60 p

Agricultural and Horticultural Series

BEEF CATTLE HUSBANDRY

BEEF CATTLE HUSBANDRY

BY

ALLAN FRASER, M.D., D.Sc.

Lecturer in Animal and Dairy Husbandry,
University of Aberdeen, Lately Research
and Advisory Officer on Sheep. Rowett
Institute, Aberdeen.

LONDON
CROSBY LOCKWOOD & SON LTD
39 THURLOE STREET, S.W.7

First published 1953

Printed in Great Britain by
Billing and Sons Ltd., Guildford and Esher
G 3242

To
LORD LOVAT
(in fealty)

Preface

IT is a very old saying that a cobbler should stick to his last, and I presume that in somewhat the same way a shepherd might be expected to adhere to his sheep. Some years ago, however— it was in 1950 to be exact—I ventured to step into the bull ring. The result, *Farming for Beef*, received more encouragement from publishers, critics and readers than it probably deserved. That encouragement, however, gave me sufficient confidence to undertake the present and more ambitious work.

Beef Cattle Husbandry is the result. It could not have been produced in any form, imperfect though that form may be, without the willing assistance of a multitude of people. I am indebted in the first place to my publisher, Mr. John W. Wilson, who persuaded me to undertake the task. To the staff, both past and present, of the Cambridge School of Agriculture, I owe a very obvious debt. Anyone who writes anything on the subject of Animal Husbandry must use the solid and enduring foundation laid by John Hammond. To A. J. Brookes, also of that great school, I am particularly indebted for the most generous manner in which he has allowed me to make free and frequent use of his ideas, publications and illustrations.

I have quoted quite freely, I hope not too freely, from the excellent works of Mr. Frank Gerrard on " Meat Technology ", of Mr. Frank Garner on the " Cattle of Britain ", of Mr. A. R. B. Haldane on " The Drove Roads of Scotland ". I have, with the permission of the Controller, H.M. Stationery Offices, quoted at even greater length from the Ministry of Agriculture Economic Series, No. 20, and, with the assent of Messrs. Geoffrey Bles, from Osgood Mackenzie's *A Hundred Years in the Highlands*.

All the Breed Society Secretaries, from South Devons down to Dexters, have been most courteous and helpful. I am indebted to my friend, Mr. Arthur Wannop, of the Department of Agriculture for Scotland, for digging up some information concerning beef grading on my behalf.

To the memory of William M'Combie of Tillyfour, I offer my respectful homage. I have read and re-read his little book so often that sometimes when I am pondering questions concerning beef cattle, he seems to be at one side of the fire, speaking his wisdom, while I sit at the other side, absorbing it.

Finally, to my wife I offer my gratitude for preparing an Index, and for persuading me to stick to my desk when on so many and diverse occasions I was inclined to desert it.

Contents

Contents

List of Illustrations

ACKNOWLEDGEMENTS

Thanks are due to the following copyright holders for permission to reproduce the
illustrations mentioned.
The Farmer and Stockbreeder for Figs. 1, 2, 14, 29, 30, 31, 32, 35, 37, 41, 43, 44.
The National Federation of Young Farmers' Clubs and the Smithfield Club for Figs.
    1, 2 from their publication *Just Your Meat.*
The Controller, H.M. Stationery Office for Figs. 3–11 from " Report on the Marketing
    of Cattle and Beef in England and Wales " (Economic Series No. 20).
Messrs. Edward Arnold and Co. for Figs. 12, 13, 45, 46 from *Farm Animals, Their
    Breeding, Growth and Inheritance,* by John Hammond.
A. Brown and Co., Lanark for Figs. 15, 36.
The Perthshire Advertiser for Fig. 17.
The Aberdeen Angus Society for Figs. 18–21.
The Hereford Society for Figs. 22–24A.
The Devon Society for Figs. 25, 26.
The Sussex Society for Figs. 27, 28.
The Highland Cattle Society for Figs. 33, 34, 39.
The Welsh Black Society for Fig. 38.
Aberdeen Journals Ltd. for Fig. 40.
Mr. Duncan M. Stewart, Millhills, Crieff, for Fig. 42.
A. J. Brookes, School of Agriculture, University of Cambridge for Figs. 47–56.

" THE rearing and feeding of cattle primarily for the production of beef is a typically British industry. In other European countries beef is essentially a by-product of the slaughter of dairy cows or draught oxen." (1)

This statement, true within its limitations, applies to Britain only since the later eighteenth century. The trade in specialised beef and beef cattle is, even in Britain, a relatively recent affair and one moreover, to-day, a little less specialised and not quite so much of a trade as it was even so recently as thirteen years ago.

That " The rearing and feeding of cattle primarily for the production of beef " *began* in Britain is incontestable fact. It began there, at the period of the industrial and agricultural revolutions when British farming was changing from champion and subsistence to several and commercial. The period was Georgian; the instrument the Enclosure Act. Two thousand six hundred of these Acts were passed between 1702 and 1810. Previous to that period, beef in England was a by-product of draught and milk just as it is in many parts of Europe to this day. The roast beef of Old England must have required a deal of roasting!

Towards the close of the eighteenth century the substitution of horses for oxen as the main motive force in agriculture released an increasing number of steers for slaughter, and these too at a younger age. An industrial people, ever increasing in both numbers and purchasing power, was eager and able to purchase the beef these steers supplied. Meat rather than draught quickly became the main product of cattle and was to remain so in Britain until meat refrigeration on the high seas, the milk churn on the railways, and the motor lorry on the highways, from the last quarter of the nineteenth century onwards, began to drive the cattle industry of Britain into the more profitable paths of milk.

Beef, then, became the chief product of British cattle somewhere about 1775 and remained such for the better part of a hundred years. It was during this period that the specialised

I

beef breeds of Britain were evolved and stabilised. It was towards the latter part of this period that these same specialised beef breeds spread abroad to supply high-quality beef for other nations. Or, what was perhaps more common, to supply beef to the industrial population of Britain from whence those breeds first came.

Britain in the nineteenth century, at the height of the country's industrial and financial supremacy, drew beef derived from British breeds off the prairies of North America, the pampas of Argentine and Uruguay, the cattle ranges of Australia. Refrigeration was introduced in 1882 as a practicable means of preserving perishable food over a sea passage. Improvement of technique and acceleration of passage permitted beef, from less distant sources, to be sold chilled instead of frozen.

This vast importation of beef into Britain certainly had a depressing effect upon beef production in Britain herself. The natural prejudice against frozen meat—people being strangely conservative about their food regardless of what brand of politics they profess—protected British beef to a certain extent and for a considerable period of time, British home-killed and unfrozen beef retaining a substantial price premium over the best chilled and imported far into the twentieth century. For example, Shaw, in comparing the " Prices of Home Killed and Imported Beef at Certain Wholesale Markets in England and Wales ", in the years 1927–1931 (2), arrived at the following monthly average for English, Argentine, and Australian beef, prices being stated in pence per lb.:

English Beef	Argentine Beef (Chilled)	Australian (Frozen)
$8\frac{1}{8}$	$5\frac{5}{8}$	$4\frac{1}{2}$

Although the flood of imported beef most certainly depressed the price of British beef in general, it is possible that in certain important respects the direct importance of this competition has been somewhat exaggerated.

Since English fresh beef fetched almost double the price, for example, of Australian frozen, it is a little difficult to see how two articles, so differently priced, could have been in direct competition. Presumably, if imports of Australian frozen beef had an adverse effect upon the production and sale of British beef, it must have been mainly upon the inferior and cheaper grades. This beef of lower quality and price being mainly cow beef, it would seem that the importation, let us say of Australian frozen beef, could have had relatively little influence upon the prosperity or otherwise of those branches of British agriculture producing beef from specialised beef cattle.

The point is raised here because of the following considerations. Previous to 1939 approximately half the beef consumed in Britain was produced in Britain, the other half being imported from outside Britain. It has often been assumed that had there been no beef importations, then, and in consequence, double the quantity of British beef would have been produced and sold and that actually at a higher price because of a British beef monopoly and the elimination of all outside competition. That, indubitably, is to assume a great deal.

Had it so happened during the nineteenth century or in the first quarter of the twentieth century that Britain had had to depend on her own production entirely in respect of beef, it seems just as probable that beef *consumption* would have fallen as that beef *production* would have increased. In other words, unless beef were cheap, fewer people could have afforded to have eaten beef and those that could would have had, perforce, to eat less of it. These considerations, based it is true on an economic situation which ended in 1939, remain strictly relevant to the beef policy of this country to-day.

Perhaps the main decision to be made in formulating that policy is to decide to what extent the future beef supplies of Britain can be imported and to what extent it may be necessary to rely upon home production. Before doing so it is necessary to examine some of the factors affecting the world trade in beef.

Now, in taking the widest possible view of the beef situation throughout the world the first, and perhaps the most surprising, consideration that requires to be taken into account is the relatively small fraction of the world's beef production that enters into the world's international trade. That is no new phenomenon.

" Pre-war, world production of beef averaged some 220,000,000 cwt. per year, of which approximately only 16,000,000 cwt. represented the exportable surplus that annually reached the world's markets." (3)

Obviously it is the size and price of the world's exportable surplus rather than the world's total production of beef that is of most immediate concern to the beef consuming public of this country, " . . . still much the largest importer of beef . . . " (4)

World beef production may increase while the exportable surplus shrinks as has, in fact, happened since the late war.

" In total, the present position is that, contrary to general opinion, there is actually to-day a rather higher world production of beef than in the years preceding the war. Instead of 220,000,000 cwt., the average annual pre-war output of beef, there was in 1947 approximately 227,000,000 cwt. produced, but as against the pre-war exportable surplus of 16,000,000 cwt. per year, there is now only a surplus of approximately 13,250,000 per year—a drop of 15 per cent despite a slight overall increase in production." (5)

The reasons for this decrease of the world's exportable surplus of beef are certainly complex and in some cases debatable. It would seem, in general, to be associated rather more with a change in the balance of wealth in the world than to be, *at the moment*, attributable to an increasing shortage of foodstuffs throughout the world. What appears to have happened since the war is that beef-importing countries, especially Britain, have been unable or unwilling to pay a sufficiently high price to induce beef-producing countries to export, with the result that these exporting countries have, it may be perforce, consumed rather more of their own product. Thus,

" Between the years 1937 and 1947, the *per caput* consumption of beef and veal has risen in the United States from 63 lb. to 80 lb., an increase of 27 per cent; in the Argentine from 176 lb. to 193 lb., an increase of ten per cent; in Canada from 67 lb. to 77 lb., an increase of 15 per cent; in Eire from 32 lb. to 54 lb., an increase of 68 per cent . . . " (6)

This situation might be expected to right itself in time. It might be anticipated that beef-producing countries, such for example as the Argentine and Uruguay, might be forced eventually, if only to retain national prosperity or even solvency, to export more beef at a price more agreeable to importing countries. Such an argument, however, is inclined to over-emphasise the financial importance of beef to the exporting countries concerned. This has never been so great as is frequently supposed.

Argentina, of all countries is that most generally associated with the export of beef. In pre-war days, as is well known, the export of chilled beef of high quality to the British market was an important feature in international trade. Yet, even in pre-war days, beef, in terms of value, was only one relatively small part of Argentina's total exports and, since the war, that value has declined.

" In 1938 beef exports accounted for about 15 per cent of the total value of Argentina's exports; this proportion, after fluctuating around 5 per cent in the early post-war years, rose sharply to 11 per cent in 1949 but has since declined to 3 per cent owing to smaller beef exports at a time when the value of total trade rose considerably." (7)

In all other beef-exporting countries the value of beef in proportion to total exports is less, and usually substantially less, than in the case of Argentina. Thus, in Uruguay, the proportion has never reached much more than 11 per cent. In all other beef-exporting countries the value of beef exports in proportion to total exports is little more than 1 per cent. (7)

The proposition, therefore, that beef-exporting countries will in time be forced to resume their exports to the British consumer market in pre-war quantity and quality, seems of very doubtful validity. It seems equally probable that they might decide to export their beef elsewhere or not at all.

Additional to this interruption of pre-war trade, due mainly to the financial readjustments between nations consequent upon that war, there is also the altogether more serious and permanent shadow of the continuous increase in the world's human population affecting the future of beef supplies as well as that of all other foodstuffs.

" Secondly, the increase in world population, associated in many areas with an acute protein shortage, has increased the size of the market and the volume of supplies needed." (6)

These factors, both those possibly temporary and those certainly permanent, have very seriously reduced the quantity of beef imported and, in consequence, the total quantity of beef consumed within the United Kingdom. Thus, the estimated supplies of beef and veal available for consumption in the United Kingdom (military consumption excluded) in 1938 was 1,190 thousand tons, reduced in 1951 to 804 thousand tons. This reduction in supplies, associated with an increase in human population over the same period of some two million, led necessarily to a substantial reduction in the *per caput* consumption of beef of from 55 lb. in 1938 to 33 lb. in 1951, a decline of some 40 per cent. (8)

Of the total beef supply of 804 thousand tons consumed in the United Kingdom in 1951, no less than 646 were from home supplies and only 158 from imported, the proportion of home-produced beef being, therefore, some 80 per cent of total supplies. (9)

"Of Great Britain's total supplies of beef and veal during 1951, home production provided 80 per cent, compared with 65 in the previous year and with just about 50 per cent in 1938. The sharp rise in the home proportion last year was accounted for largely by a substantial decline in the volume of imports." (9)

It is absolutely plain from this brief summary of relevant statistics that Britain is being driven towards a position of increasing self-support in regard to beef. This is equally true of the store cattle which form the raw material as it were of finished beef. As is very well known, the Irish Republic (Eire) has for many years supplied a vast number of store cattle for feeding and finishing in the United Kingdom. This store cattle trade was, and still is, of particular importance as between Ireland and Scotland.

"An indication of the importance of the Irish store animal to the Scottish farmer may be obtained from figures available for the years since 1940 of the numbers of fat cattle graded at the Scottish collecting centres. These returns, which distinguish between home-bred and imported animals in the case of steers, heifers and cow heifers, show that 41 per cent were of imported origin in 1940, 22 per cent in 1942 and 42 per cent in 1944." (10)

The low figures quoted for 1942 were due to interruption to normal trading through F. and M. restrictions. The general picture arising from this study is, however, that ". . . nearly half the store cattle fed off in Scotland were of Irish origin" and that ". . . the reliance on imported store cattle was even greater before 1939 than in war time". (10)

Now, there is every evidence that this supply of store cattle from Ireland has decreased and may decrease still further.

"A very large proportion of the Irish cattle output is normally exported on the hoof, but, as the increase in production has been absorbed by heavier shipments of carcase beef and veal, this trade has shown little change in the past three years and live exports in 1951, at 490,000 head, were much smaller than the pre-war figure of over 700,000 head." (11)

A reduction of over 200,000 store cattle annually must obviously have a serious effect upon the total beef production within the United Kingdom.

The most important facts as regards beef supplies in Britain are, therefore, that:

1. Imports of beef have declined from 585·4 thousand tons in 1938 to 156·9 thousand tons in 1951. This latter figure may be exceptionally low. It might be more accurate to state the decline in beef imports from those of pre-war quantity as being from 585·4 thousand tons (the 1938 figure) to 353·0 thousand tons (the average for the three years 1948, 1949, 1950). This represents a reduction of 232·4 thousand tons or 40 per cent.

2. Home production of beef during the same period 1938–1951 has increased from 604·7 thousand tons in 1938 to 652·0 thousand tons in 1951, an increase of 47·3 thousand tons or 7.7 per cent.

3. The progressive decrease in the volume of beef imports into Britain, uncompensated by any corresponding increase in home production, has led to a deficiency in the supply position which appears to be becoming more rather than less serious with the passing years.

4. The effect of the reduction in beef imports is aggravated by a simultaneous reduction in the imports of store cattle.

In view of these facts it is evident that Britain must either (a) increase imports of beef and store cattle, or (b) accept a permanent reduction in her beef supplies, or (c) increase home production to a substantial degree.

Of these three possibilities (a) might be deemed wishful thinking and (b) defeatism. Only (c) seems at all agreeable provided the task can be done. It is the purpose of the following chapters of this book to discuss the various possibilities of how it might be done. If, in the end, the conclusions reached may seem a little disappointing to those who in the past have been engaged in " . . . the rearing and feeding cattle primarily for the production of beef", I can only suggest that they continue to do so provided they can, in so doing, produce an article at a price the British people can afford to pay and at a profit which the British farmer will be content to receive.　On the other hand to go on producing an article too dear for the consumer to buy, at a loss the producer is unable to bear, is plain nonsense.　To bridge the gap by subsidy is quite as nonsensical if rather less plain, because that subsidy can only be found by the common taxation of the producer unable to bear the loss and the consumer who couldn't afford the price.

In any case we dare not—an expanding population confined to a shrinking island—neglect the beef automatically provided as it were as an inevitable and somewhat neglected by-product of our thriving dairy industry.　Some will continue to maintain that as regards beef, the dairy cow is a bad job.　That may or may not be so but, in any case, it is our duty and our business to make the best of that job.　There is no need to press for dual-purpose cattle by legislation or by propaganda.　Let the price of beef be in proper relation to the price of milk and our cattle will in course of time, and possibly in a relatively short space of time, become dual-purpose as a result of commercial incentives and without any necessity for official direction.

I have in the search for store cattle lifted my eyes to the hills as everyone must do who hopes to make the most productive use of our economically besieged island.　If I seem to be a little less enthusiastic than others, I should like to apologise again.　Nothing would give me more delight than to be proved wrong and to see many thousands of cattle come down out of the somewhat lonely and unproductive hills and glens where I was reared.

Finally my last heresy, if it be called a heresy and not true gospel, I have written in this book!

I believe, and I am by no means alone in that belief, that any substantial increase in our beef supplies must come off our own grassland.　By that I by no means subscribe to the fashionable lunacy of supposing that there is any real economy in converting summer grass into hay, silage, or dried grass and using it for *production* during the winter months.　For maintenance of breeding stock and store stock, by all means, but when it comes to production not only of beef but of all forms of animal produce, I am certain we err grievously in fighting against the seasons as we are so often and officially urged to do.　All the year round production of meat, milk, and eggs may have been a justifiable extravagance when the only known preservative was common salt. To-day, with the means of preservation, particularly cold storage, attaining ever greater subtlety and perfection, our aim should be to press for full production while summer lasts, making beef in preference to hay or silage while the sun shines.

REFERENCES

(1) Wood, T. B., and Newman, L. F. (1928). "Beef Production in Great Britain" (Liverpool).
(2) Shaw, T. (1949). "Some national aspects of beef production," *Proc. Brit. Soc. Anim. Prod.*, p. 12.
(3) *Ibid.*, p. 3.
(4) "Meat," p. 9, Commonwealth Economic Council (1952), H.M.S.O.
(5) Shaw (1949). *Ibid.*, p. 8.
(6) *Ibid.*, p. 9.
(7) "Meat," p. 7, Commonwealth Economic Council (1952). H.M.S.O.
(8) *Ibid.*, p. 5.
(9) *Farming News*, February 22, 1952, p. 3—based on data supplied by Intelligence Branch, Commonwealth Economic Council.
(10) Heath, W. E. (1946). "Irish cattle on Scottish farms," *Scot. Agric.*, **26,** 109.
(11) "Meat," p. 11, Commonwealth Economic Council (1952). H.M.S.O.

BEEF, in past history, was frequently a by-product of cattle used for other purposes. Cattle are domestic animals of diverse utility; they can be used as draught oxen or dairy cows when alive, and for meat, hides, and an infinite variety of by-products when slaughtered. The cow, when her milking days were over, probably always found her final destination in the abattoir. Working oxen, once they had grown too old for the plough, were fattened for beef, and work oxen are not so very old-fashioned as agricultural things go. They were a common feature of the English landscape in Wordsworth's time. They were used in parts of Scotland far into the nineteenth century.

The prime steer of more modern times is the direct successor of the working oxen of a former age. The keeping of cattle primarily for beef production followed hard upon the substitution of horses for oxen as the main motive power on farms. This specialised beef production was in the beginning a British industry and, so far as Europe is concerned, has remained so.

" The rearing and feeding of cattle primarily for the production of beef is a typically British industry. In other European countries beef is essentially a by-product of the slaughter of dairy cows or draught oxen." (1)

As has been remarked upon in the chapters of this book dealing with breeds, there are certain well-known beef breeds of to-day— Hereford, Devon, and Sussex are notable examples—that were renowned as work oxen at the close of the eighteenth century. In fact, the massive weight, strength, solidity, and muscular development of the leading beef breeds of to-day probably have rather more than an accidental association with the powerful ox teams of yesterday.

The close of the eighteenth century, remarkable for numerous changes and improvements in British agriculture, saw the development of roots and clovers, typified in the Norfolk four-course rotation, which made the fattening of immature animals possible. Improvements in cattle breeding resulting in earlier maturing animals, carrying better quality beef in more desirable distribution upon the carcase, followed these improvements in crop husbandry. British beef cattle began to differentiate and develop into modern breeds.

Later, the introduction of protein concentrates—largely the by-products of expanding industry—was another, although more indirect, advance in husbandry, leading to further developments in breeding for beef. It brought, as it were, the stored protein reserves of the world's crops to the British cattle breeders' byre door. It was by this means that the production of baby beef and beeflings became possible. Without this abundance of cheap imported concentrates, particularly protein concentrates, breeders who attempted to develop qualities of early maturity as exemplified in beeflings and baby beef would have failed. Breeding and feeding, in beef as in other forms of animal production, must advance together if they are to advance at all.

It so happened, however, that the emancipation of the eighteenth-century cow from the dairy did not follow the release of the eighteenth century work ox from the plough. The dairy industry persisted, at times diverging from the beef industry, at times interweaving more closely with it, but never wholly divorced from it. Beef cattle, dairy cattle, dual-purpose cattle, in a medley of breeds, ages, size and sexes have all made their contribution to the beef supplies of Britain. It follows, therefore, that while the dictionary defines beef quite briefly as being the flesh of an ox or a cow, there is, in fact, no more variable article of human dietary in Britain.

In considering the question of beef itself, what is, in short, the root of the matter, it would seem convenient, therefore, to begin with a discussion of the various classes of fat cattle as laid down in the Schedule of the Ministry of Food presently in operation. There are four such classes.

1. Steers and Heifers.
2. Cow Heifers.
3. Fat Cows.
4. Fat Bulls.

CLASS 1: STEERS AND HEIFERS include the majority of cattle of either sex that have been reared and bred for beef and for no other purpose. The definition of *steer* is given in my dictionary as " Young ox, especially a castrated one from two to four years old ". In general usage the word is, however, applied to any castrated male of the cattle species and is synonymous with the term " bullock ".

The dictionary's definition of " heifer " as a young cow is hardly sufficiently exact for the purposes of the schedule. The more general agricultural usage of the word is for a female bovine, not necessarily maiden, but definitely one that is neither pregnant nor one that has calved.

In the Ministry's Schedule, steers and heifers are classed together. Butchers, however, other things being equal, used very definitely to prefer heifers to steers, largely because they were said to kill out rather better, with less wastage and lighter bone. In fact, a well-bred, well-fed heifer of one of the specialised beef breeds, or of a first cross between two of them, is possibly the nearest approximation to the fleshers' ideal. This preference for heifers over steers was, however, never universal. Thus, Gerrard states:

" Some buyers consider that heifers mature more quickly and provide better flesh with a smoother finish, whilst others contend that steers have the advantage as they are reputed to carry a greater ratio of more valuable cuts." (2)

CLASS 2: COW HEIFERS. The official definition of a cow-heifer is as follows:

" For the purpose of these price schedules a cow-heifer is defined as any female bovine animal which has calved but which has not grown more than 7 permanent incisor teeth and still retains at least one temporary incisor tooth (calf tooth)." (3)*

To make this definition quite clear it is perhaps desirable to give a brief description of some relevant points concerning

---

* As a result of the most recent Price Review (March 1953), a new class of *Home-Bred Special Young Cows* (Grade S.Y.C.) has been substituted for that of *Cow Heifers*.

" Special young cows will be defined as female cattle which have calved and been properly dried off; which have an estimated killing out percentage of 56 per cent or over; which are firm, deep and even in the flesh when handled and are not unduly patchy in fat; and which weigh not less than 8 cwt. net live weight."

Intermediate Cows, Grade I.C., are cows of type similar to Grade S.Y.C. but estimated to kill out between 54 and 56 per cent.

All cows, excluding Special and Intermediate, are classified as *Other Cows* corresponding to the *Fat Cow* category of previous schedules.

bovine dentition. As is well known cattle, like men, have two sets of teeth, a temporary or milk set and a permanent set, the permanent replacing the temporary gradually and systematically,

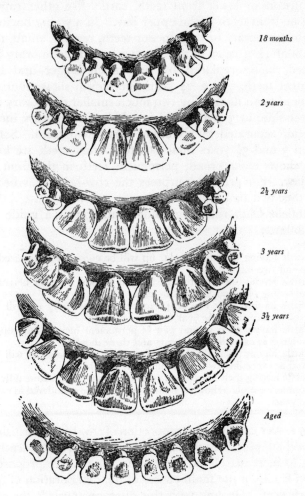

18 months

2 years

2½ years

3 years

3½ years

Aged

BOVINE DENTITION

Reproduced from *Farm Livestock of Great Britain* by Robert Wallace (Oliver and Boyd)

so that the older the animal the more permanent and the fewer temporary teeth it shows. In consequence, but within rather wide limits, the teeth of cattle, like those of horses and other domestic animals, permit an estimate to be made of their approximate age.

The teeth examined in making this estimate are chiefly the eight incisors or lower front teeth, cattle, like other ruminants, having no front teeth in the upper jaw. In a young bovine there are eight temporary or milk incisor teeth, regular, small, narrow.

At about $1\frac{1}{2}$–2 years of age the two central temporary incisors are shed, being replaced by two much bigger and broader permanent teeth. At 2–$2\frac{1}{2}$ years the mouth shows four central permanent teeth flanked by two much smaller temporary incisors on either side; at 3 years there is only one temporary incisor on either side separated by six broad permanent teeth. Sometime between 3 and $3\frac{1}{2}$ years these last temporary teeth are lost; the mouth shows eight broad, permanent teeth in the front of the lower jaw. For grading purposes the cow-heifer has become a cow. (See text figure.)

Smithfield Club rules regarding dentition as a guide to age are as follows:

> Cattle having their fifth molar up will be considered as exceeding one year and two months.
> Cattle having their central permanent incisors cut will be considered as exceeding one year and six months.
> Cattle having their central permanent incisors fully up will be considered as exceeding one year and nine months.
> Cattle having their second pair of permanent incisors fully up will be considered as exceeding two years and three months.
> Cattle having their third pair of permanent incisors cut will be considered as exceeding two years and eight months.
> Cattle having their fourth pair (corner) permanent incisors fully up and their anterior molars showing signs of wear will be considered as exceeding three years.

CLASS 3: FAT COWS. The proportion of cow beef in British home killed beef supplies is high and, at least until quite recently, was tending to increase. That increase in the relative proportion of cow beef is one of the main causes of the deterioration of quality in British beef. Dealing with this question towards the close of the 1939–1945 War, Major W. H. Warman of the Ministry of Food said:

" The recently published Agricultural Returns show that the total number of cows and heifers in the dairy and breeding herds continues to increase slightly though the rate of expansion, so marked from 1940 to 1943, is not now so pronounced. This increase in dairy stock inevitably means, of course, that there is now more cow beef going into consumption. We get in fact about four cows to every 10 clean cattle. According to the year and season this proportion is up and down and, of course, it varies widely in different districts. But in any case, we must obviously reckon with the fact that more and more cow beef will have to be consumed if the dairy herd continues to increase." (4)

This high proportion of cow beef has persisted. Thus, Mr. Thomas Shaw speaking in 1949, said that:

" The dairy cow population which was approximately 2,200,000 in 1919/20, is now three million and for the time being there is obviously a higher percentage of cow beef in the depleted home supplies than at any other previous time." (5) And that:

" To-day, the percentage cow beef is approximately 40 per cent of the total beef production in England and Wales . . . " (6)

Naturally, the quality of cow beef, within its own class, is essentially and widely variable. Thus, apart from the degree of fatness on which the Ministry's grades are based, there are very many other factors affecting the carcase quality of a cow. Age is one such factor, and it is commonly said that after her third calving the quality of a cow's carcase deteriorates quite rapidly. (7)

Again, cow beef is predominantly a dairying by-product and some dairy breeds certainly make better beef than do others. That from a Red Poll, for example, may be little behind an Aberdeen-Angus of similar weight and age. At the other extreme, Jersey cow carcases are usually judged suitable only for manufacturing purposes. The particular term " cow beef " like the more general one " beef " contains therefore the widest variation in type and quality.

Unfortunately the present system of grading is less satisfactory with cows than with other classes of fat cattle and the dressing out percentage in fat cows a somewhat unreliable index to the finish of the carcase.

" Cows are notoriously difficult to grade on a live-weight basis. This is probably because the dressing-out percentage is not a good measure of the fatness of the carcase as is the case with steers and heifers." (8)

CLASS 4: FAT BULLS. This class, obviously, is of but little importance since only a trivial quantity of bull beef is available in the market. It is not reckoned to be desirable beef, tending to be over-lean, dark in colour, and coarse in texture. In a bull carcase considered as a whole there is also an excess of weight in the forequarters and correspondingly a relative lack of weight in the hind-quarters from which the best and most valuable beef cuts are obtained. In consequence the Ministry is not prepared to pay very highly for bull beef. Since the undesirable qualities of bull beef develop with age, and are less noteworthy in youth, the Ministry instituted *Special Young Bull* classes, the Class definition being, " Young bulls which have grown no permanent incisor teeth and which in the opinion of the Certifying Authority would yield carcases of first quality beef." (3)

Schedule II deals only with calves and the basis of payment is somewhat different. Here it will suffice, however, to mention that calves are classified into three main categories.

1. Veal calves of 1st, 2nd, and 3rd Quality.
2. Other, Strong (Stirky) Calves.
3. Bobby (Slink Calves).

The maximum weight for a veal calf is laid down as being not more than that estimated to yield a dressed carcase of 200 lb.

Other Strong (Stirky) Calves are, it would seem by definition, something between a " bobby " and a " veal " calf, too old to be " bobby ", too lean to be veal.

Bobby (Slink) calves are not defined in the Ministry's schedule but the term is generally used for calves only a few days old.

Of these three classes of calves only the first—Veal calves—are considered fit for the retail meat trade. That, indeed, is the modern meaning of " veal " calf.

Stirky and Bobby calves are considered as being fit only for manufacturing purposes and some " bobby " calves are deemed unfit for human consumption.

The whole question of this trade in calf meat and of the waste involved is considered in a later chapter of this book. Here it is only necessary to stress the difference between the " veal calf " as defined in the Schedule of the Ministry of Food and the real veal calf as it was met with in the pre-war meat trade.

The true veal calf, like genuine veal, is a luxury product and, quite properly in times of meat scarcity, its production is neither remunerated nor encouraged.

The four classes in Schedule 1 of the Ministry of Food are therefore (1) Steers and Heifers, (2) Cow-heifers, (3) Fat Cows, and (4) Fat Bulls. Each of these classes is graded according to Killing Out Percentage so that it is necessary to be clear as to what a killing out percentage means.

The Killing Out Percentage, sometimes termed " The Dressing Percentage ", is an expression of the relation of carcase weight to liveweight. It means, in brief, the number of lbs. of dressed carcase obtainable from every hundred pounds of the live animal.

All cattle yield some beef, but all that cattle yield in slaughter is not beef. In the first place the gut is very capacious as it is in all ruminants and the intestinal contents—the partially digested food and unexcreted dung—weigh heavy. The weight of the intestinal contents constitutes, on the average, over 13 per cent of the total weight of the live animal. Next, the weight of what are called the offals has to be taken into account. Offals are subdivided or classified into those inedible and those edible. Inedible offals again constitute about 13 per cent of the liveweight and of these inedible offals, the hide is by far the most important both in weight and value. Other inedible offals include the feet, horns if present, and sausage casings made out of the gut walls.

Edible offals include a wide variety of internal organs and glands—the tongue, liver, sweetbreads, tripes, and the thick skirt, which is the trade name for the diaphragm. The edible offals, as it so happens, again constitute about 13 per cent of the total liveweight, just as in the case of inedible offals and of the gut contents. When the weight of the gut contents plus that of the offals (edible and inedible) are subtracted from the animal's liveweight, then the carcase weight remains.

When everything is added up together—gut contents plus offals plus carcase—there is always a slight deficiency in relation to the total liveweight. This is called the Loss and is due to the inevitable evaporation of water during slaughter. It amounts to no more than 2 per cent of the liveweight.

Figures taken from an actual weighing are shown below, expressed in percentages of liveweight.

Carcase, cold	.	.	.	.	57·6
Edible offals	.	.	.	.	13·5
Inedible offals	.	.	.	.	13·7
Intestinal contents	.	.	.	13·4
Loss	.	.	.	.	1·8

100·0

In this example the Killing Out Percentage or Dressing Percentage comes out at 57·6 which is fairly high and shows that the beast was reasonably fattened before marketing. In general the Killing Out Percentage shows how fat or how lean the animal is when slaughtered. In a very lean beast the carcase may be no more than 45 per cent of the liveweight. In a very fat beast it may be as high as 70 per cent. Anything much over 60 per cent is too high for the modern beef trade. It indicates over-fatness and consequent waste. It is said that the average figure for American cattle at slaughter is 53 per cent. To judge from grading results, the average in this country is rather higher.

The killing out percentage, then, indicates the proportion the weight of the carcase bears to that of the liveweight before slaughter. It also indicates the fatness or finish to which that animal has attained.

" The carcase percentage (other things, such as breed and amount of stomach contents being equal) is, therefore, a guide as to the composition of the carcase. For example, in bullocks killing under 53 per cent the 7th rib joint contains 18·4 per cent bone and 15·5 per cent fat, whereas in those killing over 57 per cent there is only 16·0 per cent of bone and 24·4 per cent of fat in this joint. Similarly, the amount of marbling fat in (and so the quality of) the lean meat increases from 11·8 per cent for bullocks killing under 53 per cent. to 20·4 per cent for those killing over 57 per cent. The carcase percentage, therefore, gives an indication of the meat value of the animal." (9)

Since it is in the carcase itself that the actual beef lies, it is well to give careful attention to the composition of the carcase. Not all the carcase is edible. It contains, for example, a fair weight of bone. The percentage of bone in a beef carcase is obviously of practical importance—the less of it the better. In a first-class butcher's beast it is usually reckoned that bone should constitute not more than 12 to 14 per cent of the carcase weight. Actually, the percentage of bone must depend very largely upon the degree of finish an animal has attained. For example, as the percentage of fat in the carcase rises, that of bone will tend correspondingly to decrease.

It is often said by protagonists of the pure beef breeds that one of the fundamental advantages these breeds possess over others is that the bones are lighter and the wastage from this cause far less, the assumption being that the bones of the dairy breeds are actually heavier and more massive. This is a misconception, there being no real difference between the bones of the beef as contrasted with the dairy type of cattle, " as the skeletons of the two are essentially the same." (10)

Provided both have attained the same degree of finish there is no evidence that the bones of the dairy steer weigh any more proportionally than do those of a beef steer. They may protrude more and be, in consequence, more obvious, but that is not quite the same thing.

The distribution of bone in any individual beef carcase is, of course, very unequal. That is one of several reasons for the unequal monetary value of different carcase cuts, those cuts containing the least bone—other things being equal—having the greater value.

In addition to bone, a beef carcase contains both lean and fat, and the relative proportions between the three main constituents of the carcase, the bone, the lean meat or muscle, and the fat, vary with the age and the breed of the animal, and with its nutritional history.

The study of this subject of carcase composition and quality, and of the factors both hereditary and environmental that affect it, must always be associated with the School of Agriculture in the University of Cambridge. This study began in the time of the late Professor T. B. Wood and has been enormously extended by Dr. John Hammond and by those working with him. It is now being taken a stage further in the more profound analysis being carried out by Dr. E. H. Callow, Director of the Low Temperature Research Station at Cambridge.

Hammond's observations led him to the conclusion that carcase growth proceeds in three main successive stages: (1) the growth of bone, (2) the growth of lean, and (3) the growth of fat. In a young meat-producing animal, therefore, there tends to be much bone, little lean, and less fat. In a mature animal, on the contrary, since the growth of both bone and lean has been completed, any further liveweight increase is due to the laying on of fat.

These observations of Hammond's threw new light upon the concepts of late and early maturity in cattle and of what is meant precisely by those terms.

It was found that in a slowly maturing breed, the three successive stages of (1) bone growth, (2) lean growth, (3) fat growth occur in a rather deliberate and regular succession. The beast will complete its bony frame before it will fatten, and no amount of high feeding will fatten such a beast until its framework of skeleton and muscle has been first laid down.

In an early maturing breed, on the other hand, *given a sufficiently high level of feeding*, the three stages of bone growth, lean growth and fat growth are, as it were, telescoped. The beast will lay on fat before the growth of bone and lean is completed. This capacity of telescoping growth stages is, it would appear, the essential factor in early maturity.

It cannot be too strongly emphasised, however, that without a sufficiently high level of feeding, or plane of nutrition as it is sometimes called, the capacity for early maturity can never be fully expressed.

As regards the quality of the actual beef, the great advantage arising from early maturity is that fat in sufficient quantity is laid down while the lean is still tender. In late maturing breeds, on the contrary, the lean will be growing tough before fat is laid down. Rate of maturity also has important effects upon the conformation of the beef animal. Hammond explains the relationship as follows:

" Since some parts of the carcase (back and hindquarters) are much more valuable than others (shins, neck, brisket) the butcher requires carcases which have a relatively large proportion of these high-priced parts.

" The calf with its relatively large head and legs has a high proportion of the low-priced parts of the body, but as it grows up the back and loin grows at a faster rate than the head and shanks so that the proportion of high-priced joints increases. The rate and extent to which these changes take place determine the value of the animal for beef purposes. In our improved and

Fig. I. POINTS OF A BEEF BEAST.

I, Muzzle. 2, Face. 3, Forehead. 4, Poll. 5, Crest. 6, Heart-girth. 7, Shoulder. 8, Top of shoulder. 9, Chine. 10, Back. 11, Loin. 12, Hip or Hook. 13, Rump. 14, Tail-head, the points of the pelvic bones on either side being known as the *pins*. 15, Thigh. 16, Twist or Second thigh. 17, Hock. 18, Cod or Purse. 19. Flank. 20, Paunch or Belly. 21, Ribs. 22, Fore-rib. 23, Elbow. 24, Arm. 25, Shank. 26 Brisket. 27, Point of shoulder. 28, Dewlap. 29, Neck.

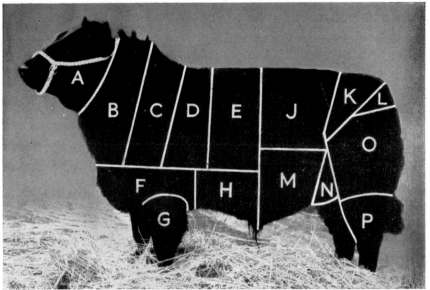

Photos: Farmer and Stockbreeder

Fig. 2. JOINTS IN A BEEF CARCASE.

A. Head	E. Six-rib	J. Sirloin	N. Thick flank
B. Clod and Sticking piece	F. Brisket	K. Rump	O. Round
C. Chuck	G. Fore-shin	L. Aitch bone	P. Leg or Shin
D. Three-rib	H. Plate	M. Thin flank	

There is some variation, from one part of the country to another, in the method of cutting up the carcase and in the names given to the various parts. The ones used here are, however, those generally used.

Fig. 3. CROSS-BRED HEIFER (prize-winner in Smithfield Club carcase competition from which the " Select " side shown in Fig. 4 (*below*) was obtained. Animals in this competition, while not so highly finished as Show animals in the ordinary classes at the Fat Stock Shows, carry too much fat for the ordinary trader except at Christmas.

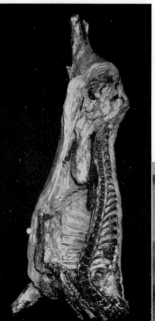

Fig. 4 (*left*). " Select " side from the heifer shown above. A typical, short, stocky side of excellent conformation, but carrying considerably more fat than is usually required.

Fig. 5 (*below*). Rib, showing the " eye " of the meat of the same heifer. The wasteful nature of the excessive fat is apparent.

quick maturing beef breeds which have been bred for killing at an early age ($1\frac{1}{2}$–$2\frac{1}{2}$ years) these changes, if the bullock is kept on to heavy weights, may go so far in depth of rib as to increase the proportions of this low-priced part and so reduce the value of the carcase to the butcher. This is one of the reasons why there is now an increasing demand for young baby beef of about $1\frac{1}{2}$ years old, well fed without check from birth." (11)

In this passage the advantage of early maturity upon conformation is explained, although the suggested practical application has a somewhat pre-war significance. It would be wrong to state in the year 1952 that, ". . . there is now an increasing demand for young baby beef of about $1\frac{1}{2}$ years old, well fed without check from birth". (11) The sentence refers, presumably, to the market conditions prevailing when the book was first written, sometime before 1940. There is no doubt, however, that when, if ever, the feeding stuff position permits it, the butchers' and consumers' demand will again be for baby beef. One reason for this preference being, that it is among early maturing strains of beef cattle, pushed to their genetic limits of growth by high and uninterrupted feeding, that the most perfect beef conformation is likely to be found.

Beef conformation is associated with a rectangular shape as opposed to the classical triangles of a dairy cow's frame. Whether looked at from above or from the side, the beast of good beef conformation is rectangular. Moreover, this rectangular body is set upon short legs. The advantage of the rectangular conformation for beef purposes is that it requires a full development of the back and hind quarters, where the most valuable cuts of the carcase are found.

A massive body close-set to the ground upon short legs presumes a shortening and thickening of the bones and, according to Hammond (12):

" Improvement of beef conformation consists in shortening the bones, particularly of the extremities and so in thickening the muscles which lie over them. This gives a carcase with blocky joints and great depth of flesh."

To understand fully the practical value of a classical beef conformation it is necessary to consider shortly how the wholesale butcher deals with a carcase of beef. The method of dividing up a beef carcase varies to a minor degree from one part of the

3

country to another. There are local customs, traditions, and terms in butchering as in other trades. The cuts are not always precisely the same nor is the one cut always known by the same name. Moreover, the wholesale cuts with which we are concerned here differ somewhat from the retail cuts with which the shopping housewife is more familiar. It must suffice, then, to select one system for description, recognising that other systems may differ from it, in detail if not in principle. Certainly the differences are not sufficiently great to affect the general principle that the practical importance of correct beef conformation in the live animal is definitely associated with the variable value of the cuts into which that animal is divided when killed for beef.

The system here selected for summarised description is what is known as " London cuts " and is based largely on the earlier and very comprehensive studies of the same subject by Wood and Newman. (1)

In the first place, then, the carcase of the slaughtered animal, after flaying and removal of offal, is divided into halves, or sides of beef, by longitudinal division down the backbone. Each side of beef, left and right, is then divided into a forequarter and a hindquarter.

In the " London cut " the forequarter comprises eleven or twelve pairs of ribs, together with the neck and shoulder. The hindquarter includes one or two pairs of ribs and all the carcase posterior to them. The hindquarters contain the best and most expensive beef.

The primary joints described as " London cuts " are fourteen in number. They are as follows.

1. *Leg, Hind Shin or Hock.*—This joint is mainly bone (tibia) and tendon or gristle. What muscular tissue there is is thin and fibrous. Consequently the meat is of the lowest value, used mainly in making gravies or soups.

2. *Round.*—This joint is the upper fleshy part of the leg, actually the thigh, enclosing the femur or thigh bone. The muscles are both large and succulent and the meat of good quality. The joint is subdivided into two retail cuts, " topside " and " silverside ". The latter term refers to the silvery appearance of the muscle sheaths.

3. *Aitchbone.*—This is a small, triangular cut from the top of the Round. It contains portions of the pelvic bones and these, in

proportion to the size of the joint, bulk large. Consequently the joint is of low value although the quality of the meat, as distinct from the bone, is good.

4. *Rump.*—This is usually the most costly joint of all and the source of the prized " rump-steaks ". The *Rump* lies between the *Aitchbone* and *Loin* and, besides well rounded and succulent muscles with masses of intervening fat, includes small portions of the pelvic bones. The flesh, of high quality, is especially suited for frying or grilling.

5. *Thick Flank.*—Sometimes called the "Bed of Beef" comprises the mass of muscle lying in the front of the thigh. The patella or knee-cap is the only bone included in this joint. The meat is of only moderate quality but the almost complete absence of bony waste raises the value of the cut.

" The large proportion of ' meat ' to waste makes it popular with purchasers who require quantity rather than quality. The cut slices are very popular both in America and in Europe, and ' flank steak and fried eggs ' is frequently served where an especially solid portion of food is required. The flesh is of good flavour, and is occasionally sold for roasting." (13)

6. *Sirloin.*—This is the best cut of the whole carcase as the name " Sir Loin " suggests. It forms the loin or lumbar region in the living beast, one reason why length and breadth of back is considered of first importance in beef conformation. The joint includes what is known as the undercut or fillet, actually the psoas muscle, which may be removed and sold separately as " fillet " or " fillet steak ". Below the undercut and included in the sirloin is a mass of suet which surrounds the kidneys.

7. *Thin Flank.*—This cut, of very little value, consists mainly of the thin muscles and fat forming the abdominal wall. It is of small weight and no great importance.

8. *6-Rib.*—This joint contains the posterior (7th-12th) ribs. Of fair quality and suitable for roasting it suffers from high wastage due to contained bone. The bone may be removed before sale of the residue as " rolled rib ".

" Rib cuts, once popular as the sideboard or cold buffet joint and almost the emblem of middle class prosperity, are now rarely purchased for household consumption, but are still popular in restaurants where heavy lunches are served. It is probably the demand for small rib cuts that has, more than any other factor, led to the popularity of baby beef, as the weight of the joints is determined by the size of the rib bones and verte-bræ." (14)

9. *3-Rib Piece.*—Similar to 6-Rib joint but of rather lower value.

10. *3-Rib and Leg of Mutton Piece* (or chuck).—Contains the shoulder-blade (scapula) and first three thoracic ribs. Because of the high proportion of bone and the tendinous insertions of various large muscles, this joint is of relatively low value.

11. *Plate.*—Includes the lower part of the breast-bone (sternum). Boned and cooked, this joint—somewhat separately or included with the *Brisket*—constitutes " cold pressed beef ".

12. *Brisket.*—Includes the upper part of the sternum and dewlap. Use similar to *Plate.*

13. *Clod and Sticking Piece.*—Includes the neck bones (cervical vertebræ) and upper arm bone (humerus). Irregularly shaped and damaged by incisions made at slaughter, the joint is of very little value.

14. *Fore-shin.*—Its uses are similar to those of the hind-shin.

It is customary to classify these wholesale cuts or joints into those of first, second, and third quality. There is a wide measure of agreement as to how such a classification should be made.

Wood and Newman (15) give the following scheme.

Round: Silverside	(boiling)	⎫
Topside	(roasting)	⎪
Rump	(grilling)	⎬ 1st Quality
Loin and wing rib	(roasting)	⎪
6-Ribs	(roasting)	⎭
3-Ribs	(roasting)	
Aitchbone	(roasting or boiling)	⎫
Thick flank	(grilling or stewing)	⎪
3-Rib and leg of mutton piece (" blade bone ") " chuck "		⎬ 2nd Quality
or " thick neck " . . .	(roasting or stewing)	⎪
Brisket	(boiling)	⎭
Plate	(boiling)	
Clod and sticking piece . . .	(stewing)	⎫
Shin	(stewing)	⎬ 3rd Quality
Leg	(stewing)	⎭

The Thin Flank, if classified as a separate cut or joint, would be considered as being of third quality.

Now, of the four cuts classified of first quality, three are in-cluded in the hindquarters and only one in the forequarters.

The rump, the round, the loin—these are the really valuable joints of beef and they are all situated on the upper surface of the posterior half of the beef animal's body. Full development in this region is therefore essential if a beef animal is to be of the highest quality.

It is, indeed, an essential part of Hammond's theories of maturation and development that these cuts, which happen to be commercially valuable, are late comers in the full development both of the individual beast and of the domesticated varieties of meat-producing animals, and that it is only in early maturing breeds of cattle on a high plane of nutrition that these most valuable cuts attain fullest development.

It is also important to appreciate the extreme variation in the value of beef from different parts of the same carcase. It raises some important considerations in the economic production and distribution of beef in relation to social conditions.

The very unequal value of the various cuts from the same carcase made beef an ideal article of diet for distribution under a feudal system. In the good old days when a feast was ordered and an ox slain, the king and his favourites ate the sirloin, the barons the rump steaks, the knights the best ribs, and the poor peasants had needs content themselves with the thin flanks, the offal and the skirt! The very names of the cuts have a mediæval sound; the " Sirloin " or Sir Loin, said to have received that title when knighted in jest by an early English king at a royal hunting feast; " The Baron of Beef " a cut seldom made now, which was a joint consisting of the two sirloins left uncut at the backbone; the " Bed of Beef " a richly pleasing title for the modern butchers' " Thick Flank ".

In more recent times the luxury price for the best cuts of beef compensated the butcher, *and*, more indirectly, the beef producer also, for the low price obtainable for the poorer cuts. A common practice in the Aberdeenshire dead-meat trade was to forward the hindquarters of a beef carcase to Smithfield for sale in the London luxury market, disposing of the less expensive forequarters to the more frugal householders of Aberdeen.

This natural inequality of beef makes it seem best suited for feudal and capitalistic systems of society. It is a desperately difficult task to divide a carcase of beef into " fair shares for all ".

There is, of course, more than one factor involved in this

inequality. The proportion of bone is obviously one such factor. For example, the relatively low value of the aitchbone compared to that of adjacent cuts—rump, round, and thick flank—is evidently due to its much higher bone content.

There is the further important difference that while certain parts of the carcase are suited for roasting and others are not, the consumer prefers and is prepared to pay considerably more for these roasting joints.

" The valuable parts of the carcase lie in the hindquarters and along the back; those are the roasting joints, which the butcher can sell at a profit because there is a good demand for them. The other parts, such as the neck, shanks, brisket and lower part of the ribs are boiling and stewing joints, for which there is a poor demand, and the butcher often has to sell them below cost price in order to clear them." (16)

It follows that the carcase proportions should have an important effect on beef quality, as indeed they do. Correct beef conformation, which is in all probability a combined effect of suitable breeding *and* feeding, by which the hindquarters are well weighted in relation to the forequarters, and by which those cuts of the hindquarters most valuable to the butcher—namely loin, rump, and round—are fully developed, is one important factor affecting the quality of beef. There are, of course, others, and it is as well to recognise at the outset that it must of necessity be difficult, and might indeed prove impracticable, to attempt to fix any rigid standards of such quality.

Hammond and Mansfield (17) have given the only true and satisfactory definition of what is meant by beef quality. Their definition is as follows:

" Quality in beef is that which members of the public like, and the butchers can sell, best."

That definition, while true, does not permit of the setting up of any precise standards, because what the public likes varies both with historical age and with geographical locality.

Change of public taste with historical period is usually assumed, in the sense that a preference for leaner and younger meat has become evident within recent times. Admittedly it is possible that there has been some slight confusion of thought upon this subject. It is often said that public taste has changed, and that the pre-war trend towards leaner beef and beef from cattle of a younger age was the beef producers' response to this change. Actually, it may rather be that public taste has always been much as it is to-day, but that the means available to the producer to satisfy that taste vary. It is an assumption, unsupported by any historical evidence, that the beef from aged work oxen was the beef of choice to the mediæval Englishman. He might, given the choice, have much preferred baby beef. The point is that, as a result of the more limited range of feeding stuffs available for cattle in his time, he was never given the choice. Nevertheless, there does appear to be evidence that the reduction in the amount and severity of manual labour in modern times has been accompanied—as indeed might be expected—by a preference for leaner meat and a growing prejudice against excessive fat in meat.

That preference and that prejudice vary with both locality and occupation, a further indication that rigid standards of beef quality are not easy to define. According to Gerrard:

" Consumers show marked preferences in the quantity of fat they require with their meat and this in turn is reflected in the degree of finish in the live animal. With the extension of the mechanical rather than the physical, the amount of fat required generally is obviously reduced. The town worker will want leaner meat than his agricultural brother, and the worker in heavy trades, iron-working, stevedores, etc. must have more calories than, say, textile workers engaged in a warm, humid atmosphere." (2)

This difference in public taste according to locality was catered for in the age of free marketing prior to 1939. Indeed one of the more useful functions of the knowledgeable cattle dealer was to sort out the various types of cattle and other livestock in the producing areas and dispatch them according to known consumer preference to different destinations. Thus, the type of meat, on hoof or on hook, sent from Scotland to Newcastle was in marked contrast to that sent to Manchester; that going to Newcastle being both heavier and fatter. The type of meat sent to London differed from both and of course, because of the size and value of its meat market, the London demand had an overriding influence over all others.

While it might prove a difficult task to fix uniform standards of beef quality satisfactory to all consumers, there is at least fairly general agreement on a number of known factors affecting that quality. One of the most important of these is the quantity and distribution of fat. In wild animals fat is the chief source of reserve energy, stored in times of plenty to be drawn on during periods of dearth. In domestic animals it has also far-reaching effects upon the nutritive value, quality, and palatability of meat.

Dr. Callow of the Low Temperature Research Station, Cambridge, has within recent years made a fresh and quantitative approach to comparative studies of meat and has already published an important series of papers on the subject. One of his main conclusions is that " . . . major changes in the anatomy of carcases and in the chemical composition of their tissues largely depend on the level of fatness of the carcase". (18)

It is because of this relationship that the estimated killing out percentage of an animal has been adopted as the basis of livestock grading by the Ministry of Food, since the level of fatness is the main factor influencing the killing out percentage.

" Since the quality of meat depends mainly on the general level of fatness of the carcase, this factor must be the major basis of grading." (19)

In addition to the *amount* of fat present in a carcase, usually expressed directly as a percentage and reflected in the killing out percentage, there is the almost equally important question of fat *distribution*.

" Just as there is a definite order in which the different parts of the body grow, so there is a definite order of the parts in which fat is deposited. In the early stages of fattening it is put on in the caul and kidney fat; in those breeds unimproved for meat production, such as in the Jersey cow, fattening never gets much beyond this stage. Next the fat goes on in a subcutaneous layer over the muscles which gives that smooth rounded appearance to the well-finished bullock and lastly it penetrates between the muscle fibres and causes the muscle to become marbled." (9)

It follows that while the level of fatness of a carcase is the fundamental factor affecting its quality, the distribution of the fat, varying as it does with species, breed, age, and sex, will have an important, although subsidiary influence upon carcase quality. As regards species, Dr. Callow has shown that:

" The partition of fatty tissue between the subcutaneous and intermuscular depots have been found to be completely different for the three species of meat animal at all levels of fatness.   Thus, cattle of average fatness have about twice as much intermuscular tissue as subcutaneous fatty tissue.   In pigs, on the other hand, the position is reversed . . . Sheep are in an intermediate position." (20)

Effects of age and breed upon fat distribution in the carcase were also found in the same series of researches.

" Thus in the case of beef when due allowance has been made for the general effect of fatness, the secondary effect of age can be seen; young beef animals have less chemical fat in their fatty and muscular tissues than older beef animals.   Similarly, there is an effect of breed; an early maturing breed such as the Aberdeen-Angus has more fat in the muscles than a late maturing breed such as the Welsh; also a dairy-bred cow (Jersey) has less fat in the muscles than a cow bred both for beef and milk; moreover, a low fat-content is found in the muscles from a steer of a dairy-bred type." (19)

These results, sufficiently interesting and important as they stand, would be still more so were they based on a sufficient number of animals to permit of statistical analysis.   Since, however, at least in some cases, the results are derived from the carcases of single individuals of unknown nutritional history, it is necessary to exercise due caution in drawing conclusions regarding the qualitative differences between the beef of various breeds.   These difficulties of interpretation emphasise the importance of a recommendation made by Dr. Callow on other grounds that experiments of this nature " should be limited whenever possible to a study of identical twins ". (21)

Studies on beef quality, using the identical twin technique, certainly promise results of the greatest interest.

Marbling of beef is always regarded as of the greatest importance in relation to its quality.   Wood and Newman in their investigations on this subject found that:

" Some fat was always found in the lean, the proportion varying in the different animals.   This fat included in the lean flesh is the fat which produces marbling of the lean, and adds greatly to the flavour, juiciness and tenderness of the meat.

" This marbling fat was found to increase fairly steadily as fattening proceeded, and to be considerably higher in the first-quality roasting joints such as sirloin or ribs, than in the rump, round, aitchbone, thick flank, and clod and sticking piece." (22)

Emphasising and explaining the importance of marbling in beef, Hammond and Mansfield wrote:

" This marbling fat is valuable, especially in the older bullocks with coarse grained meat as it breaks up the muscle bundles and so causes increased tenderness. The older the bullock, therefore, the more important it is that it should be ' well-finished ' before it is slaughtered. There is more of this marbling fat in those breeds which are early maturing and fatten easiest." (23)

These results have been confirmed by Callow in more recent work, where he writes that:

" . . . from the point of meat quality it is essential to have an appreciable amount of fat in the muscular tissue. Secondary factors which cause more fat to be deposited in the muscles, and less in the fatty tissues, thus improve the quality of meat." (19)

The level of fatness of a beef animal has a definite effect upon the *Palatability* of its beef. Tests of palatability must of necessity be qualitative and cannot by their nature be very exact. Those carried out at the Cambridge Low Temperature Research Station are conducted as follows:

" A test for the palatability of the beef from each carcase was carried out in the following way. The 12th rib joint from one side was boned, rolled and stored at 0° C. and 85% R.H. for 7 days. It was then roasted, and the hot roast beef was tasted by a trained panel of laboratory workers at the Low Temperature Research Station. Marks were awarded for texture, flavour, and juiciness. Equal importance was attached to each of these three qualities . . . " (24)

On the basis of these tests it was found that:

" The palatability of beef is greatly affected by the fatness of the animal. Tasting tests of the cooked meat showed that beef improves in palatability as the animal becomes fatter, but only up to a certain point. Beyond this point extra fatness causes a decrease in palatability." (25)

" The optimum point of fatness was attained by steers and heifers dressing out at about 58%." (25)

Colour of fat, while from the nutritional point of view of little or no import, has always been considered of significance in the assessment of commercial beef quality. Highly coloured, yellow beef fat has always been objected to by consumers and in consequence discriminated against by butchers.

" A pale primrose-yellow fat is liked rather than a deep yellow fat. This is not due to differences in nutritive value or flavour, but is because the colour is not liked by consumers." (26)

The objection—it may amount to more than a prejudice— may be due to the especially highly coloured fat of aged cows in general and of cows of the Channel Island breeds in particular. Actually, not only cows, but all cattle of the Channel Island breeds have highly coloured carcase fat due to the relatively incomplete conversion of the carotene pigments ingested in the food to the colourless fat-soluble Vitamin A stored in their bodies. Cattle coming off grass, particularly those that have suffered a check, will also have yellow fat. It follows that cattle ill-bred or ill-fed for beef production purposes are apt to have highly coloured, yellow fat. This must be contrasted with the fat of prime winter-fed beef which is creamy white in colour. Possibly, therefore, the public dislike of yellow fat in beef may be sufficiently well founded. Thus Gerrard, discussing the wide variations in colour that may occur in beef fat, writes:

" Breed plays an important part, and the characteristic yellow fat of the Jersey and Guernsey is familiar to the butcher, and possibly the public's objection to a bright yellow fat is based on its association with dairy cows. In aged cows the typical yellow fat is probably due to the concentration of pigment, as the fat is used up for the production of young and milk, and the relative increase in the proportion of connective tissue. Even in grazed beef-cattle, loss of condition, when feed is scarce, will tend to produce a rather yellow fat." (27)

Fat, therefore, is certainly the most variable and, as regards both nutritive value and general quality, not the least important constituent of a beef carcase. The lean, however, while much less variable, must by no means be neglected, especially since it is presumably because of the protein content, nitrogenous extractives, and special flavour of the lean that beef has become such an important and popular article of human dietary.

The lean meat of the butcher is the muscular tissue of the anatomist.

" The lean meat or muscle is made up, as can be seen through the microscope, of small muscle fibres grouped together into bundles. The size of these bundles determines the coarseness of the ' grain ' of meat, which is closely associated with toughness and stringiness. In small and in young animals the size of the muscle fibres and bundles is small, and so the meat is fine-grained and tender, whereas when the animal grows up the grain becomes coarser." (28)

" A rough test for the ' grain ' is to stroke the surface of the cut muscle with the thumb, a smooth velvety feel denoting a fine grain." (28)

In addition to the tactile test for the degree of tenderness in beef, the colour of the lean is also of some practical importance in judging its quality.

" The muscles of the young animal are easily fatigued, whereas as the animal grows up the power of sustained action increases. With this change in muscle comes an increase in the respiratory pigment, hæmoglobin, of the muscle and the colour of the muscle deepens. With increase in the colour in the muscle too comes increased flavour. Thus, for example, young veal is pale in colour and comparatively flavourless as compared with beef which is dark in colour. Beef, however, may be too dark in colour and too highly flavoured to suit the public taste; such, for example, is the case with bull beef."

The correlation between depth of colour and intensity of flavour is of considerable interest, and there can be little doubt that mature, dark-coloured meat, if hung sufficiently long, has the best and most characteristic flavour. Nevertheless the public dislikes dark beef, presumably because it is likely to be mature beef and the modern preference, when there is opportunity for choice, is for young and tender beef.

" The public is now paying much more attention to the softness of eating than to flavour." (28)

Considering the state of the nation's dentition that is not to be wondered at ! There is, however, a general preference for meats of a certain intermediate colour, neither too dark nor too pale.

" With beef there is an optimum colour—a bright light red . . . " (29)

There are obviously a large number of factors influencing the quality of beef. A somewhat complex subject has been very well summarised by Gerrard:

" The quality of a beef carcase can best be described in terms of *conformation, finish,* and *quality,* the latter term being a condition of the muscle. To the butcher the beast with the best conformation is one which will yield a large proportion of valuable joints and a small proportion of bone. The question of bone content is more important in beef than with mutton or pigs, as in the latter cases practically all the bone is disposed of in the various joints, but with beef a very large percentage of the bone is removed prior to sale.

" Finish refers to the external covering of fat, and correct finish suggests a smooth covering of creamy white fat evenly distributed over the surface of the carcase.

" Quality of the meat is associated with the texture, and this depends on the size of the muscle bundles and the quantity of connective tissue. Intramuscular fat, ' marbling ', is a good indication, and the question of sap, or meat juices, must not be ignored.

"A large number of factors influence this quality in beef and among the more important are: breed, condition, age, sex, activity, pre-slaughter and slaughter condition, and finally the methods of storage. A number of these are, of course, interdependent, but they all exert an important influence on the final product." (30)

REFERENCES

(1) Wood T. B., and Newman, L. F. (1928). " Beef Production in Great Britain," p. 9 (Liverpool).
(2) Gerrard, F. (1946). " Meat Technology," p. 26 (London).
(3) Ministry of Food Circular, Livestock Control (1951). 6th Ed. (Cattle).
(4) Warman, W. H. (1945). " Meat Supplies," *Repts. Brit. Soc. Anim. Prod.,* p. 11.
(5) Shaw, T. (1949). " Some national aspects of beef production," *Proc. Brit. Soc. Anim. Prod.,* p. 17.
(6) *Ibid.,* p. 18.
(7) Gerrard, F. (1946). *Ibid.,* p. 95.
(8) Callow, E. H. (1945). " The food value, quality and grading of meat with special reference to beef," *Rept. Brit. Soc. Anim. Prod.,* p. 40.
(9) Hammond, J. (1952). " Farm Animals," p. 75, 2nd Ed. (London). (Refs. to literature and illustrations omitted in extract.)
(10) Petersen, W. E. (1950). " Dairy Science," p. 186, 2nd Ed. (Chicago).
(11) Hammond, J. (1952). *Ibid.,* p. 69. (Refs. to literature and illustrations omitted in extract.)
(12) *Ibid.,* p. 74.
(13) Wood, T. B., and Newman, L. F. (1928). *Ibid.,* p. 51.
(14) *Ibid.,* p. 55.

(15) *Ibid.*, p. 30.
(16) Hammond, J., and Mansfield, W. S. (1936). "Investigations on producing quality in beef," *J. Min. Agric.*, **42**, 977.
(17) *Ibid.*, p. 980.
(18) Callow, E. H. (1949). "Comparative Studies of Meat. III, Rates of fattening in relation to the percentage of muscular and fatty tissue in a carcase," *J. Agric. Sci.*, **39**, 347.
(19) Callow, E. H. (1947). "Comparative Studies of Meat. I, The chemical composition of fatty and muscular tissue in relation to growth and fattening," *J. Agric. Sci.*, **37**, 127.
(20) Callow, E. H. (1948). "Comparative Studies of Meat. II, The changes in the carcase during growth and fattening and their relation to the chemical composition of the fatty and muscular tissues,'" *J. Agric. Sci.*, **38**, 198.
(21) Callow, E. H. (1950). "Comparative Studies of Meat. IV, Rates of fattening in relation to the deposition of fat and protein in the fatty and muscular tissue of meat carcases," *J. Agric. Sci.*, **40**, 7.
(22) Wood, T. B., and Newman, L. F. (1928). *Ibid.*, p. 34.
(23) Hammond, J., and Mansfield, W. S. (1936). *Ibid.*, p. 983.
(24) Callow, E. H. (1944). "The food value of beef from steers and heifers, and its relation to dressing-out percentage," *J. Agric. Sci.*, **34**, 179.
(25) Callow, E. H. (1945). *Ibid.*, p. 47.
(26) Hammond, J., and Mansfield, W. S. (1936). *Ibid.*, p. 984.
(27) Gerrard, F. (1946). *Ibid.*, p. 91.
(28) Hammond, J., and Mansfield, W. S. (1936). *Ibid.*, p. 983.
(29) *Ibid.*, p. 984.
(30) Gerrard, F. (1946). *Ibid.*, p. 93.

QUALITY in beef is an extremely complex affair. There is a very great difference between the best beef and the worst beef. It is only just and proper, therefore, that there be a difference in payment relative to variation in quality. Grading is the most practical method of bringing this about, yet a satisfactory system of grading is by no means easy to devise.

The first comprehensive study of the grading and marking of beef in the United Kingdom was undertaken at the instance of the Ministry of Agriculture, and the conclusions and recommendations of that study published in No. 20 of the Ministry's well-known Economic Series. (1) This publication presents the facts as they stood in 1929.

In the first place it contrasted the relatively systematic method of sale according to quality grades in the case of imported beef, with the apparently less orderly procedures applicable at that time to the marketing of home-killed (British) beef. The comparison, at least superficially, was very much in favour of the orderly method of marketing customary in the case of beef imported into Britain and of similar method of domestic marketing of beef adopted to some extent in certain other countries, particularly the United States and Canada. The Report stated (p. 106) that:

> The use of standards of quality as a basis for the physical grading of beef before sale, so that supplies are actually bought and sold according to recognised grade standards, is a feature of the trade in imported beef and is a recent development of some importance in the domestic trade of the United States and Canada. Where this practice obtains, it is obvious that information regarding market price is much more useful than when, in the absence of a grading system, a rough attempt has to be made to relate quality to value for price recording purposes.
>
> In the trade in home-killed beef, there is, as yet, no standard system of grading meat before sale; prices of steer and heifer beef on the large wholesale meat markets are customarily recorded on the basis of 1st and 2nd quality, but no precise definition of these quality distinctions exists.

It should be emphasised, however, that grading requires to be neither official nor strictly defined to be reasonably effective. Thus, in the days of the free marketing of meat previous to 1939, the dead meat market paid a substantially higher price for beef of certain type, weight, and quality suitable to what was then called the better-class trade, than it did for lower qualities of beef. In consequence the breeder and feeder of the best type of Aberdeen-Angus cross in Scotland or of Hereford and Devon crosses in England certainly received, *relative to the value of other classes of fat cattle at that time*, a higher reward than he is receiving to-day. Granted that the general level of beef prices was much lower and for all classes of fat cattle much too low for profitable beef production; nevertheless, the dead meat trade would pay up to twopence a lb. more for a carcase considered of really superior quality than it was prepared to pay for beef of less desirable type. Now, 2d. a lb. is not far short of £1 per cwt. dead-weight which, when beef prices were running at some 80s. to 90s. per cwt. constituted a very substantial price incentive for quality, always remembering that the only true definition of beef quality is that by Hammond and Mansfield, already quoted:

" Quality in beef is that which members of the public like, and the butchers can sell best." (2)

That definition is of importance because what the public liked in 1929 is not necessarily what it likes in 1952 or, rather, the section of the public best able to express its preference through payment may well have changed. Nevertheless, as an answer to effective public preferences as it then was, the pre-war (1939) marketing of beef was neither quite so chaotic nor was it quite so inefficient as certain agricultural economists of that period would have had us believe. After all, the accuracy of any rule-of-thumb method depends mainly upon the sensitivity of the thumb, and the thumb of the skilled and experienced butcher or flesher as a rule is very far from being insensitive.

Admittedly the traditional system (if it could be truly called a system) of marketing home-killed beef in Britain was less orderly than the simpler and more direct methods of marketing imported beef.

The marketing of imported as compared with home-killed beef was, however, in itself a much simpler and more direct undertaking. In the first place, imported beef was selected beef. The meat-exporting countries, in general, exported their best and ate their worst—at home! At least, that was the common custom of meat-exporting countries in the pre-war era

Fig. 6.   HEREFORD STEER from which the " Prime " sides shown in Figs. 7 and 8 below were obtained.

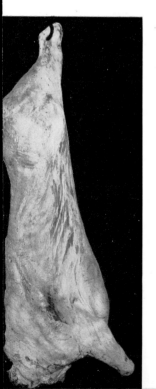

Figs. 7 & 8.   " Prime " sides from the Hereford Steer (*above*). The finish of these sides is fully sufficient for the trade, except at Christmas, for either " Select " or " Prime " grades. The interior walls of the ribs are well covered, but there is no excess of kidney fat.

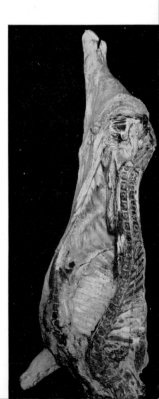

Fig. 9. CROSS-BRED STEER from which the " Good " sides shown in Figs. 10 and 11 below were obtained.

Figs. 10 and 11. " Good " sides from the steer shown above. Note patchiness on the hindquarters and slight fat covering on the interior walls of the ribs. The conformation is by no means perfect, nevertheless the carcase is a useful body of beef of a type which suits a certain class of trade.

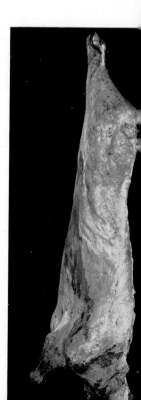

Fig. 12. Examples of undesirable and desirable beef carcases. (*Left*) Undesirable: leg long in proportion to width; neck large; ribs too deep; flat-sided. (*Right*) Desirable: leg short in proportion to width; neck small; ribs well sprung and not too deep. (Hammond and Mansfield.)

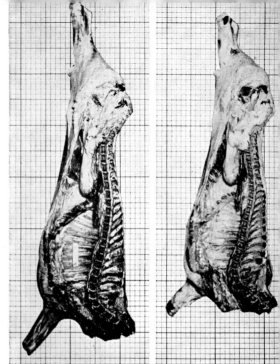

Fig. 13. Cuts through the last rib of the carcases shown in Fig. 12. (*Above*) Undesirable: shallow eye-muscle and large proportion of bone. (*Below*) Desirable: deep fleshed with a small proportion of bone. (Hammond and Mansfield.)

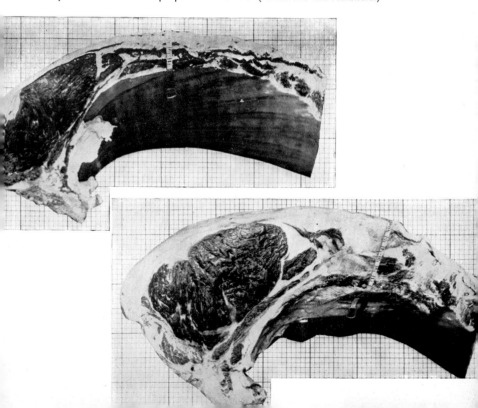

Fig. 14. BEEF SHORTHORN BULL.

Fig. 15. BEEF SHORTHORN COW.

when international competition for a share of the British meat market was at its keenest.

British home-killed beef, on the contrary, was beef from cattle as they came to be slaughtered. It might be beef from the primest of bullocks and the choicest of heifers. It might be beef from rough and over-weight cattle, frequently imported from Ireland as stores and fattened on British arable farms mainly for their dung. It might be beef from cattle turned into the fat markets at the end of an unfavourable grazing season and therefore beef from cattle unfinished and in poor condition. Finally, it might be cow beef, and that too from cows of all sizes, ages, breeds, and degrees of finish. All this beef produced in Britain, the good and the bad of it, the rough with the smooth of it, had to be marketed in Britain as British beef.

On the contrary, meat-exporting countries—Argentina for example—in pre-war days were accustomed to send only the pick of their beef to this country. The pick of Argentina beef of those days, derived from cattle of pure beef breeding, well reared, well finished, carefully selected and handled, chilled rather than frozen, was, in all probability, every bit as good, if not better, than the best of British beef. Consequently, it is probably false reasoning to attribute the capture by the Argentine of the best British markets to the superiority of her beef marketing. It might just as well, and truly, be attributed to the superiority of her beef.

It was thought, however, as the result of the Ministry's Economic survey, that the competitive position of British beef in the home market might be improved by the introduction of a system of grading and marking. In designing such a possible system, precedents taken from the marketing of beef in the United States and in Canada were carefully considered.

As a result of these and other studies, and of consultations between the Ministry, the National Farmers' Union, and the National Federation of Meat Traders' Associations, three beef grades, namely, " Select ", " Prime ", and " Good " were suggested as standard quality grades for beef suitable for market requirements in Britain. Since these grades depended primarily on the three qualitative concepts of *Conformation*, *Finish*, and *Quality*, as used in the U.S.A. Beef Grades of that period, it is necessary to quote the Definitions of *Conformation*, *Finish*, and

Quality as defined in these U.S.A. Beef Grades. They were as follows: (3)

Conformation.—The term conformation covers the general build, form shape, contour or outline of the carcase, side or cut.

Best conformation involves—Short shanks and necks, deep plump rounds, thick full loins, well-fleshed ribs, and a thickness of flank commensurate with the depth of barrel and chest cavity.

Poor conformation involves—Angularity in general outline, prominent hip and shoulder bones, long thin necks, shanks, and rounds, shallow loins, and a decided lack of symmetry in the carcase or side.

Conformation is dependent on the skeleton, the depth of flesh and the thickness and distribution of external fat. Conformation is largely a matter of breeding, although feed and care have an important influence.

Conformation has much to do with determining the relative attractiveness of the carcase or side. Its chief significance lies in the fact that it indicates the ratio between meat and bone, also the ratio between the more desirable cuts, such as round and loins, and the so-called coarser cuts, such as chucks and plates.

Finish.—Finish refers to the thickness, colour, character and distribution of fat.

Best finish implies—A smooth, even covering of brittle, flaky, white fat over most of the exterior surface of the carcase, averaging not more than three-fourths inch thick over the top of the loin and ribs, and an even, though much thinner, covering of flaky, white fat on the interior surface of the ribs; also heavy, but not excessively " bunchy " or wasty deposits of white fat over the kidneys, in the crotch, and in the chest cavity. It also involves relatively heavy deposits of fat between the larger muscles, and a liberal distribution of fat along the connective tissues and between the muscle fibres. The latter characteristic gives the cut surface a streaked appearance and is known as marbling. Rounds, shanks, neck and belly are the last portions of the anatomy to be covered with fat; hence, generally speaking, and with due regard for the maximum depth over the hips, loins and rumps, the more extensive the fat over these surfaces, the higher the finish.

Poor finish implies—Deficiency in external fat and marbling; uneven distribution, resulting in bunches, rolls, or patches of fat on certain portions of the carcase; or that fat is soft, flabby, and yellow instead of firm, flaky and white or creamy white.

The colour, character, and evenness of distribution of fat are largely matters of breeding, but the quantity or thickness thereof is due to feeding and care.

A high degree of finish adds much to the attractiveness of a carcase or cut, but its chief significance lies in the fact that a certain amount of fat is essential to palatability. Furthermore, finish serves as an excellent index of quality of the meat.

Quality.—Quality is a characteristic of the flesh and the fat included therein. It pertains primarily to the thickness, firmness, and strength of both the muscle fibre and the connective tissue. It also involves the amount, consistency and character of the juices or extractives which surround and permeate the muscle fibre and connective tissue. It is strongly influenced by marbling, which is due simply to deposits of well-filled fat cells along the connective tissue and between the muscle fibres. Although, strictly speaking, colour does not determine quality, it serves as excellent index to quality.

Best quality in beef implies—Full, well-developed, firm muscular tissue or flesh with a minimum of strength in fibres and connective tissue. Beef of this sort possesses a high proportion of juice to dry fibre, but this moisture must be of such consistency that the flesh when chilled remains firm and resilient. There must also be liberal deposits of fat between the muscle fibres, giving the cut surface a streaked or marbled appearance. This fat, together with the juice or extractives, give the meat juiciness and flavour. The cut surface of beef of this sort has fine grain, and is smooth and velvety to sight and touch. The colour is a light or cherry red, because the blood supply has been kept at a minimum by lack of exercise and because of intensive feeding on grain or other ration producing similar effect, and because the animal was not old. The cut surface also presents a sheen or reflection not apparent in beef of poorer quality. This is due to the fine grain of the meat, the consistency of the juice, and the oil of the fat giving a smooth surface which reflects light much better than the relatively dry, or watery, coarse fibre of poorer quality beef.

Poor quality involves the opposite of most of the above characteristics. Beef of poor quality is usually of a dark red colour, because the muscle has been subjected to prolonged vigorous exercise and has therefore had a relatively large blood supply. For the same reasons, the muscles are made up of strong, tough fibres and the connective tissues are comparitively thick and tendinous. Either the amount of juice is small or it is thin and watery. There is no marbling. As a result, the meat is stringy, tough and inferior in flavour. The ratio of muscle to connective tissue is relatively low, as is also the ratio of flesh to bone. The grain is coarse, and the general appearance is watery or fibrous.

Quality depends on a number of secondary factors. Breeding and feeding are among the most important, but sex and age have an important bearing on the matter.

Quality determines the palatability of the meat and the ease with which it can be prepared for human consumption. Quality is, therefore, by all means the most important factor in determining grade. Determining quality is rather difficult, as quality pertains chiefly to the inner or concealed parts of the carcase, examination of which requires more than superficial inspection.

To determine quality exactly and absolutely it is necessary to have a cut surface, or cross section, exposed to view. But there is such a close relationship between conformation, finish and quality that the beef grader can nearly always count on a high degree of quality where the degrees of the other two factors is high.

Bearing these three detailed definitions of Conformation, Finish, and Quality in mind, it is now possible to examine with a fuller understanding the three Beef Grades proposed by the Ministry of Agriculture in 1929. These three grades, it may be recalled, were entitled respectively—" Select ", " Prime ", and " Good ", their precise descriptions being as follows: (4)

Select.—A Select Grade steer or maiden heifer beef carcase should have excellent conformation, finish and quality. It should be relatively short and stocky and heavily and uniformly fleshed. Rounds, loins and ribs should be extremely well developed and rounded. Chucks and plates should be unusually thick, compact and heavily fleshed. The neck should be very short and plump; shanks short and exceptionally well muscled. The superior muscular development of the round, extending well down towards the hock joint, should yield much beyond the average proportion of flesh in that cut. The spinal processes of the chine bone should terminate in fresh pinkish white cartilages.

The finish should be ideal, fat being neither excessive nor deficient. The exterior surface of the carcase, including shanks and neck, should be entirely covered with smooth fat that is not excessively thick or wasty at any point, the greatest breadth, which should not exceed ¾ inch, being over the loins and ribs; the interior walls should be well covered. Cod fat, or, in the case of a maiden heifer, udder fat, and kidney, aitch and other interior fats should be abundant but not excessive, also firm and ripe.

The flesh should be firm, velvety, very finely grained and of a light rosy or cherry red colour and in the thicker cuts should possess an abundance of marbling.

Prime.—A Prime Grade steer or maiden heifer beef carcase should have good conformation, finish and quality. In all respects it should be somewhat above the average. Rounds should be reasonably thick and heavily muscled; loins and ribs should be moderately full and plump. Chucks and plates should be broad and moderately thick. The neck should be moderately short and thick.

The fat covering should extend well over most of the exterior surface and generally be firm and smooth, but it may be somewhat patchy, especially over the rumps, loins, ribs and shoulders. The neck and lower part of the rounds, shoulders and shanks generally may have little fat covering. Cod fat, or, in the case of a maiden heifer, udder fat, and kidney, aitch and other interior fats may be either in moderate supply or somewhat excessive. Interior walls of the fore-quarters may be only partially covered. Usually, the fat should be firm, brittle and reasonably white, but may have a slightly higher colour.

The flesh generally should be moderately firm, the colour ranging from a light cherry red to a slightly darker red. The " eye " of the rib and loin should be above the average in thickness. Some marbling should be present in the thicker cuts.

Good.—A Good Grade carcase may be slightly irregular or rough in conformation and quality, but should be reasonably well finished. The frame may be slightly angular, the bones relatively prominent—the back slightly irregular, chucks and plates proportionally large, shanks and neck long, and rounds long and tapering. The fat covering should be fair, and there should be at least a small amount of cod (or udder) and kidney fats; other interior fats should be present. The flesh, however, should be of average thickness. In all, the carcase should be of average quality.

Cow carcases in this grade should have good conformation, except for a slight depression just in front of the rump. The loins and ribs should be relatively thick, and the rounds, while heavy, may be slightly lacking in depth. The shanks may be relatively long and tapering. With the exception of the neck and shin the carcase should be well covered with fat. There may be an inclination to patchiness on the loins and rump. The interior fats should be either in moderate or good supply, and should be of average quality. The aitch bone when cut through should show gristle. Absence of gristle indicates old cow beef and disqualifies the carcase from the grade.

These three suggested Grades of " Select ", Prime ", and " Good " were in fact accepted as official under the Agricultural Produce (Grading and Marking) Acts, 1928 and 1931. The underlying purpose of this official recognition was to assist the marketing of home-produced beef in competition with imported beef. It is evident from subsequent legislation concerning beef in Britain that this official assistance towards more methodical marketing was certainly insufficient if not altogether ineffective in making British beef production profitable, for the principle of a direct subsidy on home-killed beef was introduced only a few years afterwards.

Thus, under *The Cattle Industry (Emergency Provisions) Acts* of 1934–1936, a subsidy became payable on all steers, heifers, and cow heifers killing out at not less than 54 per cent. The subsidy amounted to 5s. per live cwt. if the animal was sold alive, or 9s. 4d. per cwt. of dressed carcase if sold on a dead-weight basis. It is of interest to note that the somewhat elaborate system of qualitative grading accepted in the Agricultural Produce (Grading and Marking) Acts of 1928 and 1931 was ignored in the Cattle Industry (Emergency Provisions) Acts of 1934–1936. In place of this system the only guide to quality taken into account was the killing out percentage, estimated on the hoof (live-weight) or ascertained on the hook (dead-weight). The minimum figure of 54 per cent corresponds to the B+ Grade under the present grading system of the Ministry of Food. The four lowest grades, B, B—, C+, and C would not have qualified for subsidy.

In an attempt to differentiate to a greater extent between the variable standards of quality above a killing out percentage of 54, the Livestock Industry Act, 1937, in revoking the previous Act of 1934–1936, introduced two standards of grading that qualified for subsidy. These two standards, *Ordinary* and *Quality*, had pre-scribed killing out percentages of 54 per cent and 57 per cent respectively. No further definition was laid down for these two grades.

The provisions of the 1937 Act were short-lived, because in 1938 the regulations were again changed. Subsequently the system of grading on killing out percentage alone was combined with the more qualitative definitions as laid down in the Agricultural Produce (Grading and Marking) Acts.

Subsequent to 1938 a differential subsidy was paid on two grades of Ordinary and Quality according to the following regulations:

> 1. In order that a steer, heifer or cow-heifer may be certified for the purposes of Part II of the Act, the animal, in the case of a steer or heifer, shall be one which, in the opinion of the Certifying Authority, conforms to one of the two standards hereinafter defined (which standards are in these Regulations referred to as the " Ordinary Standard " and the " Quality Standard " respectively), and in the case of a cow-heifer, shall be one which, in the opinion of the Certifying Authority, conforms to the ordinary standard.
>
> 2. (i) The Ordinary standard shall be as follows:
> The animal shall be reasonably well finished, the fat covering shall be fair, there shall be a reasonable amount of cod (or udder) fat, the flesh shall be of average thickness, and the animal shall be likely, so far as conformation and finish are concerned, to furnish a carcase conforming at least to the definitions of quality for the Good grade as prescribed in Regulations in force for the time being under the Agricultural Produce (Grading and Marking) Acts, 1928 and 1931.
>
> (ii) The Quality standard shall be as follows:
> The animal shall be compact, heavily and uniformly fleshed throughout, and relatively short in the leg; the hind quarters, buttocks, loins and ribs shall be well developed and rounded; the animal shall be ripe with excellent finish; the fat covering shall be uniform and the cod (or udder) fat shall be adequate and firm; the animal shall be likely, so far as conformation and finish are concerned, to furnish a carcase conforming to the definitions of quality for the Select grade as prescribed in Regulations in force for the time being under the Agricultural Produce (Grading and Marking) Acts, 1928 and 1931.
>
> 3. No certificate shall be issued for the purposes of Part of the Act in respect of:
> (i) A steer, heifer or cow-heifer unless the animal, as estimated by the Certifying Authority, has a killing-out percentage of not less than fifty four per cent . . . (5)

There was, of course, a difference in the subsidy scale according to whether the carcase qualified for Quality or Ordinary Grade. For a steer or heifer bred in the U.K. and of Quality standard, the subsidy payable was 7s. 6d. per live cwt. or 1½d. per lb. deadweight.

For a steer, heifer or cow-heifer, bred in the U.K. and of Ordinary standard, the subsidy payable was 5s. per live cwt. or 1d. per lb. dead-weight.

The corresponding subsidies for cattle imported into the U.K. (in practice these would be mainly Irish stores) were substantially less, being 5s. or 1d. for Quality grade and 2s. 6d. or ½d. for Ordinary grade.

This Beef Subsidy Scheme as modified from time to time continued until the outbreak of the Second World War in 1939 when the whole business of the marketing of fat cattle was taken over and completely reorganised by the Ministry of Food. The system of grading introduced then has continued, with numerous minor modifications from time to time, until to-day. It has been in operation for over a dozen years and has become by now a well-established agricultural institution.

There are two main principles involved. The first principle is that grades are fixed according to estimated killing out percentage. The second principle is that the payment for each grade varies according to season. The precise figures as regards pounds shillings and pence change according to the findings of the Annual Price Reviews but, throughout, the basic principle of payment according to estimated killing out percentage has been maintained. There are ten such grades.

	Estimated killing out percentage
1. Super Special . .	59 and over
2. Special . . .	58
3. A+ . . .	57
4. A	56
5. A— . . .	55
6. B+ . . .	54
7. B . . .	53
8. B— . . .	52
9. C+ . . .	51
10. C . . .	50

These grades are those applicable to steers, heifers and cow-heifers. Those applicable to fat cows differ in detail although not in principle. In the case of fat cows, the grades, eight in number, are as follows:

	Estimated killing out percentage
1. Special . . .	56 and over
2. A+ . . .	55
3. A	54
4. A— . . .	53
5. B+ . . .	52
6. B	51
7. B— . . .	50
8. Manufacturing . .	50–53

The definition of Manufacturing Grade of cow is as follows:

> Cows weighing 8¾ cwt. or less net live weight with an estimated killing out percentage of not less than 50 per cent and less than 53 per cent which in the opinion of the Certifying Authority will yield carcases fit only for manufacturing purposes. (6)

The System of Grading initiated by the Ministry of Food has given general satisfaction to the farming community. Few if any farmers wish to return to the method of the sale of fat cattle by public auction common in the pre-war era. There have, as was inevitable, been criticisms of minor features of the system, these being based in the main upon the relatively favourable return for the heavy weight animal which, according to pre-war standards, would have been deemed an over-weight animal; and upon the absence of any standards of quality beyond that afforded by estimated killing out percentage.

These objections have been met, at least in part, by price reductions for cattle over a certain live-weight and by a *Quality premium* awarded to cattle of moderate live-weight killing out at 55 per cent or over. The precise figures have varied from year to year and at different periods of the same year. The general intention of these modifications has been to offer a greater reward to the breeder and feeder of specialised beef cattle and rather less to the breeder and feeder of cattle that, to a certain extent, may be regarded as by-products of the dairy industry. The arguments for and against premiums for medium weights and penalties on heavy weights are somewhat as follows.

1. The advocates *for* premium and penalty base their argument mainly on the incontestable fact that previous to 1939, it was the well-finished beast of medium weight scaling not more than 10–12 cwt. at most that was in keenest demand. Animals above 12 cwt. were in fact somewhat difficult to sell. At least such was the case in Scottish markets.

2. The advocates *against* quality premiums and penalties for over-weight cattle argue that in times of meat scarcity, quantity is of far greater importance than quality and that, in any event, there is no conclusive evidence that the beef from heavy weight cattle is in any way inferior to that of others.

Actually, it depends very largely on what type of cattle individual farmers or districts are producing as to which set of arguments is advanced. There are vested interests as well as calories involved. Those in favour of premiums for medium and penalties for heavy weights are very frequently breeders or feeders of specialised beef cattle breeds in districts which in the past have been reputed to produce the best beef.

Those opposing both premiums and penalties are, in the main, rearers or feeders of dairy type cattle, beasts capable of reaching a high degree of finish provided they are given sufficient time to do it in. Consequently such cattle, before attaining a killing out percentage so high as 55 per cent, will, in all probability, have reached very heavy weights indeed.

The Ministry of Food's regulations are, to a certain extent, a compromise between these two points of view. There is a quality premium, but not a very high one. There is a price reduction on heavy weight cattle but not a very heavy one. In spite of quality premium and price reduction it still pays to go for weight.

Now, the Ministry's grading system is based on two and only two lines of strictly quantitative evidence and that, probably, is the strongest argument in favour of the Ministry's system. The system depends primarily:

(*a*) On the animal's live-weight.

(*b*) On its killing out percentage.

The first determination (*a*) can be made anywhere where adequate weighing facilities are available. The second determination, while based in the first place on a visual estimate, can be and on occasion *is* checked by actual weighing of the dressed carcase. The real strength of the Ministry's grading system lies in the fact that it is, for all its imperfections, a *quantitative* as opposed to a *qualitative* system of grading beef. It is, moreover, a simple system, which is of first importance. It is also a system taking into full account two of the most important points concerning beef, namely, weight and finish.

It does not, however, deal specifically with quality although quality, in all probability, is fairly closely correlated with finish. Nor does it deal specifically with conformation and that would seem to be its weakest point. Another weakness, although a minor one, is the somewhat unfortunate designations of the highest grades. Special and Super-special are words suggesting nearly perfect or perfect beef whereas much of the beef qualifying for these grades is very far from being perfect. It is of a high degree of finish, that is all, and finish is a quality that can be quite easily overdone.

At the same time the Ministry's system of grading while, like all things, imperfect, would seem, both because of its simplicity and the strictly quantitative data on which it is ultimately based, to be preferable to the pre-war systems, whether British or American. These earlier systems were very far from being simple and depended largely, it would seem altogether too largely, on data which were neither quantitative nor definable with any real degree of accuracy.

As an example, consider the definition of the grade called " Select " as prescribed under the Agricultural Produce (Grading and Marking) Acts of 1928 and 1931. The first sentence reads:

> A Select Grade steer or maiden heifer beef carcase should have excellent conformation, finish and quality.

What exactly is meant by the term " excellent "? Is it, by any conceivable stretch of the imagination, a standard that could be expected to remain constant from Grading Centre to Grading Centre and from one grader to another?

The definition goes on to say that the carcase should be " *relatively* short and stocky and heavily and uniformly fleshed. Rounds, loins and ribs should be *extremely* well developed and rounded. Chucks and plates should be *unusually* thick, compact and heavily fleshed. The neck should be *very* short and plump; shanks short and *exceptionally* well muscled." (Italics mine.)

This plethora of superlatives and comparatives can, in practice, mean very little to the guidance of a grader. It would happen, inevitably, that any grader would come to base his judgement on qualitative data, comparing them unconsciously if not deliberately rather with the average of his own Grading Centre than with national standards considered as a whole. Moreover, terms like " relatively ", " heavily ", " uniformly ", " extremely ", " unusually ", " very ", and " exceptionally " can never mean precisely the same thing to any two men, let alone to a numerous body of men working at widely dispersed Grading Centres throughout the country.

While it must be frankly admitted that many of the finer distinctions in beef quality are based on qualitative judgements, that does not and cannot upset the overriding consideration that any system of grading, if it is to be both useful and reliable, must above all things be quantitative in its nature and simple in its administration. It is greatly to be hoped that these fundamental considerations will be kept in mind if and when the present grading system under the Ministry of Food is superseded by one sponsored by the National Farmers' Union and embodied in a Fat Stock Marketing Scheme. The N.F.U. has already given some indication of its policy in this respect in its recent publication on the "Marketing of Fat Stock." (7)

In the first place the present system of sales on a live-weight basis is criticised on the grounds of its inaccuracy, and that with good reason. Dealing with this matter the Report states:

> It is recognised that some producers would prefer the continuation of the present practice of grading stock on the hoof at a local centre. The apparent advantage of such an arrangement is that the procedure of weighing is carried out literally under the eye of the producer, who knows at once the return which he will receive for the animals sold by him. It cannot be denied, however, that the method amounts to no more than intelligent estimation of the weight of carcase meat which the animal will yield on slaughter. It is true that *on an average* gradings have been reasonably close to the dead weight results but within these averages there is little doubt that considerable discrepancies occur in respect of individual animals. For this reason the system cannot be regarded as satisfactory to stock owners. (8)

This is perfectly fair criticism. The method is not nearly so accurate as is generally supposed. It is even less so in the case of cows than of other classes of cattle (9), and it must be remembered that cows constitute about half the total number of fat cattle coming to slaughter. Considering the present method in its entirety, it is probably true to say that the over-grading or under-grading of one week's consignment is corrected by a tendency in the opposite direction in the succeeding week; and that, occasionally, wide discrepancies occur between estimate and actuality. These discrepancies, if frankly revealed, would startle consignors, who might be jubilant or indignant, but in either event would most certainly be justifiably surprised.

The alternative suggested by the Report is that of payment of producers on a dead-weight and grade basis on the argument that:

> The grading of meat on the hook is a much more exact method of determining the quality and market value of an animal than grading on

the hoof. The farmer obtains a return on the known realisation of the
animals fed by him and thereby has the greatest incentive to produce in
accordance with market requirements. (10)

Leaving aside certain other considerations such as the individual
producer's freedom of action, the possibilities of mistaken identity
of carcases and so forth, there can be no doubt whatever that,
considered *purely as a question of grading*, grading on the hook is,
and must always be, incomparably more accurate than grading
on the hoof.

There remains the further question as to what system of grading
on the hook is proposed. On this important point the Report
gives no definite guidance, merely stating as a rather pious
platitude that:

> The scheme of grading must be one in which producers and distributors
> alike have confidence and which will encourage stock raisers to produce
> the type of animal commanding the best price. (11)

Presumably, as at present, the broad basis of payment will be
on weight—although on dead-weight in place of live-weight—
and on killing out percentage, but on a killing out percentage
accurately ascertained instead of merely estimated. Further
than that, it may prove more difficult to prescribe. It would be a
retrogression rather than an advance to revive grading of the
type embodied in the Agricultural Produce (Grading and
Marking) Acts, 1928 and 1931. As already suggested, grading
of that type may easily become so vague and subjective as to defy
the most conscientious attempts at uniform grading and in
addition prove too complex in practice for simple and straight-
forward administration.

Certain, more recent, schemes of grading beef carcases aim to
avoid, so far as is possible, the difficulties involved in subjective
judgements and qualitative estimations, doing so by introducing
as many objective measurements as possible. As an example of
such schemes, that devised by a group of New Zealand workers
may be discussed in rather more detail. (12) The scheme,
following Dr. John Hammond's teaching, lays great importance
on measurements of the " eye-muscle " and of the fat overlying
it. Anatomically speaking the eye-muscle is a cross-section of
the *longissimus dorsi* muscle cut, in this case, at the level between
the tenth and eleventh ribs. The scheme, designed for the grading

of New Zealand chilled beef carcases, is based on a scale of points as follows:

By measurement		*Points*
1. Fullness of meat (eye muscle depth)		20
2. Fat cover (depth over eye muscle)		15
3. Blockiness (length of leg in crutch)		20
4. Balance of carcase (fore-end—hind-end weight) .		10
5. Weight suitability		5
		70

By eye judgement	*Points*
6. Rib cover (muscle and fat) (5), and evenness of fat distribution (10)	15
7. Colour and texture of muscle	5
8. Colour and texture of fat	5
9. Marbling of muscle (finish)	5
	30

An important advantage of this scheme is that 70 per cent of points are based on measurement and only 30 per cent on eye judgements. Actually, several of the eye judgements such as colour of fat and lean, degree of marbling, etc. could quite easily be made quantitative by comparison with accepted standards.

The system is designed to emphasise " the major importance of muscle development, blockiness and fat cover in the beef animal ". (13)

Other, although similar, schemes might aim to emphasise other desirable points in beef carcase conformation, finish, or quality. Obviously the exact number of points allotted to each measurement or eye judgement is capable of infinite variation. The two overriding considerations in any such system or scheme of beef grading would appear to be

1. To make it as quantitative as possible.
2. To keep it as simple as possible.

Finally, it would indubitably be a mistake were market requirements, as embodied in a grading scheme, permitted to dominate production. This danger is implicit in all rigid systems of grading and of payment according to grades. This was clearly proved by experience under the pre-war Pigs Marketing Scheme where market standards for bacon pigs were prescribed with such mathematical and minute accuracy, that the range of husbandry conditions under which bacon pigs could be successfully produced was becoming dangerously limited. Bacon pig production was developing into a specialist enterprise not, as had been hoped, into a profitable venture on the average mixed farm.

This danger is far greater in the case of beef. The specialist production of beef in this country is likely to be limited, unless beef is permitted to rise to an almost prohibitive price. There might well be a limited market for such luxury beef, as there is still, in spite of attempted income equalisation, a market for fresh salmon and caviare.

On the other hand the main beef supplies of the nation are likely to come, as they do now come, from dairy herds. Beef in Britain, despite a great deal of sentimental nonsense about the roast beef of old England, has been to an ever-increasing extent a by-product of the English dairy since it ceased to be one of the English plough. It would therefore be an error to be too harshly critical in the grading of such beef. In this connection a recent remark of Mr. Maurice Passmore is very relevant. He has said:

" Can we be critical of cow beef and heavy-weight cattle when we are eating donkeys, whales and reindeer? " (14)

We may be critical but we dare not be too unfriendly. Whether we like it or not, in future years a great proportion of this country's beef supplies will come out of the dairy as an inevitable by-product of milk production. A great deal of that beef will be cow beef and although cow beef is not the best beef it is very greatly preferable to no beef. Consequently any system of grading adopted must not be too severe upon cow beef. Encouragement and reward for the best beef, certainly, but nothing in the nature of penalties for beef of rather lower standard if we are to make the best use of the source of beef most readily available to our hands.

What is true of the dairy is equally true of the hills. Too high grading standards for beef might discourage rather than encourage the greatly desired extension of cattle rearing on hill land. In this connection a very pertinent warning was sounded by Mr. Duncan M. Stewart of Millhills in a paper read before the British Society of Animal Production in 1949. (15) While admitting that the main reason for the disappearance of cattle from the hills of Scotland was their replacement by sheep, he drew attention also to another, less widely recognised cause yet one which, to quote Mr. Stewart, " . . . can flare up like a scourge and again drive the hardy types of cattle from our hills. This second cause was the premium paid, prior to 1939, for what was called baby beef. If our arable farmer, who fed cattle, wanted to fill his fields or courts with beasts, he looked for the small, neat beast that had never lost its calf flesh and that could be sold at between 12 and 18 months of age. That kind of a beast can never be raised successfully on our Scottish hills, although on marginal farms it had an undoubted hold. If the ' powers that be ' extend their generosity too far in paying a premium for what is called ' quality ' and if they ever come to judge quality by age, then the day of the hardy hill cow is done."

That such a warning is by no means superfluous is suggested by the N.F.U's Joint Working Party's statement of Marketing Objectives which reads: (16)

> Since the objective of good marketing must be to supply the public with best quality meat which will command the best prices the policy of the Board must be to give the producers the greatest incentive to cater for this class of trade and, conversely, to discourage the sale of stock which could produce inferior grades of meat.

The sentiment expressed in the first part of this statement is altogether praiseworthy. The producer of first-class beef should have his due reward provided customers are available to pay him that reward. The second clause in the Statement of Objectives would, however, appear to be somewhat premature. This is unfortunately no time to discourage the producer of any class of genuine beef by a particular system of quality grading nor in any other way while, " we are eating donkeys, whales and reindeer ", in the words of Mr. Maurice Passmore's arresting phrase.

REFERENCES

(1) Report on the Marketing of Cattle and Beef in England and Wales, *Economic Series*, No. 20, p. 106, 1929, Min. Agric. and Fish.
(2) Hammond, J., and Mansfield, W. S. (1936). " Investigations on producing quality in beef," *J. Min. Agric.*, **42,** 977.
(3) Report on the Marketing of Cattle and Beef in England and Wales, p. 168, 1929, *ibid.*
(4) *Ibid.*, p. 116.
(5) The Cattle Subsidy Regulations, 1938.

(6) Ministry of Food, " Livestock Control—Prices of Fat Cattle, etc."
    16th Ed. (Cattle), March, 1951.

(7) " Marketing of Fat Stock " (1952).   Report and Recommendations of a
    Joint Working Party of the National Farmers' Unions of England and
    Wales, Scotland, and Northern Ireland.

(8) *Ibid.*, p. 10.

(9) Callow, E. H. (1945).   " The food value, quality and grading of meat
    with special reference to beef."   *Report Brit. Soc. Anim. Prod.*, p. 40.

(10) " Marketing of Fat Stock " (1952).   *Ibid.*, p. 9.

(11) *Ibid.*, p. 42.

(12) Kneebone, H., Marks, T., McMeekan, C. P., and Walker, D. E. (1950).
    " Evaluation of the chilled beef carcase," *N.Z. J. Science and Technol.*,
    Vol. 31, Sec. A (5), 3.

(13) *Ibid.*, p. 4.

(14) Passmore, M. (1951).   " Cattle feeding in the Midlands," *Proc. Brit. Soc.
    Anim. Prod.*, p. 68.

(15) Stewart, D. M. (1949).   *Rpt. Proc. Brit. Soc. Anim. Prod.*, p. 43.

(16) " Marketing of Fat Stock " (1952).   *Ibid.*, p. 19.

Fig. 16. WHITE SHORTHORN BULL.

Fig. 17. PERTH BULL SALE. Judging the Shorthorns.

Fig. 18. ABERDEEN-ANGUS BULL.

Fig. 19. ABERDEEN-ANGUS COW.

IN opening the discussion on the British breeds of beef cattle, it is only right and proper to commence with the Shorthorn. No breed has had a greater influence upon the world's cattle. No breed has had so many ardent disciples devoted to its breeding, its distribution, its history. At times the breeding of Shorthorns has threatened a divorce from commercial stock husbandry in becoming a cult. So much has been said, written, and published about Shorthorns that the results of specialised Shorthorn documentation and research would crowd the shelves of a capacious library. It would be superfluous, even were it possible, to go into the whole classical story in detail here. Suffice it, then, to say that in the latter half of the eighteenth century there existed, in that corner of North-Eastern England of which the town of Darlington is the market centre, a variety or breed of cattle, no doubt diverse in colour and in type, but distinguished by the fact that they bore short horns as contrasted with the Longhorn breed of cattle, at that time predominant over the greater part of England. Whether these short-horned cattle owed something or more than something to the importation of Dutch cattle must remain a matter for argument and speculation. Apparently there is no certain evidence either for or against the possibility. That grounds for such speculation exist may be supported by the known fact that certain of the cattle breeders of North-East England visited the Low Countries so convenient to their shores, and that the representations of cattle in Dutch paintings of that or earlier periods are strongly reminiscent of the rougher type of Shorthorn sometimes seen in England to this day.

In any case it so happened that from the matrix of Teeswater short-horned cattle was fashioned the Shorthorn cattle breed as we know it in our times. The tool used was the selective in-breeding practised, some would say initiated by Robert Bakewell (1726–1795) of Dishley Grange, Loughborough in the county of Leicester. To Bakewell, as pupils, came the brothers Colling,

Charles and Robert. Charles Colling of Ketton (1750–1836), at the suggestion of George Culley (author of *Observations on Live Stock* and a great admirer of Bakewell), made a prolonged visit to Dishley Grange in the year 1783, and was for a time joined there by his brother, Robert.

" After their visits to Bakewell about 1783 they returned with the determination to do for the Shorthorns what they conceived he had accomplished for the Longhorns, and to adopt the same system." (1)

In fact, they did a great deal more. Possibly because they had better initial stock to breed from, the Collings succeeded in beating their master at his own game. It came to pass that it was the Shorthorn as fashioned by Charles and Robert Colling that drove the Longhorn, both improved and unimproved, from the meadow lands of England. The game itself, however, remained Bakewell's game, " systematic principles of breeding, as opposed to the chance mating of nobody's son with everybody's daughter ". (2)

Taking the dual-purpose Shorthorn cow of their native district as a foundation, they began the long road to beef specialisation which was to lead the Shorthorn, first to Scotland, and then abroad over the entire pastoral world.

" The Colling brothers aimed to improve the general symmetry and flesh points of their animals. They were concerned first with the cheap production of meat, taking milk as a by-product." (3)

" The improvement effected by the Collings in the conformation of the Shorthorns was very marked, but their animals were stated to be inferior to the unimproved Teeswater cattle as milk producers." (4)

It is probably wrong to suppose—although to-day the point is one mainly of theoretical interest—that the Collings, in breeding towards beef conformation, made any *deliberate* sacrifice of the milking qualities of their cattle. It may not even have occurred to them that specialisation towards beef involved any sacrifice of milk. Even after the experience of one and a half centuries there are still breeders of Beef Shorthorns who are prepared to deny such a proposition. Thus Marson, writing in 1950, states that " . . . nine-tenths of the milk supply of Buenos Aires comes from Scotch Shorthorns ". (5)

Very possibly the Collings presumed that their native Shorthorn cattle, in their time noted for dairy qualities, would go on milking deeply however they were bred.

In any case, in the England of their time, it was beef rather than milk that was in greatest demand and the Collings achieved success with their beef specialised and in-bred cattle.

" It was by the use of Collings' bulls upon stock of the same kind from which the Collings had made the bulk of their earliest selections, that the Shorthorns were multiplied rapidly enough to meet the demand which occurred when the merits of the improved breed became generally known." (6)

Nor were the Collings wanting in appreciation of the sweet uses of advertisement.

" Advertisement was resorted to by the exhibition, for a time, of breeding stock at the few shows then available for them; while a wider public was reached by the fattening and exhibiting of such animals as Chas. Colling's ' Durham Ox ' and R. Colling's ' The White Heifer that Travelled ' both by Favourite 252." (7)

The success of the Collings in breeding Shorthorns was sealed at the Ketton dispersion sale where Charles Colling sold the bull " Comet 155 " for one thousand guineas. In an age when guineas were still golden and taxation trivial, a thousand guineas was a great deal of money. " Comet's " sale became a Shorthorn legend and so did " Comet " !

" It is mentioned by Mr. Thornton in the article on ' Ancient Shorthorns ' that when Comet died he was buried in the centre of the paddock at Cleasby, three miles from Darlington, where he had been kept, and a chestnut tree planted on his grave. The paddock is known as Comet's garth to this day." (8)

Following the dispersion of the two Collings' herds, that of Charles Colling in 1810 and of Robert Colling eight years later, the apostolic mantle of Shorthorn breeding descended first upon the shoulders of the Booth family and of their contemporary Thomas Bates, and later on those of the Cruickshank brothers, Amos and Anthony, in far-off Aberdeenshire.

The Booths and Thomas Bates came near to rending the mantle between them and, for a time, the Shorthorn world was divided into two camps around their respective standards. The Booth policy was to continue that of specialisation towards beef which the Collings had laid down.

" Thomas Booth (died 1835) started before 1790 to use a succes-

sion of inbred Colling bulls in his herd and followed them with
home-bred sires, selecting primarily for ' flesh making capacity
and breadth of back and loin '." (9)

The Colling strain of Shorthorns had, apparently, already
become a specialised beef breed. The " nurse cow ", that
symptom of milking capacity deterioration, was already in use
in the Collings' herds. (10)

The Booth family continued along the same beef road.

" The striking feature, however, is the almost complete lack
of reference to the Booth strain as milking animals." (11)

Thomas Bates (1775–1849) had rather different views regarding the degree of beef specialisation to which Shorthorn breeding
should go.

" Mr. Bates . . . paid special attention to the milking properties
of his cattle." (12)

Not that there is any evidence of his intention of transforming
the Shorthorn into a specialised dairy animal. His aim seems
rather to have been to resist any further sacrifice of milk in pedigreed Shorthorns because, even in Bates' time, the non-pedigree
Shorthorns were already reputed superior in that respect. Thus,
dealing with Bates' Shorthorns, Stewart writes:

" His cattle were of fine appearance and though generally
held to be good milkers were said to be inferior in this particular
quality to the non-pedigree or unimproved Shorthorn." (13)

That divergence in milking capacity between pedigreed and
non-pedigreed Shorthorns was destined to grow with the years,
until the foundation of the Dairy Shorthorn (Coates' Herd Book)
Association in the year 1905.

This Herd Book of Coates had its origin, of course, at a much
earlier date. It was the child of a Mr. George Coates, himself a
Shorthorn breeder, who in 1822, after spending ten years collecting
information, published the first Shorthorn Herd Book as a private
venture. This record of Shorthorn pedigrees was taken over by
the Shorthorn Society of Great Britain in 1872, but it is still
known as " Coates' Herd Book ". It has always been a hospitable
publication, willing to embrace sections of the Shorthorn world
returning to the fold; and to cling to those sections showing a
restless disposition to break away from the fold. It might, indeed,
have clarified matters, and certainly simplified discussion, had
the Dairy Shorthorn Association broken away from the parent

Shorthorn Society in 1905, thereby establishing an autonomous dual-purpose breed. It must be difficult to combine two separate ideals of what a Shorthorn should be within a single breed society.

Quite evidently, even so early in Shorthorn history, much of the somewhat embittered rivalry between Bates and Booths was due to this divergence of breeding purpose as well as being based on more personal considerations. Bates was a very pious person—he was, in fact, nicknamed " Bible Bates "—but he never learnt to love his neighbour's cattle as his own.

The rivalry between the Bates cattle and the Booth cattle tended, as the years went on, to degenerate into a scramble for paper. Pedigree, in the Shorthorn world, became more important than cattle, so that representatives of a great cattle breed, bred primarily for one or for two solid agricultural purposes, came to be bought, sold, and exported as though they were articles of antique furniture.

According to Stewart (13), there developed very early a divergence between the preferences of the home breeder and those of the export trade, " the general preference in Britain being for Booth stock, Bates' cattle finding more favour with overseas buyers ". Thus to the divergence of opinion as to what kind of animal a Shorthorn should be at home was added the further complication of what the export trade expected in a Shorthorn to satisfy the preferences of buyers from abroad.

" Concentration on the pedigrees rather than the individual merits of animals continued until the disastrous farming year of 1879; this year marked the beginning of the decline in Shorthorn breeding as a business, a hobby or a fancy." (14)

Cattle diseases, meat refrigeration, and depressed agricultural prices certainly brought the majority of Shorthorn breeders tumbling down out of the realms of breeding fancy on to more solid ground.

Of these various depressing factors, meat refrigeration was, undoubtedly, the most potent and prolonged in its effects. Prior to its invention and the importation of meat of high quality that so swiftly followed, the generality of British farmers were very probably, at times, tempted to follow the lead of the Collings and the Booths in their efforts to change the old dual-purpose Shorthorn into a purely beef breed. The economic results of refrigeration led them away from temptation.

To appreciate that point it is necessary to understand the sequence of economic changes that influenced the developmen of English agriculture during the nineteenth century. The generat picture is that of a prosperous country with a rapidly increasing population, with expanding industry, and a rising standard of living; a country clamorous for food and able to pay well for that food. So long, therefore, as any product of British agriculture continued to be free from foreign competition, it remained a profitable product. Whenever foreign imports became plentiful, however, that profit vanished because production costs in the newer countries of the world were so very much lower. The British farmer, therefore, during the course of the nineteenth century was in the unfortunate position of finding his monopoly of the home market first threatened and then finally broken in one commodity after another, first wool, then grain, then meat, finally dairy produce. He was left with an effective monopoly of liquid milk and of that alone, and it was very fortunate for him that rapid revolutions in transport, first from horse to rail, and later from rail to road, enabled him to take advantage of a potential demand in exploiting that new market, for the monopoly of beef supply to the British consumer was no longer his.

" From 1880 onwards the increasing costs of production and the appearance of overseas meat in the British market in increasing quantities began to affect the British cattle industry." (15)

The prospects of a thriving British beef industry were fading. At the same time those of the British dairying industry, provided always it was catering for the liquid milk market, were expanding.

" In 1865 only three million gallons of country milk were brought to London. In a year the quantity had doubled. The present figure exceeds a hundred and fifty million gallons." (16)

Both the tendency and the incentive in the British cattle industry during the last quarter of the nineteenth and during the first half of the twentieth centuries have, therefore, been to swing from beef to milk production. It so happened, however, that the Shorthorn, of the old, dual-purpose, unpedigreed type, was the predominant cattle breed throughout the greater part of England when the change began. Admittedly many of these unpedigreed Shorthorn dairy herds were termed " Shorthorn " more by courtesy than by right. " ... many so-called Shorthorns are of mixed, or even of mongrel, origin." Nevertheless they were of predominantly Shorthorn type, so that " As regards the ordinary stock of the country in 1908, according to the census taken by the Board of Agriculture in that year, no less than five-eights of the cattle in England were of the Shorthorn type." (18)

Very naturally, under the new market conditions of the twentieth century, when milk became the salvation of English agriculture, the English farmer became more determined than ever to keep his unpedigreed Shorthorn cattle to the dual purpose type, and let the British Shorthorn Society develop its pedigreed Shorthorn cattle as it thought fit, in a splendid but increasing isolation. This resistance by the breeder of unpedigreed Shorthorns was increased by the influence of the Scotch Shorthorn in turning the whole breed further towards beef specialisation.

The Shorthorn, whatever its type, is, of course, an English breed. Scotsmen borrowed it. The breed was introduced into Scotland first by Robertson of Ladykirk in the county of Berwick, and by Rennie of Phantassie in East Lothian. Both were in touch with early breeders of Shorthorns in England, including the Collings. The first Shorthorn bull to be sent into Aberdeenshire is said to have come from Phantassie. Actually, the estate of Ury, where Captain Barclay bred his Shorthorns, lies in Kincardine to the south of Aberdeen, but it was Captain Barclay—laird, farmer, sportsman, and eccentric—who, by twice dispersing his herd chiefly among local buyers, distributed the best type of the Shorthorn cattle of his time among the tenant farmers of the more northerly county.

These Aberdeenshire breeders had inherited a tradition based on beef cattle, first in rearing beef stores for the Southern market and later in fattening these stores on the basis of the turnips and oat-straw their county grew so well. They were uninterested in milk. There was no convenient market except the relatively small city of Aberdeen. They were too far distant, considering the transport facilities of their time, to take advantage of the expanding demand for milk in the bigger industrial centres of the South, the nearest of which lay in the Clyde and Forth basin. In the relative isolation, therefore, of North-Eastern Scotland, the task of developing the Shorthorn into a purely beef breed, a task begun by the Collings and the Booths in North England, was carried to completion. There came to be developed what was in essence a new breed, the Beef Shorthorn or the Scotch Shorthorn, these terms being synonymous, a breed differing essentially from the type of dual-purpose Shorthorn the average English farmer still wished to preserve. Amos Cruickshank, of the farm of Sittyton within easy riding distance of the town of Aberdeen, was the real founder of this new breed.

Marson, writing of the Scotch Shorthorn, states that: " . . . its creation was due to the brothers Cruickshank of Sittyton, who began by one Shorthorn from Durham in 1837 and by 1855 had over 300 head, the largest herd of pedigreed Shorthorns in Britain." (2)

Great cattleman though Amos Cruickshank undoubtedly was, perhaps too much credit is customarily accorded him in developing the reputation of his own herd in particular and of the Scotch Shorthorn in general. Cruickshank's real success began with the birth of " Champion of England " sired by " Lancaster Comet ", and " Lancaster Comet " was not bred at Sittyton. Nor was the purchase of " Lancaster Comet " by Amos Cruickshank any chance affair, although he is reported to have expressed disappointment when that somewhat aged bull was delivered to his farm.

To John Wilkinson, tenant of the farm of Lenton near Nottingham, some of that credit is due. Amos Cruickshank paid a visit to Lenton in the year 1852. He went there on the recommendation of a Mr. Sanday of Holme-Pierrepont farm, also near Nottingham, with whom he happened to be staying. Of the Lenton herd Amos is reputed to have said: " I accordingly went to Lenton, and to my surprise I there found the finest herd of Shorthorns I had ever beheld. I had never met with anything like them before." (20)

It would seem, then, that at Lenton, in 1852, Amos Cruickshank saw in the flesh the ideal he had been striving to attain for fifteen years, ever since " in 1837 he paid a visit to Durham and brought home his first Shorthorn, a single heifer ". (21)

It was with the picture of the Lenton herd in his mind that from the farm-house of Sittyton and in the autumn of 1858, he wrote to Wilkinson of Lenton, asking him whether he had a good young red-coloured bull he could sell.

" Wilkinson replied he could not, but recommended him to take ' Lancaster Comet 11, 663 ' then about eight years old, which he offered to let him have at little more than butcher's price." (22)

After some hesitation and further search in other Shorthorn herds, Amos accepted Wilkinson's offer. The sequel is classical Shorthorn history. " Lancaster Comet " arrived, was thought lightly of; was turned out into the bleak Aberdeenshire autumn pastures with some cows. There he took rheumatism and died, but before his death he had sired " Champion of England ". Perhaps, more fittingly, this historic calf might have been named " Champion of the Americas ", for his progeny was destined to populate the prairies and pampas of that great continent.

The importance of " Champion of England " in establishing a fixed type in the Sittyton herd is thus described by Marson (23):

" At Sittyton, Lancaster Comet sired Champion of England (17526) out of Virtue by Plantagenet (57868). This deep-bodied, short-legged roan (calved November 29, 1859) was remarkable for his covering of natural flesh and abundant coat of hair, and proved one of the greatest Shorthorn characters that ever lived, for he consolidated Sittyton and founded a world dynasty. His prepotency was great, his daughters being as good as his sons, of whom fourteen were used at Sittyton, and in addition, grandsons and great grandsons."

It is, in fact, to the in-bred progeny of " Champion of England " that the foundation of the Scotch Beef Shorthorn in its modern form is really due. The export trade to the Americas, a main support of the breed to-day, must be awarded to the credit of the same great bull.

" . . . American buyers gave the new type a trial; it throve on the prairies, and the buyers came back for more, and then for more again. Meantime new herds, destined to be almost as famous as the Sittyton one itself, were being built up with Cruickshank blood in Aberdeenshire—by Marr of Uppermill, Duthie of Collynie, and many others." (24)

Amos Cruickshank sold his bulls for export or for crossing among his neighbours' cattle.

" Almost the whole of Cruickshank's young stock was exported and it was not until 1889, when a Sittyton sire figured prominently in the Royal Show, that English breeders recognised the value of the Scottish Shorthorns." (25)

The recoil of the Scotch Beef Shorthorn—like a boomerang—into the English Shorthorn herds, was to have important repercussions on the history of the whole breed. The return of the

Scotch Shorthorn, after its prolonged sojourn in the Northern wilderness, was the return of a prodigal son, purified in that it had become a true beef breed, without any pretensions to dual purpose. Once Scotch Shorthorn bulls were used in the pedigreed English Shorthorn herds, they served to widen the gap between the pedigreed Shorthorn, already leaning to beef rather than to milk, and the unpedigreed English Shorthorn, retaining the dual-purpose character of the original stock from which the pedigreed Shorthorn sprang. These unpedigreed dual-purpose Shorthorns were then, and were to remain until a much later date, the almost universal dairy cow of English town byre and dairy farm.

" The distinction between registered and non-registered cattle appears to have been a real one at the beginning of the twentieth century based not only on entry into Coates' Herd Book, but also on the predominant characteristics of each group. There were, of course, notable exceptions, but registered Shorthorn cattle were of high repute mainly because of their carcase qualities, while a large proportion of the commercial non-registered Shorthorns were popular primarily because of their dairy qualities." (26)

It was this increasing divergence between the registered and unregistered sections of the Shorthorn breed, rapidly becoming a dangerous schism between what the breeder of pedigreed Shorthorns bred and what the majority of those who kept unregistered Shorthorns wanted, that led to the foundation of the Dairy Shorthorn (Coates' Herd Book) Association in the year 1905. The objects of this new association—a breed society within a breed society—are best explained in the words of Mr. C. R. W. Adeane, chairman of the inaugural meeting:

" It was necessary something should be done to maintain the position of the Shorthorn as a dairy cow. The farmer required an animal which would yield a large amount of milk, and was capable at the same time of carrying flesh; the Dairy Shorthorn was the ideal animal for the purpose. The association would, by offering prizes for milk tests, by securing classes for Dairy Shorthorns, and by recommending judges, do their best to sustain and popularise the Shorthorn for dairy purposes—a breed which had for so many years been so justly famous for beef. There was no question of starting a separate Herd Book, and they had the approval of the Shorthorn Council." (27)

Perhaps, for the future of the Shorthorn it might have been sounder policy to split the breed. Breeders of Beef Shorthorns had, by 1905, established too valuable an export trade to the great beef-producing countries to risk any renewed flirtation with the dual-purpose ideal. Those interested in the Shorthorn as a dairy animal needed an undivided allegiance to that ideal in order to meet the menacing competition of another dairy breed. For in 1909, only four years after the foundation of the Dairy Shorthorn Association, the British Friesian Society was formed in this country. This relatively new breed in Britain was to prove the greatest rival the Dairy Shorthorn has yet had to face.

The partnership of the Scotch Beef Shorthorn and the English Dairy Shorthorn in the same Herd Book and Breed Society has never seemed a very sensible one and from time to time moves towards separation have been made, most recently (at the time of writing) at the annual meeting of the South-Eastern Shorthorn Breeders' Association held in London in February 1952. There the suggestion was put forward of splitting Coates' Herd Book into two sections, one for dairy stock and one for beef. It was also stated that Britain is the only country without separate sections for the two types of Shorthorns.

In addition to containing two very different types of cattle, one pure beef, the other dual-purpose, the capacious lap of Coates' Herd Book has from time to time received the Lincoln Red Shorthorn, described briefly below. It will also, through its Dairy Shorthorn Association, accept the up-graded progeny out of approved unregistered cows. Contrasted with the other two main beef breeds of Britain, Aberdeen-Angus and Hereford, which have closed herd books, the open nature of the Shorthorn Herd Book is at first sight surprising. The arguments for and against open or closed herd books are much too wide for adequate discussion here. It might be suggested, however, that the open Shorthorn Herd Book is associated with the determination of certain sections of the Shorthorn Society to maintain dual-purpose type, and with the indubitable fact that for a long term of years the best milking strains of Shorthorn were unregistered.

To outline the history of a livestock breed is one thing, to assess its present or future utility quite another. History can only be fairly questioned on the grounds of inaccuracy of statement or of bias in interpretation. To attempt any assessment of the absolute or relative value of any one breed, especially compared with others, is to invite criticism. To any man breeding livestock his own breed appears the best, otherwise, presumably, he would not be breeding it. He resents, naturally and sometimes fiercely, any suggestion that *his* breed is *not* the best. The result is that in most publications concerning cattle each breed in turn is painted in the most glowing colours. All cattle, it would seem, are productive, hardy, beloved of butchers or dairymen, some-times by both, adaptable, thrifty, economical. Such encomiums, while warding off criticism, are plainly useless to student, farmer, or interested reader. They say nothing and mean nothing. Admittedly any criticism or comparison must of necessity be based on what is, at best, a personal judgement and opinion. These cannot be final, they dare not be dogmatic. Yet, if a man does not write what he, in all honesty, thinks, why write at all?

Leaving aside the Dairy Shorthorn for the moment for later consideration among the dual-purpose breeds, let us consider the Beef or Scotch Shorthorn as a breed on its own, claiming world renown on its beefing properties. First of all, what have the breeders themselves to say of the Beef Shorthorn? (28)

> What are these characteristics which have made the "Scotch" Shorthorn a favourite with cattle breeders throughout the world? They are those which are built round the ideal frame of the Shorthorn, a frame squarely set on four short legs, set well apart, a frame with a wide spring of rib and well down in the fore-rib; a great broad back with plenty of scope for a good constitution; a frame with length from the hook bones to the tail-head where the best of the meat is formed. The fleshing characteristic too, is one which gives the Shorthorn a smooth back line with a springiness to the touch, a fine deep flank with flesh well let down, the loins well covered right back to the tail and square and not sloping in the manner of the poorer grades of cattle, the hind-quarters from the tail almost to the hock joint covered with even flesh both to the back and the side, the whole animal having a blocky appearance, without either unevenness or thinness of flesh. The fine large quiet eye in a head with strength of character lets the discerning breeder know that the "Scotch" Shorthorn is a good feeder.

Actually, the qualities of the Beef Shorthorn require no adver-tisement. With the Aberdeen-Angus and the Hereford it holds an unchallenged position as one of the three great beef cattle breeds of the world. Yet the position of the Beef Shorthorn in Britain to-day is a trifle ambiguous. More than any other breed of British livestock it is one with its eyes turned overseas.

"What is the potential market for the 'Scotch' Shorthorn?

At present there are two distinct market demands for the breed—one from the pedigree breeder in Great Britain and overseas; the other from the commercial breeder of good store cattle in Great Britain who requires a beef bull for crossing with his cows. The former of the two markets embraces both the home market and a considerable export trade, largely to the Argentine, U.S.A. and Canada, but also to Australia and South Africa." (29)

As is well known, it is the export trade, particularly to the Americas, North and South, that has governed the development of the Beef Shorthorn from its beginning.

Amos Cruickshank made a name for the breed in America long before it was appreciated at home. Indeed, only a financial accident saved the whole Sittyton herd from going to the Argentine once Amos decided to retire. Since Cruickshank's time the eyes of every ambitious breeder of Beef Shorthorn cattle have been fixed on the export market. To hold that market Shorthorn breeders, for many years now, have produced, and must continue to produce, what the export market requires and what the export market *does* require is an early maturing, heavily fleshed beef bull. It prefers a Shorthorn bull to be of certain colours, most frequently a dark red, but the essential feature of its requirements is that the Shorthorn shall be bred purely for beef.

In direct contrast to the export market, the largest section of the potential home market for pedigreed Shorthorn bulls is the commercial non-pedigree, dual-purpose English herd. This market does not want Shorthorn bulls bred purely for beef. It wants a Shorthorn bull with a good recorded milk pedigree behind it. Consequently there is no opening for the Scotch or Beef Shorthorn there.

The main potential demand for Beef Shorthorn bulls at home—and it is still a limited one—is for crossing with heifers and cows of certain of our native hill breeds, particularly the West Highland. This question is discussed more fully in the section of this book dealing with Hill Cattle, but it may be said here that the Beef Shorthorn is by far the best breed to use in getting earlier maturity and an improved beef conformation on to the calves from a Highland cow. Practical breeders often talk of using the Beef Shorthorn to " break down " the Highland towards beef, and the term is expressive. It was for a rather similar purpose, namely, in the breaking down of more slowly maturing and rangy cattle towards beef, that the Scotch Beef Shorthorn first made its great reputation abroad.

The white Beef Shorthorn bull has a special value in crossing with the Galloway, since the uniform blue-grey calf resulting from this cross has gained a very high reputation as a feeder.

Nevertheless, it must be admitted that the existing stocks of hill cattle, not all of which, in any case, are of Highland or Galloway breed, are quite insufficient to induce any breeder of pedigreed Beef Shorthorns to cater for their demands. Even were the hill cattle stocks of this country greatly to increase, they would still offer too small an incentive. Apart altogether from a possible increase in the *number* of bulls such hill stocks might require, there is the further difficulty of price. The cost of production of a pedigreed bull calf of one of the leading beef breeds cannot be less than £200, and breeders of hill cattle have grown accustomed to buying their bulls at a figure far lower than that. At the present time the home market for Beef Shorthorn bulls, such as it is, is being quite heavily subsidised by the export market. To put the matter shortly, bluntly, but I believe quite honestly, without the export demand, or the ambition to reap the benefits of that export demand, there would be no Beef Shorthorns bred in Britain to-day.

While no British breed has had a greater influence on the world's cattle, at the same time, probably no breed is less in touch with the agriculture of its country of origin.

For the breeder of Beef Shorthorns, the continuance of the export demand is therefore of first importance. He could hardly go on breeding Shorthorns without it. What, then, are its future prospects? Consider the Argentine export demand, for it is still the most important, although compared with former days perhaps relatively less so. Other countries, particularly Canada and Australia, take more of the high-priced Shorthorns away from Perth than they used to do. Argentine takes away more bulls of other breeds, particularly of the Aberdeen-Angus breed, than she used to do. Will the Argentine, and other overseas countries, continue to buy the best of the Scotch Beef Shorthorn bulls at a price which enables those bulls they reject to be sold below production costs on the home market?

The Argentine demand for these bulls is, in any case, somewhat of a biological puzzle. There is an abundance of pure-bred

Beef Shorthorns in the Argentine already. There have been many of them there for quite a long time. The up-grading of slowly maturing, rangy native cattle to the standard of the Beef Shorthorn has been completed.

" Most of the big herds have been graded up from the native cattle, but they are now absolutely pure Shorthorn, Aberdeen-Angus and Hereford." (30)

Why then the annual importation out of Scotland?

Is it in search of superior genetic material? Surely, after at least seventy years of buying the best Scotch Shorthorn bulls, not to mention the importation of female stock, the Argentine must by now contain an adequate sample of all the desirable genes the Shorthorn breed contains.

Is it the persistence of a tradition—a fashion if one cares to call it so—from the latter part of the nineteenth century, when the Argentine was rapidly grading up its native cattle to take advantage of meat refrigeration and the London Smithfield market and when the importation of bulls was an easily understood necessity? The history of the international Beef Shorthorn trade in the present century hardly gives support to that view. Twice already in this century the trade has been completely interrupted by world war, first between 1914 and 1918 for a four-year period, and again between 1939 and 1945 over a six-year period. Had the importation of Scotch bulls been due to the inertia of tradition, to fashion, to misconception, or to mere superstition, then two repeated interruptions of normal trading would have proved to the Argentine cattle ranchers beyond cavil that they had been wasting money and time, and that they could breed as good Beef Shorthorns for themselves in the Argentine as they could hope to buy at the Perth sales in Scotland.

On the contrary, the export demand for Scotch Beef Shorthorns has never been so keen as at the first sales held at the conclusion of the two world wars. It seems as though overseas countries, the Argentine especially, were literally hungry for Scotch bulls and almost desperate to make up for lost time and opportunity.

Thus in 1919, at the conclusion of the First World War, the Beef Shorthorn herd of Mr. William Duthie of Collynie, Aberdeenshire, was supreme. How keen was the demand when exportation was again feasible is shown by the wonderful sale Mr. Duthie held in that year.

" . . . in 1919 twenty-four Collynie bull calves averaged £1,400. 8. 9, with a top price of £5,655." (31)

In the first Perth sale after the Second World War, the prices, based on export demand, were even more extreme.

" The eighty-second Show and Sale at Perth, 1946, will long be remembered for the record prices realised. There were 39 transactions of 1,000 guineas and over, and the 417 animals sold realised £182,755 14s., with an overall average of £438. Some 100 bulls and 20 females were bought for export at a cost of upwards of £80,000. Five bulls from the Pittodrie herd, all sired by Bapton Upright (316211) realised 35,700 guineas, an average per head of £7,497, and the Kirkton herd's Female Champion made 3,000 guineas." (32)

Granted that these high prices were, at least in part, a direct consequence of the depreciation of British currency due to war-time inflation, nevertheless the fact remains that, even after two enforced and prolonged interruptions—interruptions which can have a most disastrous effect upon normal trading connections—the Argentine buyers returned to Collynie or to Perth to purchase Scotch bulls with undiminished enthusiasm and vigour. In any case, it is difficult to imagine cattle-breeders as skilful and experienced as those of the Argentine spending hundreds of thousands of pounds over a period now approaching a full century, merely because of a tradition, a misconception, a superstition, or a fashion !

Is it conceivable that the skill of Scottish cattle husbandry produces what may at least *appear* to be a superior Beef Shorthorn bull? It is a very old truism that " Half the breeding goes in by mouth " and it was shown long ago, as the result of a series of experiments conducted in the U.S.A., that if well-bred beef steers are poorly fed they fail to develop true beef conformation and when mature have every appearance of being ill-bred cattle. Indeed Hammond (33) goes so far as to say:

" It is highly probably that the stockman's art in the feeding and management of animals to fit them for the show ring consists in an adjustment of nutritional environment during the different stages of growth designed to bring out the desired form of animal which the judges of stock require."

In the Shorthorn world it is also a matter of common observation that when a cattleman leaves a namely herd, the success and reputation of that herd quite often goes with him, even although the genetic constitution of the same herd is in no way affected by his departure. Naturally it is impossible to give the actual names of herdsmen and herds to prove this important point, but it is one well recognised by breeders of Beef Shorthorns and, indeed, of other breeds of cattle. The craft of the Scottish cattleman in bringing out cattle for sale and show may quite possibly be un-equalled in the world. Yet were that the true explanation of the Argentine demand for Beef Shorthorn cattle, why is it that the Argentine imported the cattle rather than the men? Certainly the men would have been more cheaply bought.

These various possibilities have been examined in detail to clear the way, as it were, for the almost unanimous opinion of those actually engaged in the Shorthorn trade. Quite simply it is usually stated in these terms: that the Scottish Beef Shorthorn, particularly in the Argentine, but to a less extent in certain other countries overseas, tends to lose type; that it tends to grow more leggy and rangy in succeeding generations, losing thereby the low-set, blocky, and massive beef conformation of the original breed, and that this deterioration can be checked by returning to the breed's original home for fresh stock and that it can be prevented in no other way. If that explanation be true—and certainly most men actively connected with Shorthorn breeding believe it to be true—the future export trade for Beef Shorthorns, on which the prosperity of its breeders in Britain depends, would seem assured for at least as long as the Argentine remains a great cattle-breeding country.

Admittedly, similar claims are made on behalf of many other cattle breeds. It is usually maintained by Breed Societies in this country that the breed they sponsor loses its true type when removed to a distance from its district of origin. The possibility of such statements being influenced by a certain measure of commercial bias is too obvious to merit discussion. In some breeds the assertion is certainly untrue; in others it may be partially true. In the case of the Scottish Beef Shorthorn exported to South America it is a little difficult, in face of the evidence, to judge it entirely untrue. That the facts are difficult to interpret on accepted biological theory does not make them any the less factual on that account alone. Russian biologists would find no difficulty in interpreting them, because on modern Russian

6

biological theory—whatever the value of that theory may be—the explanation offered by the Shorthorn breeder is precisely the one the Russian biologist would himself advance.

That, then, would seem to be the future of the Beef Shorthorn in Britain: a stud farm for overseas countries, becoming progressively further divorced from the cattle breeding system of its own country now firmly based on dairying, unless, indeed, the breeding of beef cattle in hill areas can be substantially revived. The possibilities of such revival are fully discussed in later chapters of this book.

REFERENCES

(1) Sinclair, J. (1907). "History of Shorthorn Cattle," p. 25 (London).
(2) Marson, T. B. (1950). "The Scotch Shorthorn," *Brit. Agric. Bulletin*, **3**, 3.
(3) Stewart, A. (1950). "The Development of the Dairy Shorthorn in Britain," *J.R.A.S.E.*, **3**, 63.
(4) Stewart, A. *Ibid.*
(5) Marson, T. B. *Ibid.*, p. 7.
(6) Sinclair, J. *Ibid.*, p. 101.
(7) Sinclair, J. *Ibid.*, p. 26.
(8) Sinclair, J. *Ibid.*, p. 67.
(9) Stewart, A. *Ibid.*, p. 63.
(10) Sinclair, J. *Ibid.*, p. 63.
(11) Stewart, A. *Ibid.*, p. 64.
(12) Sinclair, J. *Ibid.*, p. 136.
(13) Stewart, A. *Ibid.*, p. 64.
(14) Stewart, A. *Ibid.*, p. 65.
(15) Stewart, A. *Ibid.*, p. 68.
(16) Watson, J. A. S., and Hobbs, M. E. (1951). "Great Farmers," 2nd Ed. p. 168 (London).
(17) Mackenzie, K. J. J. (1919). "Cattle and the Future of Beef Production in England," p. 29 (Cambridge).
(18) Mackenzie, K. J. J. *Ibid.*, p. 78.
(19) Marson, T. B. *Ibid.* p. 3.
(20) Sinclair, J. *Ibid.*, p. 183.
(21) Sinclair, J. *Ibid.*, p. 397.
(22) Sinclair, J. *Ibid.*, p. 409.
(23) Marson, T. B. *Ibid.*, p. 5.
(24) Watson, J. A. S., and Hobbs, M. E. *Ibid.*, p.147.
(25) Stewart, A. *Ibid.*, p. 66,
(26) Stewart, A. *Ibid.*, p. 69.
(27) Wallace, R. (1923). "Farm Live Stock of Great Britain," 5th Ed., p. 83 (Edinburgh).
(28) "British Pedigree Cattle," National Cattle Breeders' Association, p. 90.
(29) "British Pedigree Cattle," p. 92.
(30) Stewart, D. M. "Proc. Hill Cattle Conference, Oban, 1945," p. 24.
(31) Marson, T. B. *Ibid.*, p. 6.
(32) Marson, T. B. *Ibid.*, p. 7.
(33) Hammond, J., Edwards, J., and Walton, A. (1941). "Animal Breeding in Relation to Environmental Conditions," *J.R.A.S.E.*, **102**, 166.

" THE Aberdeen-Angus was the last of the three great Beef Breeds to become established in this country and in consequence was the last to enter the ring in beef production abroad." (1)

Although the breed in its more modern form is relatively recent, the antiquity of origin sometimes claimed for it is sufficiently remote. The official history is given as follows:

" The Aberdeen-Angus breed originated from a group of closely related local breeds in North-Eastern and Central Scotland, whose existence goes back to a very remote period. There are, for example, illustrations of polled cattle on sculptured stones in this area, black homyl (hornless) cattle are mentioned in the middle of the 9th century, and among other traces there are Latin Charters as early as the beginning of the 16th century mentioning black hummel or hornless oxen." (2)

While there were almost certainly cattle in Scotland in very early times, some of which were black, others polled, there is no reason to suppose that cattle of this type formed anything in the nature of a distinct breed as we know it to-day.

The origin of the Aberdeen-Angus suggested by Wallace in the year 1907 is much more in keeping with the known facts. He wrote: " The Aberdeen-Angus breed, from Aberdeenshire, Forfarshire, and the district largely embraced within the adjoining counties, is most probably the result of the amalgamation of a number of different, local, polled and also horned breeds, associated with careful selection and in-and-in breeding, together with, it is asserted, the infusion, within comparatively recent times, of a greater or less degree of alien blood." (3)

Again, according to Wallace, in addition to experimental outcrosses with " Ayrshire, Guernsey, Fife, Shorthorn and Galloway cattle, . . . there is good reason to believe that the very extensive and successful use of Shorthorn bulls in breeding grazing cattle for the Southern markets, led to the incorporation of Shorthorn qualities into the breed during the early years of its improvement." (4)

Aberdeen-Angus cattle, or perhaps it would be truer to say

71

the progenitors of that breed, were sufficiently variable in appearance in the earlier half of the last century.

"The absence of horns and the prevailing almost uniformly black colour, although ranking among the most persistent characteristics of the Northern Scotch polls, were by no means uniform features in olden times. Black cattle without horns were recorded nearly four hundred years ago, but long after the beginning of last century very many of the cattle from which the existing breed sprang had horns. The colours were extremely variable; some were yellow, red, or brown; others brindled (red and black, sometimes with white mixed or broken in an irregular fashion), black and white, 'belted' and 'rugged'—the latter black with a white or brown stripe along the back. Certain herds had a brown ring round the muzzle associated with the brown ridge. The late Lord Southesk, himself at one time a considerable breeder of polled cattle, writing on July 19, 1889, reflected upon the change of colour in Highland cattle from black to reds and yellows and the possibility of the blacks becoming nearly extinct, and added; 'Just as the red, brindled, and dun Polled Angus, common in my youth, are now hardly ever seen'." (5)

Similar reminiscences of old time breeders are recorded in a correspondence printed in the *Aberdeen-Angus Review* dealing with white markings on Aberdeen-Angus cattle. There the late Mr. P. Chalmers of Aldbar recalled that: "There were many herds of Angus cattle in the Brechin district when I first remember it, about 1850. The cattle were not all of them black in colour, some being red, others brindled, and some of a black colour, but black was the usual colour. Many breeders preferred cows with white udders, thinking they were better milkers."

Another letter in the same correspondence from a Mr. Marshall of Bleaton refers to " . . . the varied colouring of the cattle from which the present Aberdeen-Angus is descended ". (6)

There is no reason to suppose that these early cattle were any less useful because of a certain diversity in colour and appearance. Nor is it likely that their breeders were particularly concerned with the matter since it was only towards the middle of the nineteenth century that the breed received showyard recognition. Whatever the arguments for an ancient origin may be it is admitted that "official recognition of the breed is of much more recent date, and may indeed be put down to the year 1835 ". (7)

Nor is the modern name of the breed, Aberdeen-Angus, any more ancient since:

" In early times it was quite the custom to designate an animal either by the name Aberdeen or the name Angus, according to the place of birth." (7)

From this somewhat heterogeneous beginning, the Aberdeen-Angus breed was formed, and successfully formed, because there is no better or more uniform breed among beef cattle existing to-day. How and by whom was the task performed? According to Wallace:

" In-and-in breeding has been adopted to fix the good qualities which have from time to time been spontaneously produced by nature under the influence of the tendency to change brought about by crossing. In the matter of consanguineous relationships the Aberdeen-Angus is not an exception to the rule which applies to Shorthorns and other well-known breeds. Hugh Watson of Keillor, in Forfarshire (born 1789, died 1865), was the Colling of the Northern polled breeds, carrying out the principles laid down by Bakewell and his followers. But it was reserved for William M'Combie, of Tillyfour (born 1805, died 1880) to make the breed known to the outside world. After a long and successful showyard career, he eclipsed all the previous performances of the breed by carrying off two champion prizes of £100 each at the Paris International Exhibition in 1878—(1) For the best group of foreign cattle, and (2) for the best group of beef-producing animals —both bred by the exhibitor." (8)

Aberdeen-Angus breeders of to-day give the highest honours to Hugh Watson:

" . . . what Watson did for the Aberdeen-Angus deserves to be mentioned in the same breath as the work that the Collings accomplished for the Shorthorns, and that Tomkins achieved for the Herefords." (7)

Hugh Watson was little more than a boy when he started his cattle-breeding, for when only nineteen years of age " . . . which was in the year 1808, he became tenant of the farm of Keillor in the county of Forfar. To his new home he took with him, from his father's herd, six cows and a bull, all black and polled. To these he added ten heifers and a bull, which were acquired in Trinity Muir Market, Brechin. . . . With these sixteen cows and two bulls, Mr. Watson began his system of breeding for a

specific result, and for the fixation of a definite type of animal."
(7)

Hugh Watson owed much to his contacts with the Shorthorn breeders of his time and it was from them, undoubtedly, that he learnt the in-breeding methods of Bakewell, so potent in the establishment of clearly differentiated breeds from among the somewhat heterogeneous cattle of eighteenth-century Britain. Whether he borrowed more than advice from Shorthorn breeders is a matter for discussion and possibly of mainly academic interest to-day. The use of Shorthorn bulls by Watson is officially denied:

" Hugh Watson, as befitted an associate of Shorthorn breeders like Captain Barclay of Ury, was not above having a Shorthorn ox in his byres occasionally, but in his grading up of the blacks he never mixed the breeds . . . " (9)

The task of breed formation that Hugh Watson undertook must have been made much easier through the fact that two of the most striking characters he bred for, namely, a uniformly black coat and a polled head, happen to be strongly dominant in inheritance, so that at least a superficial breed uniformity was quite readily achieved.

If Hugh Watson made the breed in Angus, it was William M'Combie of Aberdeenshire who both saved and popularised it.

" In the county of Aberdeen, the outstanding personality in the improvement of the breed was Mr. William M'Combie, Tillyfour, who, taking up the mantle of Hugh Watson, was successful in raising the Aberdeen-Angus from a local to that of a national and international breed, and it is his name that is most closely associated with its evolution, if not, indeed, its rescue from entire extinction as the result of the craze for crossing which followed the introduction of the Teeswater or Shorthorn cattle into the North of Scotland about the years 1830–40." (7)

He was born in 1805 and died in 1880 and during those seventy-five years of life succeeded in establishing the Aberdeen-Angus of his native Scotland as one of the three great beef breeds of the world. After a brief sojourn at Aberdeen University, where he did not stay long enough to secure a degree, he escaped to the more adventurous occupation of cattle droving and cattle dealing, a business in which his father was already well established. After a thorough apprenticeship to the store cattle trade—probably

the most highly skilled branch in the whole of cattle farming—
M'Combie turned first to cattle feeding and, finally, to the breeding
of his Black Polls. Possibly no man ever had a finer and more
thorough training in cattle husbandry. Probably no man who
ever lived knew more about beef cattle, and in his volume of
memoirs—*Cattle and Cattle Breeders*—he has passed on some of the
wisdom based on experience for the benefit of posterity. He
learnt how to breed for beef, how to select individual beasts that
would make beef, and finally, and not least important, how to
feed for beef. His early training in dealing helped him to display
and advertise his chosen breed to the best advantage.

Hugh Watson was actually the first breeder of Aberdeen-Angus
to send beasts up to Smithfield where one of his heifers secured
very high commendation " as a sample of the excellence to which
this breed of Scottish cattle could arrive ". However, it was left
to M'Combie to begin that series of sweeping victories in fat
stock competitive shows that has never been equalled, let alone
surpassed, by any other breed of beef cattle.

" Hugh Watson merely tested the defences of the other beef
breeds at Smithfield. It was William M'Combie who stormed
the citadel. His greatest triumphs in London, however, were
preceded by victories equally resounding in Europe. In the
1850's the French International Exhibitions had become the
cynosure of agricultural eyes. Three such shows were held of
breeding cattle, at all of which the Aberdeen-Angus breed was
represented, before the French Government in 1857 staged a
Fat Stock ' International '. At the 1857 Show he put forward
six entries, with which, in the polled sections, he won two firsts, a
second and a third, and in the championships two gold medals,
a silver medal, a bronze medal, and £178. He led in the class
for oxen three-year-old and over, his best at 2,744 lb. being the
heaviest of all the breeds and giving the highest dead-weight
of 72 per cent. In 1862 there was another Paris Fat Stock
International, and M'Combie sent over an ox and a heifer which at
Smithfield in 1861 had been respectively best Scots polled ox and
best Scots polled heifer. Despite the fact that they both took
foot-and-mouth disease and the heifer was still showing the effects
when she was exhibited in Paris, the two Aberdeen-Angus with
two companions from Tillyfour swept the boards. M'Combie
had best ox under three and best ox over three years old, second

best heifer (there was no first in the class) under three and best heifer over three; Great Gold Medal of France for the best ox among the foreign stock, and the Cup for the best beast, French or foreign. This grand champion ox, girthing 9 ft. 8 ins. and weighing 2,750 lb. led the 450 select cattle of Europe; as his cattle-man, John Benzies, remarked, he was ' beef to the reets o' his lugs '. M'Combie's last fat stock victory in Paris was won at the International of 1878 when, with a group consisting of the bull Paris and the females Gaily, Pride of Aberdeen 9th, Sybil 2nd, Halt 2nd and Witch of Endor, which twelve out of fourteen judges had already selected for the Prize of Honour for the best group for breeding purposes in the Exhibition, he secured, by twenty-four votes to seven, the prize for the best group of animals for beef-producing purposes. He won from 1,314 French and 370 non-French cattle, and of his six cattle only Gaily was more than twenty-five months old." (9)

M'Combie's international triumphs attracted the attention of Queen Victoria and he showed loyal appreciation of royal patronage and notice in a practical way. Some of his most memorable Smithfield successes were won by " the celebrated steer Black Prince, which he sent south in 1867 to capture every possible honour at both Birmingham and Smithfield Fat Stock Shows. . . . A baron of beef from this leviathan was sent to Her Majesty Queen Victoria, who had already seen him alive at Windsor Park." (10) This baron of beef—the two sirloins left uncut at the backbone—was, moreover, sent at M'Combie's own expense.

The Great Queen, while resident in Deeside, visited M'Combie at his farm of Tillyfour in the adjacent valley of the Don, especially to view his prize-winning black, polled cattle on their native heath. A legend tells how the International Showman, equally great in his own more domestic sphere, staged a really Royal Show, by having the cattle led in endless succession round and round the house, while the Queen, seated in the porch, marvelled at the number of cattle he possessed !

" While M'Combie was still in his prime, another great im-prover appeared on the scene in Sir George Macpherson Grant, of Ballindalloch, who began to reside at the castle there in 1861, and whose successes continued to dominate the breed until his death in 1907. It was in 1861 that Sir George purchased Erica which was bred at Kinnaird in 1857 and was probably descended from Beauty of Keillor. ... Sir George's part in the history of the breed, apart with providing it with its greatest family [*i.e.*, the Ericas], was that of supplying style and fixing a type that was rather more refined than that of Tillyfour but admirably combining the qualities of beef and breeding." (11)

The founding of the Ballindalloch herd proved an outstanding event in the history of the breed. It " marked a new era in Aberdeen-Angus breeding, and began a work the beneficial influences of which are at the present day felt in almost every herd of the breed without exception throughout the whole world." (7)

Indeed, one authority has written that: " The modern Aberdeen-Angus may be said to be founded on Ballindalloch blood." (12)

" A study of Aberdeen-Angus pedigrees is most interesting and fascinating, in respect of the fact that the thousands and thousands of representatives of the breed throughout the world to-day can be traced back to some six or eight cows who roamed the fields in the valley of the Spey almost a hundred years ago." (12)

This statement emphasises the fact that, whatever may have been the ingredients which went to the formation of the original Aberdeen-Angus, the cake has been baked according to a standard recipe for a long term of years.

" The herd book, established in 1862, is a closed register—*i.e.*, no animal may be entered except such as are the progeny of parents already registered." (13)

On its first publication in 1862, the Polled Herd Book, as it was then termed, contained a register of the Galloway as well as of the Aberdeen-Angus breed. Separation was effected ten years later, in 1872, when the Galloway section was withdrawn to be published separately. The Polled Cattle Society, Banff, established 1879, conducted the registration of the Aberdeen-Angus breed until in 1909 it changed its name to the Aberdeen-Angus Cattle Society. In 1919 the headquarters moved to Aberdeen.

" The English Aberdeen-Angus Cattle Association which publishes no Herd Book was formed in May 1900 mainly with the object of holding an annual show and sale at a convenient centre for English breeders and buyers." (14) It was reabsorbed into the parent society in 1948. The Standard of Excellence for the breed is given in the A.A. Herd Book.   That for the Aberdeen-Angus bull is as follows:

> *Colour.*—Black.   White is objectionable, except on the underline behind the navel, and there only to a moderate extent.   A white cod is most undesirable.   Red is undesirable.
>
> *Head.*—Forehead broad; face slightly prominent, and tapering towards the nose, with fairly large mouth, nostrils wide and open; distance from eye to nostril of moderate length; eye mild, full, and expressive; ear of good medium size, well set, and well covered with hair; poll well defined, and without any appearance of horns or scurs; jaws clean.
>
> *Throat.*—Clean, without any development of loose flesh underneath.
>
> *Neck.*—Of medium length, muscular, with moderate crest (which increases with age); spreading out to meet the shoulders, with full neck vein.
>
> *Shoulders.*—Well laid in, covered on the blades and on the top, which should be on a line with the back, and moderately broad.
>
> *Chest.*—Wide and deep.
>
> *Bosom* (or Brisket).—Standing well out between the legs, and moderately covered with flesh and fat.
>
> *Ribs.*—Well sprung from the backbone, arched and deep, neatly joined to the crops and loins.
>
> *Back.*—Broad and straight from crops to tail-head, loins strong; hook bones moderate in width, not prominent, and well covered; rumps long, full, level, and rounded neatly into hind-quarters.
>
> *Hind-quarters.*—Deep and full; thighs thick and muscular, and in proportion with hind-quarters; twist full.
>
> *Tail.*—Fine, coming neatly out of the body on a line with the back, and hanging at right angles to it.
>
> *Underline.*—As nearly as possible straight; flank full and soft.
>
> *Legs.*—Short, straight, and squarely placed; hind legs slightly inclined forward below the hocks; forearm muscular; bones fine and clean.
>
> *Flesh.*—Even, without bumps or patchiness.
>
> *Skin.*—Of moderate thickness and mellow touch, abundantly covered with thick and soft hair.
>
> *General appearance.*—Gay, well-bred, and masculine.

Allowing for minor differences related to sex, the Standard of Excellence for an Aberdeen-Angus cow is identical with that of the bull.

That, then, is the Aberdeen-Angus breed as it stands to-day—pure-bred, indeed in-bred, uniform, famous.   What are its qualifications to its present position as one of the leading, if not *the* leading, beef breeds of the world?

The claims made by the Breed Society are as follows:

> The special characteristics of the Aberdeen-Angus breed are the small proportion of bone and offals in the carcase to the total dead-weight; the hardiness; the adaptability to a great range of climates—for example, the black skin renders them immune from many diseases like cancer eye and udder burning, which attack cattle in very hot climates, while in dry countries like Queensland they are very tolerant to fly and

do not suffer from worm infestation; quick maturity; a peculiar quality of the flesh which takes the form of marbling the beef with fat rather than separating the fat and the beef into layers; a high rate of fertility; a racial dominance which results in the elimination of horns from progeny of animals inter-bred with Aberdeen-Angus; and the capacity to transmit their beef qualities to other breeds with whom they are crossed. (15)

These are the claims made for the breed by its sponsoring society. Naturally, they are unlikely to suffer from under-statement. Some, in the light of available evidence, appear to be rather better founded than others. In this connection it is only sensible to remember that a great deal of the credit customarily accorded to the various breeds of cattle, both beef and dairy, may be more truly ascribed to the conditions under which they are usually reared and fed.

Many of the problems affecting meat quality—killing-out percentage, marbling and so on—are discussed more fully in other sections of this book. It will be found there that surprisingly little experimental work has been undertaken so far in assessing the relative importance of the multitude of factors affecting beef quality, let alone in deciding the relative superiority of the beef from one breed of cattle over that of another. As only those who have attempted to perform critical experiments upon productivity in livestock know, it is extraordinarily difficult even to measure the relative importance of heredity and environment in the de-velopment of those productive characters which give farm animals their economic value. Yet an assessment of the variation in response of different cattle breeds to different planes of feeding and management, as determined experimentally, must be an essential preliminary to a critical judgement of the beef-producing capacities of the various breeds. Only the high cost of cattle has delayed such experimentation. A good start, however, has been made at Cambridge in a series of highly important experi-ments described and discussed later, and it must be admitted that so far the lesson of these experiments has been that, at least under the conditions of feeding and management appropriate to commercial beef production, there would seem to be far less difference between breeds than has been previously supposed.

On the contrary, that may not be—and, indeed, most probably is *not*—true where both feeding and management are the best that can be designed. In preparing cattle for Fat Stock Exhibi-tions, for example, there is no economic brake upon the fullest expression of an animal's inherited capacity for beef production. Cost of production is quite unimportant. No champion at a Fat Stock Show was ever produced at a cost commensurate with the economic value of its carcase.

Under the somewhat specialised conditions of the Fat Stock Show, the Aberdeen-Angus has established its supremacy both at Smithfield in London and at Chicago in America as the diagrams facing p. 84 (Figs. 20 and 21) clearly prove. The pure-bred Aberdeen-Angus has gained 46·4 per cent of the Smithfield Championships and its crosses with a variety of other breeds, but chiefly with the Shorthorn, 32·3 per cent. At Chicago, pure-bred Aberdeen-Angus cattle have secured no less than 74·6 per cent of the Championships. Crosses of any variety have been far less prominent in Chicago than at Smithfield, nevertheless 3·2 per cent of the Championships at Chicago have been won by Aberdeen-Angus crosses compared with a mere 0·7 per cent by crosses of any other breed.

There can be no doubt, in view of these convincing figures, that, at least under optimum conditions of feeding and management, the Aberdeen-Angus is the outstanding breed of beef cattle for Fat Stock Show purposes. Admittedly this purpose is a specialised one, for in addition to its quite uneconomic production, a Fat Stock Champion is inclined to be altogether too fat to be eaten. Because of this divorce of Show standards from commercial realities, the carcase competition, within more recent years, has become an accepted method of breed comparison. The Aberdeen-Angus and its crosses have been outstandingly successful in these competitions also, although the supremacy has been scarcely so overwhelming as in the Championships awarded to animals on the hoof. Thus:

" In the Carcase Competition at Smithfield from 1919 to 1938 the total entries were 894 and the respective percentages of total entries, of first prizes, and of second and third prizes together, may be compared in the following categories.

	Percentage of entries	Percentage of prizes	Percentage of second and third prizes
Aberdeen-Angus . .	24·04	27·06	29·35
Other Breeds . .	39·48	36·47	35·33
Aberdeen-Angus Crosses .	29·97	35·30	28·74
Other Crosses . .	6·26	1·17	6·58

Thus the Aberdeen-Angus made a far better showing in the prize list than the number of their entries warranted, while, compared with Aberdeen-Angus crosses, other crosses were insignificant in the aggregate both of their entries and their prizes." (16)

Because of the accepted fact that, as regards beef production, the Aberdeen-Angus is a particularly high-quality breed, it is often assumed that it is also a small breed. Presumably this is because since the two factors of quantity and quality are so frequently opposed, it has become customary to assume that this must inevitably be so. Actually, there is no proof that small size and high quality of carcase in livestock are in any way correlated, as Mr. Maurice Passmore pointed out very forcibly at a recent summer meeting of the British Society of Animal Production. (17) Numerous examples —one such is the Large White Pig—might be suggested to prove the contrary.

In any case the Aberdeen-Angus is not nearly so small as it looks. Its neat head, short legs, and compact body give good specimens of this breed a deceptively small appearance. They weigh heavier than their appearance suggests. Compared with some of the cross-bred steers out of certain dairy breeds such as the Friesian frequently seen in British abattoirs to-day, and which at mature ages may attain very great weights, the Aberdeen-Angus may seem relatively small. Matched with other specialised beef breeds, such as the Shorthorn or the Hereford, however, there is no very great difference. Watson and More (13) state that the Aberdeen-Angus is some 4 per cent lighter than the Shorthorn and that, very probably, is a fair summary of the case.

Again, because of the high quality of the Aberdeen-Angus, it is frequently assumed that it must of necessity be a delicate breed, since there is a tendency to assume a correlation between quality and delicacy. Obviously the environmental conditions under which the average pure-bred Aberdeen-Angus herd is reared in Britain does not favour hardihood, nor, under such a specialised and sheltered environment, can there be any selection towards hardihood. That, however, is a criticism, if it be a true criticism, of our methods of livestock breeding in general and is no reflection on the Aberdeen-Angus cattle breed in particular. Certainly the climate of North-Eastern Scotland, where the breed arose and where many namely herds still thrive, is not one especially conducive to delicacy. The most probable derivation of the name " Tillyfour " where M'Combie built up the breed is from the Gaelic " Tigh fuar " meaning " Cold House ", and upper Donside in winter can, in verity, be bitter cold. The Aberdeen-Angus is, moreover, the common hill cattle breed of New Zealand and has in many parts of the world proved its utility on the range.

The question of immunity to various diseases claimed for the Aberdeen-Angus is, of course, a much more debatable one. It is essentially a veterinary problem unsuited for discussion here. That of the breed's black coat is, however, one of animal husbandry in general.

" From time to time some scientist does a bit of witch-doctoring, and announces upon wholly inadequate data or from the result of some half-digested experiment that the Aberdeen-Angus, because of its black coat, is of no use in hot climates." (18)

These are strong words and possibly somewhat unfair to those people of scientific training who attempt to extract a kernel of fact from the encrusting shell of competitive breed propaganda. Nevertheless, in view of the universally accepted fact that among the various races of mankind the nearer the equator the darker the pigmentation of the skin becomes, it would be, at first sight, surprising were blackness *in itself* to prove a disadvantage to the Aberdeen-Angus under tropical conditions. On the other hand, no sane man would select a black coat for a hot country! Obviously, the matter is one for further and *scientific* investigation.

In any event, were it proved that a black coat is inimical to the thriving of cattle in a tropical climate, it would be the easiest thing in the world to breed Aberdeen-Angus of red colour instead. Red coat colour is a Mendelian recessive character in the genotype of the breed, which has never been bred out entirely, so that an occasional red calf is dropped among its black brethren even in the best herds. Red is, in fact, a recognised although undesired breed colour, and a red calf, if otherwise qualified, is eligible for registration in Britain and in the Argentine, although not in U.S.A., Canada, or New Zealand. In this country Aberdeen-Angus calves of red colour whose sire and dam are both registered in the Herd Book may themselves be registered, provided the name given to the calf contains the word *Red* or an indication otherwise that the animal is red.

At one time an attempt was made to establish an Aberdeen-

Angus Red Poll breed much as in the same way to-day a similar enterprise is on foot in connection with the British Friesian. Wallace (19) described the situation as it existed in 1907:

"The Aberdeen-Angus Red Poll is a pure strain of the Northern Scotch Polls derived from red specimens that have appeared from time to time among the best Black Polled herds. This sub-section of the breed has been collected by W. K. Mac-Donald, Windmill House, Arbroath, N.B., whose herd numbers about forty animals. He began by purchasing from George Wilkin 'Waterside Elena 2nd'—whose dam was champion heifer at Birmingham Fat Stock Show, first prize cow at the Highland Society's Show at Dundee, and first at the Royal Northern Show at Aberdeen. With the founder of the herd and her progeny some half a dozen cattle of the best strains of blood in Scotland have been mated. The females keep easily up to the level in quality of well-bred herds; but the difficulty in dealing with such a limited number of cattle is to find a stock bull good enough to mate with them. Resort has been had to a black bull, who usually gets red calves. The red colour being more in favour than the black in the River Plate countries, an offshoot of the Windmill House herd has been established in the Argentine by Knight & Porteous, at Las Tres Lagunas. The cattle are found to be hardy, and the bullocks feed to 1,500 lb. live-weight. The difficulty about the quality of the bull occurs there also."

To-day there is only one red Aberdeen-Angus herd in Great Britain and Ireland, that owned by Mr. Eric L. C. Pentecost, the Elms, Cropwell Butler, Notts, but there are many pedigree herds of red Aberdeen-Angus in the Argentine.

Whatever objections—valid or invalid—may be raised against the dominant black coat colour of Aberdeen-Angus cattle, there can be no conceivable quarrel with the equally dominant polled character of the breed. The future of the pastoral world lies with polled cattle. Horns, under all conditions and in all countries, are becoming ever less popular. In a number of breeds naturally horned, including both Shorthorn and Hereford, polled varieties already exist. Certain breeders of Sussex cattle have embarked on a carefully planned programme, based on modern genetic theory, to produce a polled variety of their breed. A vast number of calves, born with horns, are, at some degree of trouble and expense, dehorned by one means or another shortly after birth. A naturally polled breed, such as the Aberdeen-Angus, therefore has an initial advantage in full conformity with the trend of modern times.

The dominance of both black coat and polled character are extremely valuable qualities in the Aberdeen-Angus when crossed with other breeds of cattle. The calves born are uniform in superficial appearance, being both polled and black in the great majority of cases. " In 90 per cent. of cases, whatever the colour or type of the dam, the colour of the calf is black, and in 95 per cent. of cases the horns disappear." (20)

In consequence of external uniformity, and of the valuable beefing qualities transmitted to many of its cross progeny by an Aberdeen-Angus sire, the black polled cross bullock or heifer has gained a high reputation with feeders, particularly with winter feeders who find, apart from any other consideration, that polled cattle are best suited to feeding in courts.

It would be a profound error, however, to claim or to imagine that the Aberdeen-Angus crosses equally well with *all* other breeds of cattle. That is, indeed, very far from being the case and, at least in Scotland, it may be suggested that crossing bulls of the breed have been used too frequently and freely for casting a black blanket and a hornless crown over some rather indifferent feeding constitutions. Indeed, to obtain the best results in crossing with the Aberdeen-Angus, the circumstances and conditions in which this particular breed is preferred to certain others might, with advantage, be more carefully considered than is always the case, particularly in Scotland, to-day. To obtain the best results the Aberdeen-Angus bull should be crossed with a cow of fair beefing qualities and good frame and substance. The best cross of all is with the Beef Shorthorn and this cross is, in fact, frequently preferred by breeders aiming to produce a calf suitable for bringing out for the specialised purpose of the Fat Stock Show. The Aberdeen-Angus will also leave a very useful calf from dual-purpose cattle such as the more beefy strains of Dairy Shorthorn. Recently it has been widely used—and by all contemporary accounts—successfully used, to cross with the Friesian.

Mr. Alexander Keith, Secretary of the Aberdeen-Angus Cattle Society, has kindly supplied me with information regarding another Aberdeen-Angus cross with a dairy breed. He writes:

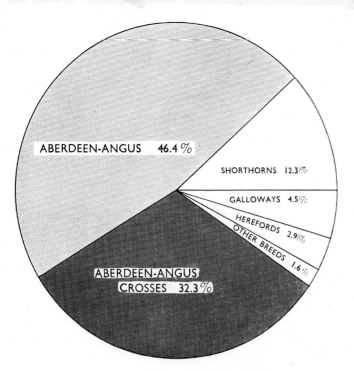

Fig. 20. SMITHFIELD CHAMPIONSHIPS.

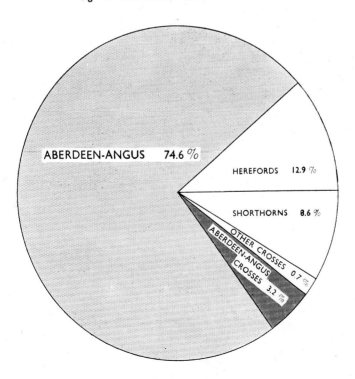

Fig. 21. CHICAGO CHAMPIONSHIPS (see page 80).

Fig. 22. HEREFORD BULL.

Fig. 23. HEREFORD COW.

" Incidentally, it may interest you to know that in Australia one of the most satisfactory crosses is the Aberdeen-Angus second and third cross on Jerseys. There are several herds of this kind in Australia, the cows milk well, and the steers make good carcases. I happened a few months ago to meet the President of the American Jersey Cattle Society and on hearing who I was he stated, ' You will not know that your bulls make the best cross on our cows.' As I have two second and two third cross cattle of this description on my own farm, I was able to tell him I knew all about it."

On the other hand, the Aberdeen-Angus does not cross quite so successfully with the Scottish breeds of hill cattle, where the Beef Shorthorn is certainly to be preferred as the first cross both with the Highland and the Galloway, particularly with the Highland for, as Mr. J. A. Cameron has written from long experience, " . . . the Highland cow and the Angus bull is a known bad cross ". (21)

Nor, although very frequently made, is the Aberdeen-Angus cross with the Ayrshire entirely satisfactory. Wallace wrote that (22):

" The polled bull on an Ayrshire cow produces a small thinly made up animal . . . "

Fraser Darling has written more recently (23):

" Even if we have a black polled bull and get black calves from our Ayrshires we are not really playing fair by the man who buys these calves, not knowing the Ayrshire side of the parentage, for they will never make good bullocks."

On the contrary, the Aberdeen-Angus will leave an excellent feeding calf out of the Beef Shorthorn first crosses from any of these breeds. Thus, of the Shorthorn Highland first-cross cow, Mr. J. A. Cameron has said (24):

" On the Highland cross, the Angus bull of substance is excellent."

Mr. George Jamieson, lately farm manager at the North of Scotland College's hill farm at Glensaugh, writing of the Aberdeen-Angus cross on the Shorthorn Galloway first cross states that:

" I have seen some very fine specimens of butchers' beasts of the latter breeding." (25)

The Aberdeen-Angus also gives an excellent calf out of a Shorthorn–Ayrshire cross cow.

The general conclusion to be based on the variable value of the Aberdeen-Angus bull is that the cow on which he is used must be half-way towards beef herself. In beef cattle husbandry, therefore, the real function of the Aberdeen-Angus is to complete the up-grading towards beef which other breeds, particularly the Beef Shorthorn, have already begun.

This principle, if accepted, serves to explain the history of the Aberdeen-Angus abroad. The breed, as already mentioned, is of more recent origin than the Shorthorn or Hereford and, in the beef cattle colonisation of the New World, it therefore got away to a late start. In fact, general interest in what up to that time was essentially a local Scottish breed, was first aroused by the resounding successes of M'Combie's black polled cattle in the International Cattle Shows, particularly those of Paris, between 1857 and 1878.

Nor was the initial entrance of the Aberdeen-Angus into the international cattle arena altogether auspicious. Foreign buyers had become accustomed to horned cattle, and both Shorthorn and Hereford had already established high reputations abroad. An exception may be made of Eire where the Aberdeen-Angus was introduced at a relatively early date and where the breed has done an immense service in improving the quality of store cattle.

" In Ireland, where there went Hugh Watson's Grey-Breasted Jock in 1843, there has always been a strong representation of Aberdeen-Angus cattle." (26)

" The invasion of North America began in 1873 when three bulls from Scotland were imported to a ranch in Kansas." (26)

" The first Aberdeen-Angus bull arrived in the Argentine in 1876, and its appearance, black without horns, created a sensation that did not seem to presage any very satisfactory future for the incomer." (26)

These early prejudices were, however, soon overcome and the Aberdeen-Angus has come to occupy an increasingly important place in the beef cattle industries of America, both North and South so that to-day:

" . . . Aberdeen-Angus blood predominates in the cattle of the Eastern States and the Eastern part of the Middle West, while it is steadily expanding West of the Mississippi. This year the Aberdeen-Angus Cattle Breeders' Society in America passed the

10,000 mark in membership and in 1945 it registered over 62,000 pure-bred calves." (26)

" There are, at the present moment, not less than 400,000 pure-bred Aberdeen-Angus cattle in the United States of America, as compared with a sum total of 25,000 in Great Britain." (12)

" The breed has been an outstanding success under arable or semi-arable conditions—for example in the maize-growing districts of the United States." (13)

The history of the Aberdeen-Angus in the Argentine is interesting and instructive of the use and abuse of a great breed.

The early prejudice in the Argentine against the breed was not, however, entirely based upon its novel appearance. The first results of crossing it with the native cattle appear to have been unsatisfactory and not nearly so beneficial as crossing with the Beef Shorthorn of that time. The Argentine cattle of the nineteenth century were not sufficiently far up-graded to benefit from the Aberdeen-Angus cross.

As W. J. Grant wrote from personal experience:

" There is no doubt the Aberdeen-Angus cattle are the finest beef cattle in the world, but to obtain good results the bulls must be mated to large-framed cows and not to mean little scrubs as were the native cows of the Argentine." (27)

Since those early days of the Aberdeen-Angus introduction, the improvement in the standard of Argentine cattle has, of course, been tremendous. The " mean little scrubs " have been converted by up-grading with the three leading breeds of British beef cattle—Shorthorn, Hereford, Aberdeen-Angus—to the finest commercial beef cattle in the world.

The improvement in the general standard of Argentine cattle is reflected in the growing popularity of the Aberdeen-Angus breed.

" . . . since the end of the first European War the breed has expanded there by leaps and bounds. In 1920 there were only a dozen or two Aberdeen-Angus breeders, whereas at the end of 1945 the Corporacion Aberdeen-Angus de Argentina had 674 members and an Aberdeen-Angus bull had established the record price in that country for imported bulls by fetching £10,000 under the hammer." (15)

The Aberdeen-Angus has by now spread to all parts of the world where beef is produced.

" In New Zealand a large proportion of the beef cattle are Aberdeen-Angus and many herds are to be found in Australia, South Africa and Canada and in places as diverse in climate as the high Andes of Chile and the warm Pacific island of Hawaii." (15)

Compared with the Beef Shorthorn and the Hereford, the Aberdeen-Angus has certain advantages and certain defects. The comparison is very fairly summarised by Watson and More (13):

" The Angus is particularly well adapted for intensive feeding and for ' baby beef ' production. It has not proved so widely adaptable as the Shorthorn, nor so useful under poor range conditions as the Hereford. For grading up thin-fleshed and slow-maturing types it is less useful than the Shorthorn, but for imparting quality to herds that are already improved to some extent, it is excellent."

The Aberdeen-Angus is, in fact, to the beef world what the Southdown is to the sheep world.

" The Aberdeen-Angus is to cattle what the Southdown is to mutton sheep. It is the breed with the highest development of carcase qualities." (28)

There could be no higher tribute.

REFERENCES

ABERDEEN-ANGUS

(1) " Memorandum on Aberdeen-Angus Cattle," p. 1, Breed Society Publication.
(2) " British Pedigree Cattle," p. 1, National Cattle Breeders' Association.
(3) Wallace, R. (1907). " Farm Livestock of Great Britain," p. 163. 4th Ed. (Edinburgh).
(4) Wallace, R. (1907). *Ibid.*, p. 165.
(5) Wallace, R. (1907) *Ibid.*, p. 164, 165.
(6) *Aberdeen-Angus Review* (1919), **1**, 28.
(7) *Ibid.*, p. 5.
(8) Wallace, R. (1907). *Ibid.*, p. 166.
(9) " Aberdeen-Angus," Breed Society Handbook, p. 6.
(10) *Ibid.*, p. 10.
(11) " British Pedigree Cattle," p. 2.
(12) Maclaren, T. (1951). *British Agric. Bull.*, **4**, 69.
(13) Watson, J. A. S., and More, J. A. (1949). " Agriculture," p. 564, 9th Ed.
(14) Wallace, R. (1907). *Ibid.*, p. 170.
(15) " British Pedigree Cattle," p. 6.
(16) " Aberdeen-Angus," Breed Society Handbook, p. 21.

(17) Passmore, M. (1951). " Cattle Feeding in the Midlands," *Proc. Brit. Soc. Anim. Prod.*, p. 63.

(18) " Aberdeen-Angus," Breed Society Handbook, p. 15.

(19) Wallace, R. *Ibid.*, p. 172.

(20) " Aberdeen-Angus," Breed Society Handbook, p. 16.

(21) Cameron, J. A. (1948). " Hill Cattle," *Trans. High. Soc.*, **55**, 34.

(22) Wallace, R. (1907). *Ibid.*, p. 169.

(23) Fraser Darling, F. " Crofting Agriculture," p. 118.

(24) Cameron, J. A. (1948. *Ibid.*, p. 52.

(25) Jamieson G. Personal Communication.

(26) " British Pedigree Cattle," p. 4.

(27) Grant, W. J. (1920). " Aberdeen-Angus in the Argentine," *Aberdeen-Angus Review*, p. 46.

(28) Hammond, J. Quoted in " Aberdeen-Angus Breed Society Handbook," p. 34.

WHEN cattle are discussed among men in this country of Britain to-day, there is talk of beef and of milk and of the compromise between these two, called dual-purpose, that lies between. Two hundred years ago, when the solution of the country's relatively undifferentiated cattle began to crystallise out into separate breeds, there was an equal interest in cattle considered as draught animals. The work oxen that drew the plough were essential to cultivation and the work oxen of some counties were reckoned to be better than those of others.

Those bred in Herefordshire had a particularly high reputation, indeed:

" The main object for which the breed was kept till well into the nineteenth century was the supply of work oxen for land cultivation." (1)

Of the cattle of Hereford at the beginning of last century (1804–1805) one John Duncumb wrote: " The cattle of Herefordshire have long been esteemed superior to most if not all the other breeds in the island. Those of Devonshire and Sussex approach nearest to them in general appearance. Large size, athletic form, and unusual neatness characterise the true sort; the prevailing colour is a reddish brown with white face. The rearing of oxen for the purposes of agriculture prevails universally, nearly half the ploughing being performed by them, and they take an equal share in the labours of the harvest. They are shod with iron in situations which frequently require their exertions on hard roads, but it has already been noted that grazing is not generally pursued except for provincial consumption. The show of oxen in thriving condition at the Michaelmas fair in Hereford cannot be exceeded by any similar annual collection in England; on this occasion they are generally sold to the principal graziers in the countries near the metropolis, and there perfected for the London market." (2)

During the eighteenth century, therefore, and indeed for some time afterwards, beef was a by-product of draught oxen, the main purpose for which Hereford cattle were then kept.

" The chief function of the Hereford of the present day, viz. the production of the finest quality of grass-fed beef, was during the eighteenth century quite a secondary consideration. "(1)

It was, presumably, the substitution of oxen by horses as the main motive power in the cultivation of English farms, together with the increasing demand for beef by the growing industrial population of the England of that time, which led certain breeders of Hereford cattle to concentrate upon the beef-producing possibilities of their county's cattle.

Just as in Shorthorn cattle, the names of certain of the more prominent of these pioneers have come down in agricultural history.

" Benjamin Tomkins (1745–1815) occupies in the history of the improvement of this breed a corresponding place to that assigned to Bakewell in regard to Longhorns, and to the brothers Colling in connection with Shorthorns." (3)

" Tomkins adopted Bakewell's system of in-and-in breeding. It is on record that the best of his famous herd sprang from two cows and one bull." (3)

It would be a profound error, however, to imagine that Tomkins' cattle, in-bred though they were, had anything approaching the uniformity and quality of the modern breed. Nothing to-day is more characteristic of the Hereford than its colour markings, the well-known and supremely attractive red background to the the distinctive white facings, yet:

" Tomkins put no store upon uniformity of colour, and for a time (as late as 1845, when the *Herd Book* appeared) the breed was subdivided into four classes, mottle faced, dark grey, light grey, and white faced." (4)

Indeed, it is true of the Hereford as of most other breeds of cattle, that as late as 100 years ago, there is recorded a surprising diversity of type. For instance, Youatt wrote in 1835:

" Hereford oxen are considerably larger than the North Devon, they are usually of a darker red, some of them are brown and even yellow, and a few are brindled, but they are principally distinguished by their white faces, throats and bellies. In a few white extends to the shoulders. The *old Herefords* were brown or red-brown, with not a spot of white among them. It is only within the last fifty or sixty years that it has been the fashion to breed for white faces." (5)

The relatively recent origin of the modern Hereford markings was confirmed by Rowlandson in 1853:

" The old Herefords are said to have been brown or reddish brown, and it is only within the last eighty or ninety years that it has become the fashion to breed for white faces." (6)

What were the origin of these markings and from whence they came it would by now be rather futile to inquire. There is the legend—it can be deemed little more—of Hereford cattle being derived from the Flanders cattle introduced into the county at the instance of Lord Scudamore, who died in 1671.

What is probably the soundest summing up of the origin of the Hereford, as of other modern breeds of cattle, was given by Low in 1845, when he wrote:

" Some of the finest of the breeds of England may be termed artificial with relation to the means employed to give them their distinctive characters; such was the variety of the Long-horned formed by Bakewell; such is the modern Durham improved by Colling; and such is the highly esteemed breed of Hereford perfected by Tomkins." (7)

The Hereford Herd Book was established in 1864 and in the United States has been closed since 1883, but was not closed in Britain until 1887, four years later. This divergence of dates has, on occasion, led to difficulties in the export of British Herefords to America.

The points looked for in the modern breed are as follows:

" A Hereford bull should have a head of strong, masculine character, with a bold, alert eye.

The eyes should be set well apart from the muzzle; the two eyes and tip of nose forming an equilateral triangle.

The nose should be dewy pink, black marks being objectionable with breeders.

The horn should be flat and of wax-like texture, with the tips turning slightly down. Again, any black on the horn is looked upon with disfavour as, for that matter, are black hairs, which indicate coarseness in the animal's quality of fleshing.

The head should be set on a moderately short neck, well set into the shoulders, with well-developed crest.

The back should be broad and smoothly fleshed, and when viewed from the side present a level top line, as should the underline.

The tail-head setting should be level with the back, any gaudiness of flesh around tail-head being undesirable.

At the same time the animal should be fully and smoothly fleshed from hooks to tail-head, with great length from hooks to pins.

If possible, also, the animal should measure three equal parts from pin bones to hook, from hooks to back of the shoulder, and from there to the head.

The animal must therefore be well coupled up and not appear long. He must also show a good depth through the body.

His legs must be short and with plenty of good oval bone and well set on his fetlocks. Leggy animals are usually long in the bone between knee and fetlock—a fault to be avoided.

The shoulder should be well laid, not too upright, and with the top of shoulder blades set well apart but not prominent.

Viewed from the front, the animal should have great width between his front legs and through his chest and when walking should step out well and straight.

Viewed from behind, the legs should again be well set apart with the hooks straight, not turned in, and when walking the legs should lead out straight. He should be well let down behind, well fleshed between the thighs.

Viewed from the side the hind leg should be moderately straight, with meat carried well down on the hock and with second thigh well developed.

The bull should have a skin that is supple, resilient, and mellow to the touch. The hair should also be soft and silky.

The animal should be fleshed evenly and firmly, ties in the back and patches of fat on the ribs and at the tail-head being undesirable.

The animal should have a white head and a white crest, white dewlap and throat and white underside, white socks and white brush to the tail. The rest should be a deep rich red colour.

The female should have the body conformation as outlined, though she must be of feminine character.

She should have a placid, open countenance, bright but soft eyes and pleasing appearance.

The neck should be fine, cleanly cut, and neatly set into the shoulders. Too much dewlap or heavy fleshing under the neck makes the animal too ' steerlike.' " (8)

The modern Hereford is closely associated with grassland fattening.

" Hereford cattle have always been in high repute *as grazing animals* throughout the midland and eastern counties of England." (9)

" The Hereford breed . . . provides some of the best cattle fattened on grassland in this country . . . . " (10)

The Hereford "will fatten readily on good grass alone . . . ." (11)

It is this presumed superiority of the Hereford as a converter of grass into beef that has, within recent years, led to the great extension of both the breed itself and of its crosses throughout the whole of Britain. Economic factors that have favoured summer grazing contrasted with inside winter fattening as the main method of producing this country's beef have, undoubtedly, also favoured the Hereford breed. Admittedly, there is little or any experimental evidence to support this presumed superiority. Nevertheless, the widely held opinion of graziers, based on their personal experience, cannot well be ignored.

There are, however, certain other factors, less complimentary to the breed, which have also favoured its increase. The standards of beef in Britain have, very obviously, declined, so that the preference of the high-class butcher for the crosses of certain other beef breeds, particularly of the Aberdeen-Angus, are no longer of equal importance. In fact, the preferences of the butcher based on those of his customers and expressed in price are to-day, in Britain, of no importance at all. The Ministry of Food buys all beef according to a schedule of prices which, in essence, favours weight rather than quality, so that the aim of the feeder is to produce the maximum weight of beef at the minimum cost. This influence of price schedule upon the economics of beef production in Britain to-day is discussed more fully in later chapters of this book. The point deserving emphasis here is that the recent extension of range of Hereford and Hereford crosses in this country has a very definite connection with the price schedule. So long as summer production of beef off grass remains more profitable, or less unprofitable, than the winter feeding of cattle in courts or byres; and so long as beef is paid for on weight and degree of fatness without regard to more subtle points of quality, so long will the territory of the Hereford in Britain continue to expand.

Until the Ministry of Food became the monopoly buyer of British beef, the Hereford—*in Britain*—was of somewhat limited distribution. Wallace (12) wrote in 1907 that " in this country it is distinctly a local breed ".

" As regards Britain, the Hereford is rather a local breed. Nearly all the prominent pedigree herds are found in the English and Welsh counties adjoining the border, from Cheshire in the North to Monmouth and Gloucestershire." (11)

That situation is changing to-day.

The characteristic white markings left by the Hereford on its crosses are to be seen on summer pastures in many districts where they were previously unknown. The extension of the breed in Scotland and in the last decade has been quite remarkable. There the expansion has been at the expense of both Beef Shorthorn and Aberdeen-Angus.

Compared with the Hereford there can be little doubt that the Aberdeen-Angus, at least under optimum conditions of feeding and management, produces the better carcase of beef, as is demonstrated unequivocally by the results of the major Fat Stock Shows.

In the early days of Smithfield Show, the Hereford had a very impressive record of successes. Thus " during the first fifty-two Annual Meetings of the Smithfield Club, when all breeds met in competition with each other, 185 prizes were awarded to Hereford steers or oxen, while only 190 fell to the lot of all the other breeds or cross-breeds put together ". (13)

Since the arrival of the Aberdeen-Angus as a recognised breed of improved beef cattle towards the latter part of the nineteenth century, that situation has altered and the Hereford has had to take a quite secondary place in both the Smithfield and Chicago Championships to the rival breed.

It is, of course, very easy to exaggerate the practical importance of these shows and it would be quite wrong to belittle the Hereford on that account alone. Actually, although somewhat overshadowed in competition with the Aberdeen-Angus in more recent years, there is a good deal of evidence that the quality of Hereford beef has, nevertheless, actually improved since the days of its greater prominence at Smithfield. Thus, according to Garner (10):

" At times butchers criticised cattle of this breed because of their heavy fore-ends, but during later years the breeders have developed the hindquarters so that this criticism is no longer valid."

Apart from the question of carcase quality, on which the evidence suggests that while good the Hereford is not so good as the Aberdeen-Angus, the breed has many other virtues of practical utility.

" *Natural Aptitude to Fatten and Early Maturity.*—These are perhaps the predominant characteristics of the breed which have always been carefully maintained and developed, with the result that no breed can be marketed as prime beef, of greater weight for age in so short a time and at so low a cost." (14)

This claim to the Hereford's capacity for early maturity, made by the Breed Society, is one that is generally agreed on by authorities and one, moreover, that can be supported by figures.

" The breed and its crosses may also be fattened in yards as baby beef since it is an early maturing breed . . ." (10)

At the 1938 Smithfield Show, the average weights for steers under fifteen months were, as regards the three leading beef breeds, as shown in the following table:

			cwt.	qr.	lb.	
Herefords	.	.	9	3	27	
Shorthorns	.	.	8	0	27	
Aberdeen-Angus	.	.	8	0	2	(14)

While the days of " baby-beef " in Britain have vanished and are unlikely to return it is, nevertheless, of profound theoretical interest to find clear evidence of early maturity and a robust constitution, commonly called hardiness, associated together in the same breed of cattle. It is generally assumed, very possibly on evidence that is somewhat insufficient, that these two important characters in livestock—early maturity and hardiness—are necessarily opposed. There may be a fallacy in reasoning underlying this assumption. Under hard environmental conditions an animal must of necessity be hardy if it is to survive. Its slow rate of maturity, however, may be merely the necessary consequence of its poor nutrition, while a latent capacity for rapid maturity may never have an opportunity for display.

Certainly, the Hereford, while having sound claims to early maturity, is very far from being a delicate breed.

Wallace (5) wrote of its " hardiness of constitution ", Watson and More (11) refer to its " robust constitution ".

The Hereford Herd Book Society (14), in making the same claim attribute the robust constitution of their breed, at least in part, to the way in which Hereford pedigree herds are customarily managed.

" Hereford cattle have always been and are still bred and reared under the most natural conditions, and, with the exception of the bulls and a few show animals, are seldom housed. The cows and heifers run out in the pastures all the year round, receiving no extra food except a little rough straw or hay during the most severe weather and at calving time. It is moreover the practice of many breeders to allow their cows to calve out in the open. This treatment has the effect of keeping the cattle healthy and making them extremely hardy, and it is for this reason that

Herefords have gained a world-wide reputation for withstanding every kind of hardship." (14)

Perhaps this passage somewhat exaggerates the spartan conditions under which pedigree Hereford cattle are maintained. Nevertheless, it is very definitely my impression from personal observation that the husbandry in the leading Hereford herds is less specialised and is far less artificial than has become customary practice in Aberdeen-Angus, and still more in Beef Shorthorn, herds.

Undoubtedly the breed is relatively free from tuberculosis.

" The breed is almost entirely free from tuberculosis. Already a great proportion of English Hereford herds belong to the British Ministry of Agriculture's T.T. Attested Herd Scheme and on and after 1st January, 1947, it is anticipated that every herd will belong to the scheme; as from that date only animals from T.T. Attested Herds will be accepted for the Shows and Sales held by the Hereford Herd Book Society. For over 30 years the Society has only accepted for their Shows and Sales animals which have passed the tuberculin test." (14)

In constitution and health-record the Hereford can, therefore—it may be safely claimed—compare favourably with any other breed of beef cattle. A further and, in Britain, a very valuable additional character is the excellence and ease of recognition of its crosses.

" The Hereford breed is very dominant when crossed, the typical white faces, briskets, feet or tails being seen in the progeny no matter with what breed they are crossed, but the deep red colour of the breed disappears when crossed with stock of a black breed." (10)

". . . these colour markings being a dominant factor type mark the calves no matter what breed of cow the Hereford bull is crossed with." (14)

This clear stamping of Hereford characters on crosses could only be an advantage to the breed provided the crosses were of exceptional merit. Such is the case, and perhaps particularly out of Welsh Black and Dairy Shorthorn cows the Hereford bull produces most desirable feeding calves. The Hereford can, however, give useful crosses with a wide range of breeds.

" Herefords nick in crossing with the Shorthorn, West Highland, Galloway, and Polled Angus . . ." (16)

Hereford cattle are very numerous abroad. They were introduced to the United States in 1817, to Australia in 1839, to the Argentine and Uruguay in 1858. (17)

To-day " . . . there are many more Hereford cattle in the world than any other beef breed. . . . In the U.S.A. in 1943 there were three times as many pedigree Herefords recorded as all the other beef breeds combined; and in that great cattle state of Texas the total cattle population of the state was 98% Hereford or Hereford cross. . . . Again in Uruguay over 90% of the cattle population are Herefords or Hereford cross." (18)

While this great colonisation by the Hereford of virgin pastoral territory was in progress, the demand for English foundation stock was naturally of the keenest.—" The American trade, while it lasted, raised prices to record point." (19)

More recently, perhaps because of the large number of Hereford herds established abroad, this demand has abated.

" North America has practically ceased to take Hereford cattle from this country as there are over 70,000 pure-bred animals there." (19)

Certainly, for whatever reason, the Hereford abroad seems to be less dependent upon periodical rejuvenation from British herds than is the case with the Beef Shorthorn.

Now, the Hereford like the Shorthorn is a horned breed, and horns are becoming ever less popular among breeders of commercial as opposed to pedigreed cattle, whether these be of beef, dairy, or dual-purpose breeds. Consequently, there is a variety of the Hereford called the Polled Hereford, just as there is a variety of the Beef Shorthorn called the Polled Shorthorn. Opinion is divided on the value of these polled variants of the classical horned breeds. Let it be at once admitted that while horns are a nuisance, nevertheless a good beast horned is infinitely preferable to a poor beast polled, and that the mere fact of being polled does not and cannot compensate for other weaknesses in frame or constitution.

Polled Herefords are not bred in England. They appear to have originated first in North America.

According to Wallace (20), they " were originated and bred by the late W. W. Guthrie of Atchison, Kansas.

" In March 1889 he had a bull calf dropped without horns which he named ' Discovery ' by a pure-bred Hereford bull out of a cow that was one-half Hereford and one-half Shorthorn.

" In December 1902, the registry known as the National Polled Hereford Breeders' Association, Ill. was formed."

There are also Polled Herefords in Australia. At a recent world conference of Hereford cattle breeders held at Hereford,

" Mr Lindsay Field told the conference that Polled Herefords were making great strides in the Dominion and breeders of horned cattle throughout the world had to put their best foot forward to combat them." (21)

REFERENCES

(1) Wallace, R. (1907). " Farm Livestock of Great Britain," p. 121, 4th Ed. (Edinburgh).
(2) Macdonald, J., and Sinclair, J. (1909). " History of Hereford Cattle," p. 12, Revised Ed. (London).
(3) Wallace, R. (1907). *Ibid.*, p. 114.
(4) *Ibid.*, p. 115.
(5) Youatt, quoted by Wallace, R. *Ibid.*, p. 115.
(6) Rowlandson, T., in *R.A.S.E. Journ.* (1853), quoted by Wallace R. *Ibid.*, p. 115.
(7) Low, D., quoted by Macdonald and Sinclair. *Ibid.*, p. 19.
(8) " Target for the Modern Breeder," reprinted from the Overseas and Transatlantic Mail Agriculture and Hereford Supplement and published by the Hereford Herd Book Society.
(9) Wallace, R. *Ibid.*, p. 117.
(10) Garner, F. H. (1946). " The Cattle of Britain," p. 77 (London).
(11) Watson, J. A. S., and More, J. A. (1949). " Agriculture," 9th Edit., p. 566.
(12) Wallace, R. *Ibid.*, p. 112.
(13) Brandreth Gibbs, B. T., quoted by Wallace, R. (1907). *Ibid.*, p. 117.
(14) " British Pedigree Cattle," p. 56.
(15) Wallace, R. (1907). *Ibid.*, p. 118.
(16) *Ibid.*, p. 120.
(17) Court, T. J. C., (1950). " British Breeds of Livestock, III—The Hereford," *Brit. Agric. Bull.*, 3, 98.
(18) " British Pedigree Cattle," p. 55.
(19) Wallace, R. (1907). *Ibid.*, p. 116.
(20) *Ibid.*, p. 122.
(21) *The Hereford Breed Journal* (1951), 6, 46.

In 1907 Wallace wrote (1):

" The Devon breed is primarily divided into (1) North, and (2) South Devons. The North Devon is the original true and hardy type belonging to the elevated region in the North of Devonshire. As represented by the best specimens, this division of the breed is unsurpassed for compactness and symmetry of form. It is smaller than the Hereford and the Sussex, two breeds to which it is allied."

Nowadays, North Devon cattle are simply styled " Devon Cattle ". (2) It is an old and namely breed, often—because of the beautiful and richly red colour of its coat—called colloquially " Red Rubies ". The breed has great beefing qualities combined, at least in some strains, with fair milk production. Those responsible for the breed's future, however, prefer to regard the Devon as a beef rather than as a dual-purpose breed.

" The main function of the Devon breed is, and always has been, the production of beef of prime quality, although milk has not been entirely neglected." (3)

The word " always " is perhaps not altogether appropriate in this connection, since the Devon was known in the plough before it was famed for its beef.

" As draught animals, Devons gained a remarkable reputation. William Marshall, author of *Rural Economy of the West of England*, published in London in 1796, wrote that Devons were beyond all comparison the best draught animals he had ever seen. At the same period, the Rev. W. Quartly, of Molland, maintained that a pair of Devon oxen could plough an acre of stiff land in a day." (3)

One John Lawrence, in a book entitled *A General Treatise of Cattle, etc.*, published in the year 1805, wrote of the Devon that:

" . . . the fashionable substitution of horses made no progress in the district of these cattle, . . . " and that " the Devons are the speediest working oxen in England, and will trot well in harness ". (4)

That, then, was the reputation of Devon cattle when, at the

Fig. 24. HEREFORD CATTLE AT GRASS.

Fig. 24a. HEREFORD CATTLE GRAZING.

Fig. 25. DEVON BULL.

Fig. 26. DEVON COW.

commencement of the nineteenth century, men began to breed cattle for the butcher rather than for the plough. In that era the Devon, like most other breeds of British cattle, had its notable " improvers ". Perhaps the term is hardly a happy one, since what really happened was a change of emphasis, a new specialisation in function, by which a new breed was selected out of the old.

" Francis Quartly of Great Champson, in Molland, North Devon, filled the position in the history of North Devon cattle which the Collings did among Shorthorns and Tomkins among Herefords." (4) This Francis Quartly came of a notable family of Devon cattle breeders.

" Mr. James Quartly, the first of a leading line of Devon cattle breeders, was breeding ' Red Rubies ' (as the Devons are sometimes called) at Great Champson, Molland, in 1703. His great-grandson, Mr. Francis Quartly, probably the most successful of this famous family, did invaluable service to the breed during the post-Napoleonic period. Recognising that many of the best strains were being lost to the district through farmers being tempted by the war-time prices, he determined to buy quietly all the good stock he could meet with and so built up one of the most famous herds in Devon cattle history." (2)

In the past, Devon cattle were a somewhat local breed as they are, indeed, to-day, most of the leading herds and breeders being centred in the county which gave the breed its name. An interesting and important exception to this rule was the herd imported into East Anglia by that great pioneer of agricultural improvements, Coke of Norfolk.

" One of the most famous of the early herds outside the county of Devon was that of Holkham, in Norfolk, founded in 1791 by Coke, created Earl of Leicester in 1837. From Holkham, Devons were first exported to the United States." (5)

The history of the Devon cattle breed is peculiarly colourful and attractive. It is dealt with authoritatively in Housman and Sinclair's *History of the Devon Breed of Cattle*, published in 1893.

The official registry of the breed is in Davy's Devon Herd Book, so called after a Colonel J. Tanner Davy who published the first volume, over a hundred years ago, in 1850. The Herd Book is open, a Grading-up Scheme on the usual lines being in operation.

As described in the booklet *Devon Cattle*, the most recent and authoritative publication of the Devon Cattle Breeders' Society:

The cattle are symmetrically proportioned, their general colour being the shade of dark cherry-red. The whole red colour of the hair is frequently varied by distinct dappled markings, the skin being generally orange-yellow, but inside the ears orange-red. The horns of the female are medium in length, and elegant in their outward and upward sweep and creamy white. The horns of the bull are thicker, straighter and less elevated. The breed type has changed to some extent during the past fifty years. Whilst retaining all the best points of the " North Devon," the type most common in the hills of North Devon in the " Davy-Quartly " era, the present-day animal is of larger scale, combining early maturity with symmetrical form. (6)

The same publication claims that " the word ' Beef ' and ' Devon Cattle ' are almost synonymous terms ", and there can be no doubt that the Devon both in conformation and meat quality is a real beef breed of high standing and established reputation. Thus, the late K. J. J. Mackenzie of the Cambridge School of Agriculture wrote:

" For, *having regard to the size of the joints*, I know of no beef that shows such depth or thickness of lean meat as that cut from the carcase of the Devon." (7)

The Devon is also an early maturing breed when given the environmental opportunity to express its genetic capacity.

" . . . Smithfield Show records provide ample justification for the Devon's claim to be the outstanding breed for early maturity. In six out of the last seven pre-war Smithfield Shows, the heaviest animal in the pure-bred Baby Beef Classes was a Devon and in 1935 the breed furnished the five heaviest animals in these classes. At the 1938 Smithfield Show the average daily gain of 2·71 lb. recorded in the class for Devon Steers under 15 months old was, in fact, the best recorded for any class in the Show." (8)

In this connection Garner wrote: " The breed is famous for early maturity, it being quite common to find at the Smithfield Fat Stock Show that the breed has produced the heaviest baby beef animals. Frequently cattle under 15 months old are found weighing 10 cwt., which represents a live-weight gain of nearly 3 lb. per day from birth, which is no mean achievement." (9)

The Devon is not widely known or used as a crossing breed, although the Breed Society does claim that " for crossing with other breeds the Devon has no rival ". (10)

In fact, considering its undoubted merits the breed has remained rather strangely localised.

" . . . the great majority of pedigree Devon herds are still found in the four Western counties of England—Devon, Cornwall, Somerset and Dorset." (11)

Nor has the Devon achieved the prominence abroad equal to that of the Beef Shorthorn, Aberdeen-Angus, or Hereford. The main exports have been to Brazil and Australia. These exports have been increasing within recent years:

"Exports have increased from 2 in 1945 to 58 in 1950 . . . Brazil was the highest receiving country with 41 . . ." (12)

It is, in fact, a cattle breed that seems to do well in semitropical countries.

SUSSEX cattle are " . . . native to the Weald district and the marsh lands of Kent, Surrey, and Sussex ". (13) The breed has affinities with the cattle both of Hereford and of Devon, particularly of the latter county. It is " . . . very definitely related to the Devon cattle, for both breeds are similar in type, reddish colour and horn development ". (14)

Again, as in the cattle native to Hereford and to Devon, those of Sussex were for long bred mainly with a view to the production of work oxen. Emancipation from the plough came even later in the case of the Sussex.

"The breed continued to supply work oxen for the Wealden clays long after the horse had become the sole draught animal elsewhere." (13)

The Sussex Herd Book Society was established in 1878, the first volume of the Herd Book containing the record of stock born in 1855. The Herd Book is closed.

The modern Sussex, like the modern Hereford and Devon, claims to be a beef breed and as such it must come to comparative judgement.

"In weight it is practically equal to the Hereford, but is less compact, somewhat more muscular in build and rather later maturing." (13)

Commenting with surprise on the fact that the Sussex has not been more widely exported Garner (14) wrote: " . . . it may be that some critics consider there is relatively too little development in the valuable cuts of the hindquarters ". Similar criticism used to be levelled at the Hereford and it can hardly be denied, even to-day, that many specimens of the Sussex breed tend to be somewhat over-weighted in the fore-quarters as compared to the hind.

It is not so very long since the Sussex came out of the plough yoke and in its weight of shoulders it still shows that origin. Indeed, viewed purely from the standpoint of beef conformation, it might be argued that compared to certain other beef breeds the Sussex appears relatively unimproved.

The breed lays claim, however, to certain peculiar qualities of behaviour which, if substantiated, would seem to justify a wider field for the Sussex than the breed presently enjoys. The Sussex has a grazing habit which should endear it to the grassland improver.

" Sussex cattle are unique as graziers for apparently they have no sense of taste because they never seem to discriminate between grasses, clovers and weeds; observation shows that they eat all that comes in their paths when eating their way across a field. The breed are often used to ' trim up ' rough grass fields and marshland areas that have been mismanaged and where coarse patches have developed." (14)

It is usually taught that cattle, because of their relatively unselective grazing, are more beneficial to grass than any class of sheep can ever hope to be, and Sussex cattle appear to possess this advantage to an outstanding degree.

Abroad, the Sussex has achieved an outstanding success in South Africa, as also in South-West Africa:

" Originally a draught breed, it is not to be wondered at that the Sussex crosses well with the native Africander or Africander-cross cattle, producing grand trek oxen and imparting high quality to the beef." (15) Consequently, there " . . . is a flourishing Sussex Cattle Breeders' Association of South Africa ". (15) Indeed, there is more than a suggestion that, at least in certain respects, the South African scion is superior to the English stock. Thus, the Director of the English Sussex Herd Book Society, Mr. E. C. Trotter, visited South Africa twice in two successive years in the capacity of guest Judge.

" Mr. Trotter was struck by the great suitability of better types of Sussex for rapid beef production. They have there [*i.e.*, in South Africa] compact, deep bodied beasts with better hindquarters than are generally found in our own country. Some stock from over there would materially improve our own cattle." (16)

Proposed action along these lines was prevented by an untimely outbreak of foot-and-mouth disease in Bechuanaland but: " A suggestion that an importation of pure-bred Sussex cattle from South Africa might be undertaken is still a possibility of the future." (16)

It is clear both from the excellence of the brochure the Society has produced, and the evidence of initiative and energy its pages contain, that the breeders of Sussex cattle are an enterprising group. Perhaps it is that the enthusiasts for what is still a relatively restricted and localised breed are more apt to look towards the possibilities of future expansion than towards restrictions based on the vested interests of a famous past.

Take, as an example, the question of horns. The Sussex as it is bred to-day is a horned breed as it has been in the past, yet the Sussex Herd Book Society are by no means wedded to horns.

" Dehorned Sussex Cattle are now accepted for registration in the Herd Book, *provided the fact is stated on the entry form.*" (17)

The Society, moreover, are engaged on the lengthy programme of the deliberate and planned breeding of a Polled Sussex. The reasons for doing so are summarised as follows:

" The rapidly increasing demand for polled breeds of beef cattle throughout the beef raising countries of the world has reflected on sales of horned breeds in many parts. The United States of America has long been alive to the advantages of polled cattle.

" In order that we may compete with other Beef Breeds abroad and incidentally with polled cattle at home, it has been decided to proceed with an experiment of producing a sub-race of Polled Sussex." (18)

The breeding policy, based on the mating of a Red Aberdeen-Angus bull with Sussex cows and as advised by Dr. John Hammond, is estimated to take some twenty years—a relatively long-term project. The details of the scheme, a model of its kind, are fully detailed in the Society's Brochure.

REFERENCES

(1) Wallace, R. (1907). " Farm Livestock of Great Britain," p. 123, 4th Ed. (Edinburgh).
(2) " British Pedigree Cattle," p. 27.
(3) *Ibid.*, p. 28.
(4) Wallace, R. (1907). *Ibid.*, p. 127.
(5) *Ibid.*, p. 128.

(6) " Devon Cattle," Breed Society publication, p. 7.

(7) Mackenzie, K. J. J. (1919). " Cattle and the Future of Beef Production in England," p. 143 (Cambridge).

(8) " Devon Cattle," p. 9.

(9) Garner, F. H. (1946). " The Cattle of Britain," p. 76 (London).

(10) " Devon Cattle," p. 17.

(11) " British Pedigree Cattle," p. 32.

(12) " Devon Cattle," p. 7.

(13) Watson, J. A. S., and More, J. A. (1949). " Agriculture," p. 566, 9th Ed.

(14) Garner, F. H. (1946). *Ibid.*, p. 78.

(15) " British Pedigree Cattle," p. 100.

(16) " The Sussex Cattle Brochure and book of reference," p. 27.

(17) *Ibid.*, p. 66.

(18) *Ibid.*, p. 23.

OF the five beef cattle breeds so far discussed, three are quite outstanding. The Beef Shorthorn, the Aberdeen-Angus, and the Hereford are, beyond argument, the three leading beef breeds of the whole world. The Sussex, whilst also a beef breed, is, as regards numbers and distribution, of relatively minor importance. The Devon, also a somewhat localised breed although of outstanding beef quality, in point of milk production approaches the dual-purpose breeds now to be described.

What is actually meant by the phrase dual-purpose as distinct from beef or dairy cattle? The term, especially in certain European countries, is sometimes applied to dairy cows which are capable of supplying a carcase of reasonable beef once their milking days are over. That, be it noted, is not the meaning we attach to the term in this country.

" The really important point is not the beef value of the old cow, but the potential value, as a beef animal, of the calf which the cow produces." (1)

That quotation is taken from a small but still useful book by Sir James Scott Watson and others published a quarter of a century ago. Sir James went on to elaborate his statement as follows:

" The essential feature of a dual-purpose breed is therefore this, that the heifer calves, given appropriate treatment, should be capable of making good milch cows, while the surplus heifers and the male calves should, again with appropriate treatment, be capable of making good butchers' beasts." (2)

Dr. John Hammond, quite recently, has given a more exact and quantitative definition of what good and useful dual-purpose cattle should be able to do. He has defined them as those cattle among which a cow will give 800 gallons of milk and in which a steer at two years of age will weigh 11 cwt. and Grade A or better. (3)

These, presumably, are average figures and the great practical difficulty, of course, is to persuade the breeder of dual-purpose cattle to rest contented with an average milk yield in three figures, when rivals, using one or other of the specialised dairy breeds, are getting four.

Moreover, in a dual-purpose breed, without correct management during rearing, the heifers may prove little better than beef cattle when they come into milk, and the steers but little superior to dairy steers when they come to be graded. That the question of " appropriate treatment " mentioned by Scott Watson (2) is of first importance is becoming more clearly recognised than was once the case, very largely owing to the interim deductions to be made from the Cambridge University Farm's experiments on cattle rearing, more fully discussed in a later section of this book. The following passage, written by Scott Watson in 1926, has, in consequence, a great deal more evidence to support its important generalisation than it had when first written.

" It must be insisted that treatment, particularly the richness of the feeding during the period of rapid growth, has a very marked influence on conformation, and, provided the hereditary type is not too extreme, a particular animal can be so developed as to show a considerable measure either of beef or of dairy conformation, at the will of the rearer." (2)

Evidence of the profound influence of nutrition during the first eight months of a calf's life upon its subsequent conformation and rate of development is one of the most important results emerging from the Cambridge experiments already referred to. A general principle emerging from these results is that a high plane of nutrition in calfhood is necessary for the development of good beef conformation in the adult heifer or steer.

There is, at the moment, rather less experimental evidence upon the effect of early nutrition upon subsequent milk production either in dairy or dual-purpose cows. The subject is under investigation—using the identical twin calf technique—at the Rowett Institute at the time of writing. Results there have not yet reached the stage of publication. Practical breeders of experience appear to be convinced that a moderate rather than a high plane of nutrition in early life is most favourable to subsequent milk production, at least in the beef or dual-purpose breeds. Thus Mr. D. M. Stewart, in a recent article dealing with milk yields in Scottish Shorthorns, wrote:

" This tendency to keep your female stock in high condition does undoubtedly detract from their ability to milk when mature. Ask any dairyman how he rears his young heifers, and his answer will confirm this." (4)

Mr. J. Harrison of Gainford Hall, Darlington, who undertook the interesting experiment of developing the latent milking qualities in the herd of Scottish Beef Shorthorns inherited from his father, has recorded that in his opinion:

" The vital principle is not allowing the heifers to become too fat before delivering their first calves." (5)

In any case it seems abundantly clear that early environment, as well as breeding, has an important influence upon the future specialised productivity of cattle, whether towards beef or towards milk, and that these environmental influences are probably of greater practical importance in the dual-purpose breeds than in others.

It would be irrelevant at this stage to embark upon an examination of the case for or against dual-purpose cattle. The matter has been sufficiently debated within recent years. The point of main interest here is the extent to which dual-purpose breeds—and there are quite a number of them in this country—can contribute to the nation's beef supplies.

In the first place, then, let it be admitted that, although of less importance than formerly, dual-purpose cattle still form an important section of the cattle population of Britain, more particularly of England. Indeed, in England and until very recently, the main tradition in cattle-breeding was towards dual-purpose types. Thus Garner wrote:

" It is very doubtful whether any other country carries as big a proportion of dual-purpose cattle as are found in Great Britain." (6)

This statement, while true of England, does not apply to Scotland where dual-purpose cattle breeds never attained the same popularity.

The reasons for the earlier predominance of dual-purpose cattle in England has been discussed by Mackintosh (7):

" During the last century the dual-purpose type of cow was almost universal in England. Its popularity was due to a large and regular demand by city and suburban dairies for cows in their prime (just commencing their third or fourth lactation) which would fatten readily as their milk yield declined.

" Gradually, however, the decline in the city dairies, the importation of beef from abroad, and the increasing importance of milk induced farmers to give more attention to breeding for milk, with less emphasis on the ultimate beef value. The movement was away from the lower yielding type of dual-purpose herd towards better milking strains and single-purpose dairy breeds and their crosses."

The preference for dual-purpose cattle was, at least in part, the reason for the predominance of the **DAIRY SHORTHORN** as the common breed upon the average English dairy farm until relatively recent times. That predominance, at one time, approached monopoly.

There has, of course, within more recent years, been a tremendous advance of the specialised dairy breeds in England, particularly of the British Friesian. There has also been a tendency in the Dairy Shorthorn breed itself to press milk yields in competition with the specialised dairy breeds. In so doing there is an evident danger—or might it be an advantage?—of the Dairy Shorthorn itself becoming a specialised dairy breed.

At one time, at the beginning of the century, the tendency was in the opposite direction. The trend of *pedigreed* Shorthorn breeding during the nineteenth century was towards beef, a trend reinforced towards the end of the century by the use of Shorthorn bulls of Scotch descent in English herds. Meanwhile the English farmer owning non-pedigreed stock preferred his Shorthorns to be dual-purpose. It was because of this growing divergence between the ideals of the breeder of pedigreed Shorthorn bulls and the preference of the home buyers most likely to purchase them that the Dairy Shorthorn (Coates' Herd Book) Association was founded as already described in the previous section dealing with the Beef Shorthorn.

The claims of the Dairy Shorthorn as put forward in *British Pedigree Cattle* are detailed below:

" In addition to its constitutional hardiness, adaptability and milk-yielding ability, the Dairy Shorthorn cow has the quality of laying on an even covering of flesh and fat when dry. It has been proved, without doubt, that she has one characteristic very much desired in a heavy milker, to wit, the gift of providing a reserve to be drawn upon after calving and so enabling the maximum production of milk to be attained without undue strain.

In barren cows and heifers this same characteristic enables them to provide a good carcase of beef and steer calves offer feeders a valuable source of beef production. This assured dual-purpose merit of the breed makes it suitable for farms, where, in addition to milk production, hardy calves are wanted for rearing and growing on for steers." (8)

Data concerning milk and butter fat production would be irrelevant here. All that need be said is that the Dairy Shorthorn is capable of giving a large milk yield of moderate quality. It is sometimes suggested that a certain number of heifers prove indifferent milkers and that there is a greater number of such dairy disappointments in the Dairy Shorthorn than in the specialised dairy breeds such as Ayrshire and British Friesian. In all probability such statements are justified, but as a criticism of dual-purpose breeds in general rather than of the Dairy Shorthorn in particular.

To an outside observer—and admittedly this is a purely personal opinion—it would seem that in England to-day there are many herds of Dairy Shorthorns giving excellent milk yields but without the frame and substance of body that promise abundant beef. Indeed, I have seen at least one herd where, apart from the red, white, and roan Shorthorn colouring, the cows might well have passed for indifferent Ayrshires. That is, in all probability, an inevitable result of pushing a dual-purpose breed too fast and too hard along the milky way. The Dairy Shorthorn of genuine dual-purpose type is a beautiful cow, possessing all the attractiveness of natural balance. Nevertheless, particularly since there is already a well-defined and clearly established breed of beef Shorthorns in existence, it would seem almost inevitable that the Dairy Shorthorn will tend more and more towards milk. How it will fare eventually in competition with specialised dairy breeds is certainly an interesting speculation but one beyond the scope of a book dealing specifically with beef.

The centre of Dairy Shorthorn breeding is North-West England. Dairy Shorthorn bulls from Cumberland and Westmorland go to all parts of England. These counties are the great bull-breeding centres of the breed.

Now, the value and, indeed, in some cases the superiority of unpedigreed Dairy Shorthorns has already been mentioned. Some of the best of them were native to the dales of Northern

England and certainly there has never been a finer example of dual-purpose cattle than the old Shorthorn of the Northern English counties. During the 1939–1945 War, with the great extension of liquid milk production into that hill country, there was a temptation to depart from the dual-purpose and even from the traditional type of Dalesbred cow. There was for a time a good deal of somewhat indiscriminate crossing with bulls of the specialised dairy breeds in an endeavour, not by any means necessarily successful, to increase average milk yields. It was in an effort to save and preserve the dual-purpose Dairy Shorthorn native to the English Northern counties that the **NORTHERN DAIRY SHORTHORN BREEDERS' SOCIETY** first was formed. The progress of this young breed society has been rapid and successful due largely to the enthusiasm and energy of its secretary, Harold J. Shutt. In a recent letter to me he writes:

" Formed in 1944 for the preservation and improvement of the dales Shorthorn which has been indigenous to the hills and dales of Northern England for 200 years, we are now the sixth largest pedigree cattle Society in Great Britain, despite our being confined to a very small part of the country.

" We now operate with a closed Herd Book and seek improvement through proven male and female strains."

To an outside observer there seems to be more than a suggestion that during the formative period of the breed and while the herd book remained open a certain amount of specialised dairy blood, presumably Ayrshire, was introduced. That can have done no possible harm provided the added weight towards milk rather than beef such introduction entails be admitted. The Society lays evident stress on milk records and increased milk production in the breed it sponsors. To do so without simultaneous recording of beef production—so infinitely more difficult yet obviously essential if a true dual-purpose balance is to be struck—is to invite the evolution of another specialised dairy breed, possibly one of the greatest local value, but hardly the dual-purpose dales Shorthorn the Society was founded to preserve.

It should be emphasised that the Northern Dairy Shorthorn Breeders' Society is a completely autonomous organisation. It has no affiliation to the Shorthorn Society of the United Kingdom of Great Britain and Ireland nor are its cattle registered in Coates' Herd Book.

The last of the Shorthorn family requiring mention is the **LINCOLN RED**. The breed has an ancient and, at times, somewhat troubled history. According to the Breed Society booklet (9):

" During the latter years of the 18th century, and early in the 19th century, when the Colling Bros. were carrying on the great livestock improvement traditions of Bakewell by improving the Shorthorn, a select number of enterprising North Lincolnshire Breeders attended the Durham sales and no expense was spared in securing the very best blood the North could produce. Thus, three bulls were sent into Lincolnshire from Charles Colling's great sale in 1810; the animals being lightly shod to perform the journey south. There appears no doubt that many of these Durham Shorthorns constituted the foundation blood of a number of the early Lincoln Red Shorthorn Herds. Among the Lincolnshire breeders at this time was one Thomas Turnell, of Reasby, near Wragby, Lincoln. He reared and bred a wholly red variety of this improved kind of Shorthorn with great success, and thereby founded the variety since known as the Lincoln Red Shorthorn."

Relationship of the Lincoln Red Shorthorn Society to the Shorthorn Society and to Coates' Herd Book has varied from time to time. At first combined, the Society became independent in 1896, to rejoin in 1935, only to split off again in 1941, since when it has maintained its autonomy. The natural relationship of the Lincoln Red to the Shorthorn is, however, a very close one, so that apart from its deep red colour and unusual strength of bone the Lincoln Red did not differ fundamentally, at least until recently, from the Dairy Shorthorn.

The phrase " until recently " is of importance because in 1946 the Lincoln Red Shorthorn Society came to an important decision and one which, eventually, must affect materially its position as a dual-purpose breed.

" In October, 1946, it was resolved by the Society to divide the Herd Book into two sections, one for entries from Beef Herds and the other for qualified entries from Dairy Herds. The decision was based on the selective emphasis made between the two types of qualifying standards imposed by the Ministry of Agriculture and Fisheries under the Bull Licensing Scheme." (10)

When a dual-purpose breed splits into two such sections it is obvious that, whatever benefits may accrue, the maintenance of a dual-purpose ideal, sufficiently difficult without such division, becomes wellnigh impossible. It is undeniable that the most recent Bull Licensing Regulations do definitely favour specialisation either towards beef or milk, and, equally, are unfavourable to the maintenance of dual-purpose breeds.

As regards beef production the Lincoln Red has the capacity of reaching very great weights.

Between 1941 and 1951, " . . . when the heavier weighing bullock was the order of the day, it can be safely said that no other breed in the British Isles produced so many heavy fat bullocks. Live weights of 15 and 16 cwts. were common in every market throughout the country, week by week, and instances have been recorded where whole consignments, sometimes totalling over 100 animals, turned the scale at over 17 cwts." (11)

The Lincoln Red is a noted good grazier.

" Several of the dual-purpose breeds produce ideal stock for fattening on grassland, *e.g.* Lincoln Red Shorthorn (which was, of course, very largely developed to consume the grassland on the Lincolnshire marshes)." (12)

Heavy weight and good grazing ability are two important characters in the Lincoln Red appropriate to modern conditions. True, that under the most recent regulations of the Ministry of Food, weights over $13\frac{3}{4}$ cwt. incur a certain weight penalty, nevertheless, as discussed in another section of this book, the weight penalty is far outbalanced by the value of extra cwts. even at the reduced " over-weight " price. It is the day of the big bullock and the Lincoln Red is big.

According to the Breed Society publication, the Lincoln Red " . . . as regards early maturity or weight for age compares more than favourably with any other breed of cattle ". (13)

On the contrary, Garner, presumably with a first-hand experience of this breed, wrote:

" No attempt should be made to fatten the stock at young ages, because if fed freely they grow and they will not get fat." (14)

The **RED POLL** at the present time probably deserves the title dual-purpose better than any other breed of British cattle. It is a breed dual-purpose, not only by nature, but by declared intention.

" The cardinal aim is to keep prominently to the fore the essential combination of milk and beef." (15)

The origin of the breed rests on a peculiarly happy union of beef and milk characteristics.

" Red Polled Cattle have been formed into a general purpose breed of unsurpassed merit in this country by uniting picked specimens of the old Norfolk horned breed of superior grazing cattle with the equally meritorious milking breed of polled Suffolk Duns." (16)

This ancient cattle breed of Norfolk was described by the well known agricultural writer W. Marshall in his *Rural Economy of Norfolk* in 1787.

" The native cattle of Norfolk are a hardy thriving race; fattening as freely, and finishing as highly, at three years old as cattle in general do at four or five. They are small boned, short legged, round barrelled, well loined, thin thighed, clean chapped; the head in general fine and the horns clean, middle-sized and bent upwards; the favourite colour, a blood red with a white or mottled face. The breed of Norfolk is the Herefordshire in miniature." (17)

That was the beef side of the picture. The milking qualities of the modern Red Poll come, according to accepted breed history, from the neighbouring county.

" The Suffolk breed on the other hand were essentially polled, their colour, red, brindled or dun. Sometimes they are called the Suffolk Dun Cow. They were a dairy breed, famed for the quantity of the yield and the excellence of the butter it produced." (17)

" At the beginning of the nineteenth century a Mr. John Reeve, a tenant on the Holkham Estate, conceived the idea of crossing the two breeds of Norfolk and Suffolk with the hopeful intention of combining the hardiness and beef of the one with the milk of the other. . . . This experiment was the origin of the present Red Poll, then termed Red Polled." (18)

Such is the reputed origin of the Red Poll although no doubt, as in the case of all livestock before the days of reliable registration, there may have been an occasional introduction of desirable characters from other breeds.

To-day the breed takes its stand upon its dual-purpose character. It would be quite easy for the Red Poll to follow the Lincoln Red in splitting into Beef and Dairy sections because, undoubtedly, some strains of the breed tend naturally towards meat production and others towards milk. This, however, is quite contrary to the declared official policy of the Red Poll Cattle Society.

" As the Breed Description clearly indicates the Red Poll is a dual-purpose animal, and on dual-purpose qualities it will live or vanish. The aim of the Society and of breeders before the Society was formed has been to perpetuate and continually improve an animal that will give a consistently high-average yield of high-class milk, and from which the steers can all be reared to provide prime carcases of beef. The highest yields are not sought after, though herds of over a 1,000 gallon average are common, and the 2,000 gallon cow is by no means unknown. Generally speaking, however, a 800–900 average is considered adequate, provided of course that make and shape for beef are retained." (18)

The accepted standards for milk and beef are laid down in the statement of Breeding Policy already referred to. They are as follows:

(*a*) No excess of milk can compensate for lack of capacity to carry flesh and *vice versa*.

(*b*) A female which does not in normal circumstances give the following yields as a minimum in the first 305 days of her lactation with corresponding increases for longer periods cannot be classed as dual-purpose— 1st Calf, 500 galls.; 2nd Calf, 600 galls.; 3rd Calf, 700 galls. On the other hand, *Provided Always* that it is not obtained at the expense of the capacity of the carcase to produce the finest beef, there is no upward limit to the yield which may be obtained from a dual-purpose Red Poll.

(*c*) Every Red Poll calf should be potentially capable of being fed with a view to providing animals that will grow into healthy beasts to make Grade "A" carcases as follows—18 months, 8½ cwt.; 2 years, 10 cwt.; 3 years 12 cwt.

The chief factor in the attainment of this aim in any given herd lies in the bull, which should be well grown and of such type and breeding as to qualify for both dairy and beef licences. To provide evidence of such qualification, it is suggested that breeders secure beef licences for their bulls and furnish National Milk Records certificates regarding the Dam's and Sire's Dam's yields. (15)

What are the results, as regards beef, the subject with which we are mainly concerned here, of holding so strictly to the middle way ? The answer is that as regards beef production the Red Poll is little if anything behind the specialised beef breeds. Indeed, in certain respects it is actually ahead of them. Baby beef was first produced from Red Poll cattle, and the breed's capacity for rapid growth, say up to fifteen months of age, is greater than in

Fig. 27. SUSSEX BULL.

Fig. 28. SUSSEX HEIFER.

Fig. 29. DAIRY SHORTHORN BULL.

Fig. 30. LINCOLN RED SHORTHORN BULL.

any other breed. Baby beef, for which the breed was particularly noted, is now rather out of fashion and, because of national economic circumstances, very likely to remain so. At more mature weights and ages appropriate to the times, however, the Red Poll has also an excellent reputation as the following quotations show:

" The steers fatten readily at an early age and produce a good quality of beef." (19)

" . . . the steers and non-breeding heifers make excellent beef." (14)

The Red Poll Society was founded in 1888 and the Herd Book is closed.

As regards distribution, the Red Poll is still at its most numerous and certainly at its best in its country of origin, namely, East Anglia. There are, however, numerous rather widely scattered herds throughout the country, some of great merit. The breed, according to some authorities, is said to lose type outside its native territory. Thus, according to Garner (14):

" The Red Poll . . . has been developed in East Anglia and especially on the poor sandy soils of Suffolk and to a certain extent Norfolk also. The cattle of this breed have become so accustomed to the sparse supply of food of low quality that if they are moved to districts where food is abundant they grow excessively and become coarse in bone."

In Scotland a similar fate overtakes the Ayrshire when transported from the west to the better land and more intensive agriculture of the eastern counties.

It is possible, therefore, that there may be some grounds for Garner's criticism. It is certainly rather strange, considering its many outstanding qualities on its native heath and at its best, that the Red Poll is not more numerous and more widely distributed than it can claim to be to-day. In Britain, it remains a somewhat local breed.

In the United States of America the Red Poll is recognised as " a true dual-purpose breed ". (20)

" The Red Polled rank high among milking cattle for beef production. The steers are usually blocky and dress out high. Red Polled steers are recorded as having won first place in national carcase contests. When they are through milking, the cows fatten rapidly to produce satisfactory beef." (20)

9

In addition to the United States and South America, " . . . there is a growing demand from many of the Dominions, especially the Union of South Africa ". (21)

Other British cattle breeds usually classified as dual-purpose are the South Devon, the Dexter, and the Welsh. I have preferred to deal with the Welsh in its capacity as a hill breed, which leaves the South Devon and Dexter to be mentioned in this section.

The **SOUTH DEVON** is a horned breed of variable brown to red colour, a curly coat, and vast size. Steers of the breed attain great weight on the fattening Midland pastures. The milk yield is not especially high in relation to the cow's size but in quality is of Channel Island standard.

Because of the immense size of a fully grown South Devon, it is usual—although perhaps somewhat uncritical—to describe the beef as coarse. Actually a correlation between small size of carcase and high quality in beef or the reverse is far from being proved. A well-known London butcher assured me at the 1951 Smithfield Show that under modern British conditions where a number of small rations have to be cut from the one joint, the South Devon carcase is less wasteful than that of any other breed. This opinion is supported by a North country butcher, as quoted in the South Devon Herd Book Society's pamphlet, *You can have Triple Purpose*:

" At the 1951 Smithfield Show, the first prize-winning South Devon steer, Waddeton Boy, weighed 20½ cwt. at 2 years and 11 months, and another steer at the same Show, Wenmouth Joe, sold to a north country butcher, brought the following comment— ' The carcase of beef was the best from all standards for quality and the least wasteful of all the six beasts purchased at Smithfield. The other five were not South Devons.' "

Finally the **DEXTER**, in contrast to the South Devons, is the smallest breed of British cattle. It is of Irish origin, first introduced into England in 1882. It has certain genetic handicaps which militate against its commercial usefulness:

" Monstrous calves, of the so-called ' bull-dog ' type, are much commoner than in other breeds. Indeed, the Dexter appears to be a heterozygous form, producing, when pure bred, 25 per cent of long-legged, ' Kerry type ' calves, 50 per cent of true Dexters, and 25 per cent of ' bull-dog ' calves." (22)

It is rather a moot point as to whether or not the **BRITISH FRIESIAN** should be regarded as a dual-purpose breed in face of the Breed Society's official decision to deny the claim. Yet there is a unanimity of opinion both abroad and in this country that the Friesian produces a better beef carcase than does any other specialised dairy breed.

In its original home in the Low Countries, some Friesian strains are termed dual-purpose. This appears to mean little more, however, than that the carcase of the cow, when her milking days are over, yields rather better beef than is commonly obtained from cows of other dairy breeds. The suitability of the male calves for rearing into beef steers hardly comes into the continental picture.

In America (U.S.) the breed is best known as the Holstein. Discussing its value in beef production, Professor Petersen writes:

" The Holstein ranks highest among the dairy breeds for meat production. It has the largest carcase of the dairy breeds, is the thickest fleshed, and has the lightest colour of body fat. In some tests Holstein steers have shown up favourably with beef breeds in rapidity of gains and in the quality of beef pro-duced." (23)

There are some who claim that the British Friesian as it exists to-day may, by correct management, be made most useful for beef production. Mr. Mansfield of Cambridge University is one of them, and highly interesting and important experiments to test the beef possibilities of the breed are presently in progress on the Cambridge University Farm under his direction. Suffice it to say here that under good rearing conditions the Friesian steer appears to have done unexpectedly well in comparison with that of a specialised beef breed such as the Hereford.

Under commercial conditions Friesian steer calves are unlikely to be particularly well reared and in such circumstances must be given ample time to grow. Thus Mr. G. P. J. Hoddell writes:

" To try feeding Friesians at an earlier age would, in our opinion, be uneconomical, as they feed quicker from $2\frac{1}{2}$ years of age onwards." (24)

Given the necessary time Friesian steers will attain great weight and a satisfactory killing out percentage. Thus Hoddell describing his results in the fattening of mature Friesian steers says:

" Up to date this year, for example, all the 36 animals sent to Gainsborough grading centre were graded 'special' and averaged 16 cwt. 1 qr. in weight." (24)

A fair summing up of the value of the Friesian in beef production is that given by Watson and More (25):

" As a meat producer the Friesian is the best of the purely dairy breeds, if it be considered as such; but it is not so satisfactory as, say, the recognised type of Dairy Shorthorn. The calves are large and feed rapidly into excellent veal, but the steers tend to grow too large before they will fatten, and the meat is commonly rather poorly marbled. Some strains might be classed as dual-purpose, and a few steers of excellent quality have been exhibited at recent fat-stock shows."

There can be no doubt that the Friesian has made its presence felt in the post-war beef world. The Ministry of Food's system of grading offers the biggest reward for weight and for a high killing out percentage, the latter being about the only estimation of that very complex thing—beef quality—earning financial reward. The Friesian comes out well on both counts—it grows big and it kills well. Even an Aberdeenshire feeder, Mr. D. Fowlie, says this much of it:

" Cattle of the Friesian type have grown much more popular in the beef world. They certainly carry a big percentage of bone but they put on a lot of weight for age, and, if fat, are very good graders, i.e., they kill out very well." (26)

It must be added that the carefully controlled Cambridge experiments rather suggest that the presumed " big percentage of bone " in the Friesian may be more apparent than real.

The breed made a very good impression at the 1952 Smithfield Show and proved a capacity for early maturity with which it is seldom credited. The following extract is fairly typical of press comments made at the time:

" Another striking thing about the Smithfield exhibits was the Friesian steers, several of which weighed out at about 12 cwt. at under two years old, and it occurred to me that if they were shorter legged and a different colour they could compete in looks with some of the pure beef cattle.

" We all think of Scottish beef as the finest in the world and, no doubt, it is, but—judging by the sort of steak which is served in Holland—there is not a lot wrong with Friesian beef.

" If they can obtain such a weight in so short a time, it may be a much more profitable way of producing meat, and if all the males of that breed were reared and fattened it would help considerably in settling our meat problems." (27)

The answer to this suggestion is that, in all probability, there are not enough concentrated feeding stuffs available in post-war Britain to bring out *all* the Friesian steers at 12 cwt. when under two years of age. In considering these Smithfield successes, the important thing from the practical point of view is to know not only what *can* be done but how it *was* done.

REFERENCES

(1) Watson, J. S., Cameron, J., and Garrad G. H. (1926). "The Cattle-Breeders' Handbook," p. 19 (London).
(2) *Ibid.*, p. 20.
(3) Hammond, J. (1952). "Farm Animals," p. 245, 2nd Edit. (London).
(4) Stewart, D. M. (1952). "Milk and real beef forbye," *Scotch Shorthorn Record*, June, p. 21.
(5) Harrison, J. (1945). "Shorthorns," *Agriculture*, **52**, 26.
(6) Garner, F. H. (1944). "The Cattle of Britain, p. 107 (London).
(7) Mackintosh, J. *J. British Dairy Farmers' Association*, Sept. 1945, as summarised by H. B. Cronshaw in "Dairy Information," p. 89, Dairy Industries Ltd. (London).
(8) "British Pedigree Cattle," p. 87.
(9) Lincoln Red Shorthorn Society (1951). "Brief History and Description of the Lincoln Red Shorthorn Cattle," p. 4 (Lincoln).
(10) *Ibid.*, p. 11.
(11) *Ibid.*, p. 19.
(12) Garner, F. C. (1944). *Ibid.*, p.12.
(13) Lincoln Red Shorthorn Society (1951). *Ibid.*, p. 19.
(14) Garner, F. C. (1944). *Ibid.*, p. 115.
(15) The Red Poll—Breeding Policy—adopted by Council on April 17, 1947.
(16) Wallace, R. (1907) "Farm Livestock of Great Britain," p. 156, 4th Ed.
(17) "British Pedigree Cattle," p. 81.
(18) *Ibid.*, p. 82.
(19) Watson, J. A. S., and More, J. A. (1949). "Agriculture," p. 569, 9th Ed.
(20) Petersen, W. E. (1950). "Dairy Science," p. 159, 2nd Ed. (Chicago).
(21) Watson, J. A. S., and More, J. A. (1949). *Ibid.*, p. 570.
(22) *Ibid.*, p. 577.
(23) Petersen, W. E. (1950). *Ibid.*, p. 110.
(24) Hoddell, G. P. J. (1947). "Friesian bullocks for the fat market," *Agriculture*, **54**, 402.
(25) Watson, J. A. S., and More, J. A. (1949). *Ibid.*, p. 573.
(26) Fowlie, D. (1950). *Proc. Brit. Soc. Anim. Prod.*, p. 86.
(27) *Farmers' Weekly*, (1952), **37**, 26.

THERE are three breeds of cattle in Britain that are generally accepted and acknowledged as being hill breeds. They are the Highland, the Galloway, and the Welsh Black. Of these three breeds the first two are frequently classified as beef breeds, partly, no doubt, because neither the Highland nor the Galloway make any special pretensions to milk. The Welsh Black, on the contrary, is often regarded as a dual-purpose breed, as some strains undoubtedly are.

Nevertheless, the main importance of all three breeds is their capacity to live and to make either beef or milk, or both, under the somewhat rigorous conditions of hill-farming. One might go even further, indeed, in suggesting that, wanting this adaptation to hill-farming conditions, none of these breeds would have very much of a future. Wanting it, they might, in fact, quite readily and quite easily become things of the past. It is the recently revived interest in the possibilities of hill country as a source of beef, or rather of beef stores, that has focused attention on these three old breeds.

HIGHLAND CATTLE. This breed, sometimes called the " West Highland " or " Kyloe ", is descended from the native breed of the Scottish Highlands. It might be truer to say from native *breeds*, since historical evidence suggests that the ancient Highland cattle of certain regions, particularly those of Skye, were distinguished from those of others. It has been suggested also that the cattle of the Islands were at one time substantially different from those of the Highland Mainland, and that the title " Kyloe " applied particularly to the Island cattle. It was they that had to be ferried or swum across the straits or kyles separating the Hebridean islands from the Mainland or from one another.

The historical aspects of Highland cattle husbandry are more fully discussed in a later section of this book. Here we are concerned only with the cattle themselves.

In the first place, then, many ancient documents and some more recent refer to the old Highland cattle as " black cattle ", from which has arisen the quite erroneous notion that they were all black-coated. Actually, that was not so.

" The phrase, ' black cattle,' employed by some early writers, was used to distinguish that class of stock from horses, and did not apply exclusively to the colour of the hair of the animals." (1)

The old use of the phrase is clearly illustrated by the wording in the advertisement of William Dick's first course of veterinary lectures in Edinburgh in 1816: ". . . lectures on the diseases of horses, of black cattle, sheep and other domestic animals." (2)

Early contemporary descriptions of Highland cattle are quoted by Haldane in his book on the Scottish cattle droving industry. (3)

One description written in 1798 describes the West Highland cattle of that period as follows:

" They are of various colours, black, dun, branded and brown; but the black is the most common and most run after."

Another description, written in 1811, lists the desirable colouring of the Kyloe breed as:

" . . . black (that being reckoned the hardiest and most durable species), or dark brown, or reddish brown, without any white or yellow spots."

The most recent authoritative publication on the subject states that:

" . . . in addition to the actual black there must have been varying degrees of red, brown, and brindled. There was also said to have been a whitish dun . . . " (4)

At one time, probably towards the end of the eighteenth century, black became the most fashionable shade among the best folds of Highland cattle. Thus Osgood Mackenzie (he was himself born in 1842) wrote:

" In my grandfather's day no colour was considered right for Highland cattle but black. The great thing then was to have a fold of black cows. No one would look at the reds and yellows and cream and duns, which are all the rage nowadays." (5)

To-day, the cycle of colour in the breed has turned full circle.

" The recognised colours embrace various shades of red, yellow, dun and cream, as well as brindled and black, which last formerly prevailed but is now rare." (6)

In the modern breed horns are universal, but there is ample historical evidence to show that this was not always so. When Dr. Johnson visited the Scottish Highlands in 1773, one of his unanswered questions was whether the polled and horned cattle he saw belonged to the same breed.

In his published account of the journey which he and Boswell made through the Western Islands of Scotland in 1773, he wrote:

" The cattle of Skye are not so small as is commonly believed. Since they have sent their beeves in great numbers to southern markets, they have probably taken more care of their breed. Of their black cattle, some are without horns, called by the Scots *humble* cows, as we call a bee *humble* that wants a sting. Whether this difference be specific or accidental, though we inquired with great diligence, we could not be informed." (7)

There is universal agreement and a great deal of historical evidence to show that the old Highland cattle were of extremely small size, at least they were so in their native environment. Possibly the size of the ancient Highland cattle, like that of the common clansmen, was stunted by the semi-starvation they had to endure.

Burt, in his classical *Letters from Scotland* written about 1730, describes a drove of Highland cattle he saw being driven south as being of the size of Lincolnshire calves.

In John Smith's *General View of the County of Argyll*, 1798, as quoted by Haldane (8), the carcase weights of the Highland cattle of that time are given as 360 to 400 lb., indicating a live-weight of somewhere between 6 and 8 cwt.* Considering they were in good condition and from three to four years old when slaughtered, that is no great weight by modern standards. John Smith added, however, that:

" . . . such as are brought to better pasture as in England, may be brought to weigh 560 lb. or more."

That would indicate a live-weight of some 10 cwt., something much closer to modern standards and illustrative of the truth of a generalisation made by Mr. John Cameron of Glenfinlas:

" About the cattle themselves, if they have been bred on the holding the land will generally dictate size, whatever the breed or cross." (9)

What, then, of the breed to-day?

" It has been said time and again, with acceptable frankness, that the Highland breed is the most picturesque of all the cattle breeds." (10)

---

* According to Handley, *Scottish Farming in the Eighteenth Century*, 1953, p. 71, they weighed " between two and four hundredweights."

That statement is something more than breed propaganda, it is plain truth. In good condition and in full coat, the Highlander is certainly a very lovely creature, with its proud carriage and wild appearance (rather deceptive, because Highland cattle, even the bulls, are often surprisingly docile), the shaggy, often richly coloured coat, the wide and majestically sweeping horns, rendering the Highlander the most pictorial of all our cattle.

Pictures by themselves, however, make a bare platter. What value does the breed have for beef? On that important point, opinions differ. Highland steers are shown at all the leading shows, including Smithfield, but are welcomed there, presumably, rather for their beauty than their beef.

William M'Combie of Tillyfour, the great breeder and feeder of cattle, co-founder of the Aberdeen-Angus breed, wrote of the Highland cattle of his day, those of the mid-nineteenth century: "They consumed few turnips, and did not pay sixpence for what turnips they did consume." He admitted, however, that they might be useful "for grazing purposes in certain localities and under certain conditions". (11)

Garner, in more modern times, is little more enthusiastic over the economic value of Highland cattle as beef producers. He wrote: "The breed serves a useful function in their natural habitat, but they have spread little except as picturesque cattle to consume grass in parkland areas. The breed is slow maturing and often is not ready for sale (fat) until three or four years of age. At Smithfield Fat Stock Show animals of this breed are the oldest exhibited and even then rarely do they carry much fat." (12)

In fact, the difficulty of disposal of the male calves, unwanted for bulls, is one of the main factors against the extension of the Highland breed. The pure Highland steer is slow and ill to fatten and, apart from motives of sentiment and art, there is no particular reason why feeders when they come to the buying in of stores should come to buy it. Highland heifers, on the contrary, are easily and well sold and always in short supply, the reason being that the Highland cow will live well in hill country and, at the same time, produce a cross calf, preferably by a Beef Shorthorn, that is relatively easily fed and far more easily sold than a pure Highland steer.

The hardiness and longevity of the Highland breed is universally recognised.

" Some cows will breed on to 17 and 18 years of age." (13)

The type of coat, an outer coat of long hard hair to shed the rain; inner, thick, soft under-coat or " vest " to hold the body heat, is an important breed point in Highland cattle and one that is also of great practical importance.

" The importance of the hair in the Highlander cannot be too strongly emphasised. James Cameron summed this up beautifully when he said—' . . . At the fall of the year and in winter the brow of the well-bred bull or heifer should be like a sporran, with straight flowing hair down to the edge of the nose, and leaving not more than a mere peering opportunity for the eyes. Long hair should also fall from the ridge of the neck, the spinal column, and should be abundant down the thighs. A long fringe should also hang from the lower edge of the ears. I always think this is a sign of good breeding. It is of consequence to have a very thick, soft undercoat, or " vest " . . . '." (14)

The Highland cow, because of her hardihood and longevity, forms an excellent foundation for a hill herd. Apart, however, from the maintenance of an indispensable foundation of pure Highland stock, there is general agreement that the Beef Shorthorn cross is equally hardy and has the further advantage of producing a much more readily saleable steer calf. The calf may be either a half-bred Beef Shorthorn cross out of a pure Highland cow or a three parts bred Beef Shorthorn cross out of a half-bred cow.

The advantageous nature of the cross between Shorthorn and Highlander was recognised many years ago. Thomas Bates of Shorthorn fame " . . . in his earlier years experimented in crossing the Shorthorn with the Kyloe ". (15)

That cross has been more widely popularised in later time. It was the most common cross on the Highland cattle of my youth, and the cattle that used to be driven down to the Muir of Ord market between 1900 and 1908 from Western Ross-shire were mainly of that type. The crossing with the Aberdeen-Angus and the fashion for the black polled calf came rather later and was not altogether favourable to the old Highland breed. For, in contrast to the excellence of the cross between the Shorthorn and the Highlander, " . . . the Highland cow and the Angus bull is a known bad cross ", although, " on the Highland cross [*i.e.*, with the Shorthorn] the Angus bull of substance is excellent ". (16)

In the modern revival of interest in hill cattle farming in the Scottish Highlands, the Highland cow and her Shorthorn crosses have received some influential backing. One of the earliest and most carefully planned experiments in the reintroduction of cattle on to the Scottish hill pastures was that of the Ben Challum Estates Ltd.'s at Glenlochay, Western Perthshire. The moving spirit in this company, Mr. Duncan M. Stewart, has on several occasions, both in speech and in print, defended the choice of the foundation stock in this most interesting and successful enterprise.

Mr. J. A. Cameron of Glenfinlas, who has wide experience both of hill farming and hill cattle, has written:

" I am perfectly satisfied that the Shorthorn–Highland cross is an adequate hill cow and a sound foundation type." (16)

These testimonials to the Highlander and more especially to its Shorthorn crosses are from breeders carrying beef production to the stage of the weaned calf and no further. What of the feeder?

Mr. J. A. Stodart, writing of his experience in East Lothian, typical cattle-feeding as opposed to cattle-rearing country, states that:

" In my county the Shorthorn–Highland cross bullock has made a minor invasion during the last three or four years; so well have these cattle done for those who have fattened them that the bidding for them each October has become increasingly keener." (17)

To illustrate what the Shorthorn–Highland cross can do in the way of beef production under the most favourable conditions one may refer to a heifer of this cross that won first prize at the Scottish National Fat Stock Club Show in 1937. Aged one year seven months and one week she weighed 10 cwt. 49 lb.

The Highland Cattle Society of Scotland was founded in 1884, " to maintain the purity of the breed known as Highland Cattle and to establish a Herd Book in which to register their pedigrees ". The first Herd Book was published in 1885. Until recently open, the Herd Book is now closed.

Although the export demand for Highland cattle is still distinctly limited, there is evidence that it is growing and may continue to grow.

" They are now to be found in places far removed from their native haunts—in Canada and the United States; in Newfoundland and the Falkland Isles; in the heights of Peru; in rough stretches of country in Queensland (Australia); on the veldts of South Africa and on the Argentine plains; and some years ago a consignment was sent to Russia." (18)

GALLOWAY CATTLE. In one sense the Galloway might be termed a royal breed, since its early popularity and fame followed closely on the union under the one king of two countries previously hostile.

" In earlier days cattle in Galloway were not very numerous, as, being distant from any centre of population, there was no commercial outlet for any quantity of beef. The lands, both hill and low ground, carried mainly sheep which were kept for the sake of their wool from which in those far off days more profit could be derived. The union of the crowns, however, opened the road south across the border, and the demand from Norfolk and the south-eastern counties of England resulted in a rapid extension of cattle breeding during the next two centuries— so much so that at the close of the 18th century as many as 20,000 to 30,000 Galloway cattle were sent annually from the pastures of Dunfriesshire and Galloway, mainly to Norfolk and Suffolk." (19)

Stimulated and nourished by this export demand the Galloway increased both in numbers and in range so that it became " . . . the most prevalent breed in Scotland west of the Tweed and south of the Forth and Clyde till the first decade of the nineteenth century ". (20)

As in so many other of our cattle breeds, there seems to have been rather more variability in the external characters of the Galloway of the past than is to be found in its descendants to-day. Thus while all Galloways are now polled and either black or dun in colour, " . . . Youatt says, as late as the middle of the eighteenth century, many animals of pure blood had horns of considerable length, and not a few were red-brown in colour ". (20)

Some of these aberrations described by Youatt may well have been the result of previous crossing of the breed in the eighteenth century, then as now a recognised and common method of attempted livestock improvement. Thus James Webster in his *General View of the Agriculture of Galloway*, published in 1794, wrote: " Crosses have been made by the introduction of bulls from

England at different periods, but recently by the present Earl of Galloway, with the Westmorland bulls; from which his Lordship is of opinion that both the size and shape have been improved. Admiral Keith Stewart has lately introduced a beautiful Argyllshire bull, which he considers to have made the greatest improvement of any on the country breed." (21)

No name, however, stands out particularly in the history of the Galloway. The breed had no Bakewell, no Collings, no Tomkins, no Quartly.

" No great so-called ' improver ' ever rose to do work like that of the Collings upon the Galloway breed. But the work was well done under the fostering care of the noblemen and gentlemen of Galloway, towards the end of the eighteenth and early in the nineteenth century." (22)

The late eighteenth and early nineteenth centuries were the hey-day of the Galloway. After that there came a recession, related to economic causes and not to any deterioration of the breed.

" The increase in the feeding of crosses and half-bred sheep and the remarkable extension of dairying during the latter half of the nineteenth century have brought about a great diminution in the number of this breed, and a concurrent increase in the deeper milking Ayrshire." (22)

" From about 1840 onwards dairying increased steadily in Galloway and the surrounding counties and this resulted in the gradual displacement of Galloways from the lower-lying and better quality farms by Ayrshires and other dairy cattle. The dairying industry had its depressions also, and during these Galloways once more came into favour for short periods, but generally the change was a steady one and the Galloway was slowly but surely pushed up into the hills and marginal areas." (23)

The Galloway was, in fact, tending to fade out of the picture of British cattle. The revived interest in hill cattle first as agricultural implements for improving hill pasture to benefit sheep, and secondly and rather later as beef producers in their own right, led to a renewed interest in this ancient breed.

" . . . it is as hill cattle that Galloways have now an established place in the farming economy of the country, and an increasingly important part to play in the future." (24)

Before reviewing critically the claims made on behalf of the breed, it may be useful to mention some breed points of importance and also the connections, accepted or speculative, of the Galloway with other Scottish breeds.

The Points of the Breed were drawn up by the Council of the Galloway Cattle Society of Great Britain in 1883 and have not changed substantially since that date. Nor, indeed, was the description accepted officially in 1883 very different from that given by authorities on the breed in 1800.

The colour of the Galloway should be black (with a tinge of brown) or dun. It is of interest that the team of Galloways that won the Duke of Norfolk's Inter-Breed Trophy at Smithfield Show in 1951 were all dun coloured. On the whole, however, black is more fashionable and more common. The breed is polled without trace of horns or scurs; the general conformation of the body is that sought in beef breeds, although narrower and longer than in some; the skin mellow and moderately thick. The hair " soft and wavy, with mossy undercoat ". (25) Superficially, at least, the Galloway has a certain resemblance to the Aberdeen-Angus.

" Like the Aberdeen-Angus, the Galloway is black, polled, and of beef type." (26)

There are, however, certain important differences in the shape of the head, that of the Galloway being very short with a broad poll, while that of the Aberdeen-Angus is longer with poll sharply pointed. There is also, of course, a less perfect beef conformation in the Galloway:

" A certain slackness of back and prominence of shoulder are common faults among the ordinary commercial individuals." (27)

These are faults, however, only from the point of view of ideal beef conformation. They are actually advantageous in an animal designed to climb hills.

The relationship between the two polled breeds was sufficiently close to hold them in the same Herd Book for fifteen years, between 1862 and 1877, the Galloway Cattle Society being formed in the latter year.

" The first volume of the Galloway Herd Book was issued in 1878. This volume consisted of a reprint of the Galloway entries in the first four volumes of the Polled Herd Book which was issued between 1862 and 1877. Since 1883 a volume has been issued annually." (28)

In action, style, hardiness, and type of coat, the Galloway shows a resemblance to the Highlander. Take the horns off a black or dun-coloured Highlander and it is not so vastly different from some types of Galloway. There has never, however, been any officially accepted connection between them.

" The Galloway and the West Highland breeds are universally considered to be descended from the same original stock, but although in type of body they are much alike there is no sufficient historical grounds for the belief." (29)

With certain affinities to Scotland's premier beef breed—the Aberdeen-Angus—on the one hand, and to Highland on the other, it might have happened that the Galloway fell between two stools. Actually, the breed has made a brave and far from unsuccessful attempt to mount both stools at once.

" Two points always to be borne in mind are—(a) that the Galloway is a Beef Breed, and (b) that it is a Hill Breed; and the qualities and characteristics of the Breed all flow from these two main considerations." (30)

The beef qualities of the Galloway are undeniable; ". . . perhaps the most important testimony is the fact that between 1919 and 1938 the Breed won the Championship in the Carcase Competition at Smithfield Show no fewer than 10 times and the Reserve Championship 4 times." (31)

The success of the Galloway team at Smithfield in 1951 has already been mentioned. This capacity to lay on beef of quality is—like so many characteristics of the breed—of ancient origin. George Culley wrote of the Galloway of his time (c. 1800): " . . . few or no cattle sell so high in Smithfield market, they being such nice cutters up, owing to laying the fat upon the most valuable parts; a great excellence in all feeding cattle." (32)

It is, in fact, one of the most valuable qualities of the Galloway, considered as a hill breed, that the steer calves of the breed itself, as well as those of its crosses, can make first-class beef. As previously mentioned, the profitable disposal of the male side of a pure hill breed whether of cattle or of sheep is frequently something of a problem. This problem does not arise in the case of the Galloway because of the excellent feeding potentialities of the pure Galloway steer. Crosses with the classic beef breeds— Shorthorn, Hereford, Aberdeen-Angus—are equally if not more valuable.

Of these, the cross with the White Shorthorn—giving the Blue-grey—namely for yard-fattening, and in the case of the heifer for further breeding—is the best known and of greatest commercial importance. Actually, the cross can be made either way, but the general custom is to use a white Shorthorn bull on the Galloway cow.

" . . . trial and error had proved that the Shorthorn–Galloway cross produced an excellent animal. The white Shorthorn bull used on Galloway cows produced a very uniform polled calf which, on account of its colour became known as the ' Blue-grey '. These soon earned a very wide popularity, and Blue-grey heifers were, and still are, extensively used for breeding." (33)

Garner, in discussing Galloways, wrote: " The main function of the breed in this country is to provide the dams for crossing with the White Beef Shorthorn bulls to produce the famous ' Blue Greys ' that fatten so well in yards." (34)

The beefing qualities of the breed both in the pure breed and in its crosses, notably in its " Blue-grey " cross, together with its noteworthy successes at Smithfield and other national shows, entitle the Galloway to rank as one of the recognised beef breeds.

The qualities of the Galloway that have made it one of the two recognised hill breeds of Scotland are less easy to define. " Galloways are extremely hardy." (30) That indubitably is true, yet the definition of hardiness is sufficiently difficult. What is even more difficult is to decide how much of an animal's hardiness is due to its genetic constitution; how much to the environment in which both it and its immediate ancestors have been reared. Galloways, being prepared for Smithfield, no doubt became exceedingly soft; quite as soft, presumably, as any Aberdeen-Angus being fitted for the same competition. On the reverse side I have been informed by a cattleman of wide experience that Aberdeen-Angus reared and bred on the hill become as hardy and independent as any Galloway. Indeed, much of the difference between these two black and polled breeds, once included in the same Herd Book, may—and that possibly to a degree greater than is commonly supposed—be environmental rather than genetic. That, in a sense, although the sense is important, is by the way and speculative. What is known and certain is that the Galloway, in the type of country where it is customarily kept and under the type of husbandry to which it is usually subjected, is a true hill breed, able to with-

Fig. 31. RED POLL BULL.

Fig. 32. SOUTH DEVON BULL.

Fig. 33. HIGHLAND BULL.

Fig. 34. HIGHLAND COW.

Fig. 35. GALLOWAY BULL.

Fig. 36. GALLOWAY COW.

Fig. 37. WELSH BLACK BULL.

Fig. 38. WELSH BLACK COW.

stand vicissitudes of weather, to endure seasonal dearth, and to find an independent living on uncultivated pastures through its own initiative and by its own exertions.

" The other great Hill characteristic of the breed is its quality and ability as a rustler." (31)

That of course is true and in a sense a virtue, although some might suggest that the rustling, on occasion, is overdone. In other words the Galloway, or at least some strains of the Galloway, have been accused of becoming so independent and wild under Range conditions, as to be unmanageable. This fault, if it be a fault, has a remedy in the hands of skilful cattlemen.

Ian Jennings, of Shiel, New Galloway, writes:

" First, the complaint that Galloways are wild and hard to handle; in my experience if the stock heifers are tied up for a week or two during their first winter, they soon get used to handling, and if the necessity should arise later in their lives they can be dealt with at a difficult calving, twinning etc. without difficulty." (35)

George Jamieson, lately farm manager at Glensaugh, Kincardine, has much the same answer:

" Heifer calves to be retained for stock are best tied up for say two or three weeks at weaning. This is the time when the cattlemen ought to get busy if they are to be quiet cows later. It is not enough for him to feed only, he must spend a lot of time on kindly handling. It is worth a lot." (36)

The Galloway has not in the past attracted a great deal of attention abroad. " . . . Galloways have never been exported in very large numbers, . . . " (37)

Recently (since 1945) there has been more interest shown in the breed by foreign and Dominion buyers. Thus, while only 55 beasts were exported during the twenty-year period 1919–1939, there were 213 exported between 1945 and 1951. This is due to considerable revival of interest in the breed—particularly in U.S.A. and in New Zealand.

BELTED GALLOWAY CATTLE are close relatives of the foregoing breed but being much less common are, in consequence, of less economic importance. They are distinguished superficially by having a wide white belt around the middle of the body, hence the name " Belties ". This striking and contrasting colour pattern gives the Belted Galloway a very attractive appearance, " . . . there are two recognised colours—black with brownish tinge and white, or dun with similar markings." (38)

The white belted character is dominant and very persistent.

" It is on record that on one farm where belties were kept no Belted Galloway bull was used for over 30 years and yet the belt persisted . . . " (39)

The Belted Galloway, unlike the Galloway, make some claims to milk production:

" . . . on the whole the cows are fairly good milkers and by selection some very fine herds of good milkers have been established." (38)

WELSH BLACK CATTLE. This, by tradition, is the native cattle breed of Wales or rather, perhaps, the fusion of two such breeds, because the modern Welsh Black is the outcome of two types or breeds, at one time considered distinct. There was until recently a North breed or type and a South breed or type, the distinction arising in the first place no doubt from geographical and political separation.

" . . . in Wales itself there was little communication between North and South so that two distinct types of cattle developed— a sturdy, small, compact type adapted to the mountains in the north and a rather larger and heavier beast in the south-west. The latter (known as the ' Castlemartin ') was used for draught as well as for butter and beef—for which both north and south were noted." (40)

" The North Wales or Anglesey was a hardy, slow-maturing beef breed, well known during the past two centuries as producing the highly valued grazing cattle imported into the Midlands for fattening, under the name of ' Welsh Runts '. In the south was the Pembroke or Castlemartin breed, rather longer and looser of frame and thinner of flesh, prized chiefly for the dairy." (41)

These two types have from time to time been separated in two Herd Books or combined in one.

" The first volume of the Welsh Black Cattle Herd Book appeared in 1874. In 1883 the North Wales Breeders issued a separate Herd Book known as the North Wales Black Cattle Herd Book. But since 1905 there has only been one Herd Book including both types." (40)

As regards the characters of the modern breed:

" The accepted coat colour is black, but a little white on the udder is allowed and even welcomed so long as it is not excessive." (42)

The uniformity of coat colour demands continuous selection as in so many other cattle breeds because other colours do occur, although infrequently: " On rare occasions, red or dun calves may be born of pedigree parents, as well as calves which show some excess of white." (42)

The breed is horned and the general conformation—regarded from the beef point of view—somewhat uneven. Thus:

" Show specimens often leave little to be desired in respect of symmetry, but the ordinary run tend to be rather high at the rump, rather weak in the thighs, and hard ' handlers '." (42)

" As beef stock, they are rather slow developing and even when finished are very liable to lack in development of loin and hind-quarters." (43)

The Welsh Black does not, of course, lay claim to being a specialised beef breed. Welsh cattlemen specialising in beef cattle prefer the Hereford, a breed having a strong representation within Welsh territory. The avowed intention of the breeders of the Welsh Black is to maintain it as a true dual-purpose breed, yielding milk of high butter-fat content in moderation and producing a fair carcase of beef. For beef purposes the Welsh Black is undoubtedly improved by crossing with the Hereford.

" They are very commonly crossed with the Hereford, the first cross making excellent stock for fattening on pastures, for which they are much in demand." (43)

In this cross the black coat of the Welsh and the white face of the Hereford are both dominant, giving the first cross a characteristic, if somewhat peculiar appearance.

As hill cattle the Welsh Blacks have proven qualities. They are hardy, long-lived, independent.

" The hardiness of the breed is well exemplified in the herd of Captain Bennett Evans, whose cattle are out all the year round on Plynlimmon on the 1,500 feet line; the herd has been kept in this way since 1931." (44)

Abroad the Welsh Black is not widely known. At home, a hill breed of cattle having a dual-purpose character is unique and deserves a wider publicity. Only two other breeds in Britain

—Highland and Galloway—make serious claims to be regarded as hill breeds, and neither has ever made any pretensions to milk production beyond what is required to rear a good suckled calf. The Welsh Black, in this respect, seems to have kept closer to the original pattern of those cattle which, in historical times, formed an important element in the natural wealth of the hill lands of Britain.

CROSS-BREDS AS HILL CATTLE. So far only those cattle claiming to be pure-bred and sponsored by their appropriate Breed Societies have been considered under the general classification of Hill Cattle. There are already, however, many cattle on the hill lands of Britain that are not pure-bred and, in certain areas of the Highlands of Scotland, at least, there appears to be a growing tendency to use cross-bred rather than pure-bred cattle for the exploitation of hill pastures. This tendency is of especial interest as being in direct contradiction to what is customary, or presumed to be customary, among hill sheep.

There are, of course, several good if not necessarily sufficient reasons for preferring a pure breed to cross-breds on a hill grazing. For one thing it is possibly to maintain a hill stock of a pure breed permanently on the ground without any recruitment apart from its natural increase and the occasional introduction of fresh blood through a bought-in male.

In this connection it should be emphasised that the pure breed so-called is genetically heterogeneous and that the genetic variation between the extremes of any breed of large numbers and wide dispersion is possibly little less than that existing between one recognised breed and another. In other words, the advantages resulting from heterosis or hybrid vigour may not be entirely confined to the crossing of different breeds. In all probability it occurs also, although possibly in a minor degree, between different strains within the same breed. It would, therefore, be a mistake to assume that a hill breeding policy, based on one breed only, entirely excludes the possibility of employing the very real advantages derived from crossing and somewhat loosely described as hybrid vigour. There are, of course, other and substantial advantages of keeping a hill stock of cattle pure bred. Mr. Ian Jennings in his essay *Galloways on the Hills*, puts the case exceedingly well.

" My herd is all pure bred, and consists at the present time of about 90 breeding cows, most of which were bred on the ground. I think that this is very important. The great advantage of (and in my opinion an unanswerable argument for) having a pure bred stock, is that the stock heifers are reared on what is to be their future home and they become used to the hill conditions from birth, and in fact almost hefted in exactly the same way as Blackface sheep." (45)

In point of fact, however, it is not strictly necessary to maintain a hill cattle stock pure bred in order to obtain the undoubted advantages of hefting, acclimatisation, and disease resistance universally recognised as being of the very first importance in the successful management of hill sheep. Mr. George Jamieson suggests a practical programme by which this can be done.

" The foundation stock must be kept pure, but I think the aim should be to produce as heavy quality beef as possible and therefore cross with the more early-maturing beef bulls as much as possible. I think the ideal way is to try to make the herd self-sufficient as far as possible except for the purchase of fresh bulls. On bigger grazings it may be that a herd of pure-bred cows can be kept to supply replacements both for the pure herd and for crossing, but on the smaller farms I think the best set-up would be about 25 per cent pure cows and 75 per cent cross cows. A pure-bred bull would then be put to the pure cows about every fourth year to maintain the foundation stock." (46)

In this plan Mr. Jamieson is obviously concerned mainly with the up-grading of the pure hill breeds—Galloway and Highland—to higher beef standards. That is his main interest and plea for cross-breeding of hill cattle.

Mr. John A. Cameron of Glenfinlas has rather a different approach. He advocates crossing of the basic hill breeds—again Galloway and Highland—and in doing so makes what amounts to a direct claim to the importance of heterosis or hybrid vigour in the breeding of hill cattle. He writes:

" While generally recognised as the universal first cross beef improver, I do not know that the Scottish Shorthorn anywhere exercises a more valuable influence than when used on either the Galloway or the Highland female. *Whether it be that both hill breeds have suffered from inbreeding, I am certain that the first cross of either by a Shorthorn bull gains in constitution.*" (47)   (Italics mine.—A.F.)

And again:

" . . . my experience is that the Galloway–Shorthorn, or the Highland–Shorthorn is in essential respects a better hill cow than her mother." (47)

On the basis of this experience Mr. Cameron, with the sanction of the Department of Agriculture for Scotland, has embarked on the interesting experiment of in-breeding his Shorthorn–Highland crosses in the expectation, presumably, that the new breed so established will retain the virtues and alleged superiority of the first-cross over the foundation breed. But will it? That is an important although extremely difficult question to decide. It is one, I understand, that the Hill Lands Commission in Scotland, recently established, is preparing to investigate on a somewhat larger scale.

Additional to the use, or suggested use, of first crosses or in-bred crosses between one or other of the Scottish hill breeds and the Beef Shorthorn, there is what is customarily referred to as the Irish heifer. She has been used as foundation stock on some of the most widely publicised hill cattle enterprises of the Scottish Highlands. These heifers of beef type from the West counties of Eire are fine cattle, well bred and well reared. They are not, to the best of my knowledge, by any means of strictly uniform type. They are, however, of beef ancestry and they are cross bred. Those introduced by Mr. J. W. Hobbs on to his Great Glen Cattle Ranch near Fort William in Inverness-shire are Hereford–Aberdeen-Angus crosses.

" In selecting the foundation herd we chose the well-known and recognised Irish cross of Hereford–Aberdeen-Angus, which have proved the best beef producers in the West of Ireland." (48)

Irish cattle of similar type were used also as foundation stock on Lord Lovat's Glen Strathfarrar cattle ranch, and the lead given by these two pioneers is being widely followed by newcomers to the hill cattle adventure.

The conditions and modifications of husbandry applicable to different types of hill cattle are discussed more fully in a later chapter. Here I have endeavoured to draw attention to what I believe may prove eventually to be a most important point. First crosses, at least in certain crosses, may have a vitality superior to either of the parent breeds from which they are derived. If that be so, and the experience of breeders of both cattle and sheep suggest that it *is* so, then it would seem only reasonable to make the very widest possible use of first crosses under hill conditions. In this country, at least, there is no type of stock farming where every ounce of vitality is so urgently required.

REFERENCES

(1) Sinclair, J. "History of Shorthorn Cattle," p. 15.
(2) Watson, J. A. S., and Hobbs, M. E. (1951). "Great Farmers," p. 267, 2nd Ed. (London).
(3) Haldane, A. R. B. (1952). "The Drove Roads of Scotland," p. 235, appen. C. (Edinburgh).
(4) MacKenzie, A. (1952). "Highland Cattle, To-day and yesterday."
(5) Osgood Mackenzie (1950 Ed.). "A Hundred Years in the Highlands," p. 26. (London).
(6) Watson, J. A. S., and More, J. A. (1949). "Agriculture," p. 568, 9th Ed.
(7) Johnson, Dr. Samuel (1774). "A Journey to the Western Islands of Scotland," p. 123, 1817 Ed. (Glasgow).
(8) Haldane, A. R. B. (1952). *Ibid.*, p. 236.
(9) Cameron, J. A. (1948). "Hill Cattle," *Trans. High. and Agric. Soc. Scotland,* 5th Ser. V60, p. 56.
(10) MacKenzie, A. (1952) *Ibid.*, p. 6.
(11) M'Combie, W. (1875). "Cattle and Cattle Breeders," p. 16.
(12) Garner, F. (1944) "Cattle of Britain," p. 77 (London).
(13) Stewart, D. M. (1941). "Cattle on hill grazings," *Scot. J. Agric.*, **23,** 253.
(14) MacKenzie, A. (1952). *Ibid.*, p. 7.
(15) Sinclair, J. (1907). "History of Shorthorn Cattle," p. 136 (London).
(16) Cameron, J. A. (1948). *Ibid.*, pp. 52 and 55.
(17) Stodart, J. A. (1949). "Yarded beef production," *Agriculture,* **56,** 77.
(18) MacKenzie, A. (1952). *Ibid.*, p. 5.
(19) "British Pedigree Cattle," p. 39.
(20) Wallace, R. (1907). "Farm Livestock of Great Britain," p. 173, 4th Ed. (Edinburgh).
(21) "Galloway Cattle," (1951). The Galloway Cattle Society, p. 24.
(22) Wallace, R. (1907). *Ibid.*, p. 176.
(23) "Galloway Cattle" (1951). p. 30.
(24) *Ibid.*, p. 21.
(25) *Ibid.*, p. 33.
(26) Watson, J. A. S. and More, J. A. (1949). "Agriculture," p. 567.
(27) *Ibid.*, p. 568.
(28) "British Pedigree Cattle," p. 44.
(29) Wallace, R. (1907). *Ibid.*, p. 175.
(30) "Galloway Cattle" (1951), p. 34.
(31) *Ibid.*, p. 35.
(32) *Ibid.*, p. 30.
(33) *Ibid.*, p. 31.
(34) Garner, F. (1944). *Ibid.*, p. 76.
(35) Jennings, I. (1951). "Galloway Cattle," p. 61.
(36) Jamieson, G. (1950). Private Communication.
(37) "Galloway Cattle" (1951), p. 53.
(38) "Belted Galloway Cattle," Breed Soc. Publ., p. 5.
(39) *Ibid.*, p. 7.

(40) " Welsh Black Cattle," Breed Soc. Publication.
(41) Watson, J. A. S. and More, J. A. (1949). *Ibid.*, p. 571.
(42) " Welsh Livestock," (1951). Royal Welsh Agric. Soc., p. 11.
(43) Garner, F. (1944). *Ibid.*, p. 116.
(44) " British Pedigree Cattle," p. 104.
(45) Jennings, I. (1951). *Ibid.*, p. 58.
(46) Jamieson, G. (1950). Private Communication.
(47) Cameron, J. A. (1948). *Ibid.*, p. 52.
(48) Hobbs, J. W. (1951). " The Great Glen Cattle Ranch," *Scot. Agric.*, **30,** 181.

Chapter Ten   SOURCES OF BEEF
A.—HILL AND MARGINAL LAND

THERE are some 16 million acres of rough and uncultivated, mainly hill pasture in the island of Britain. Twelve million of these acres are in Scotland, 4 millions in England and Wales. Several million of these acres are allotted to forestry; most of the unplanted land already supports sheep. There are red deer on these hill lands, and grouse, both having a certain food value and a greater economic importance because of sport. What space, if any, remains for cattle?

Some say that there is a very great deal and that, in fact, there is a possibility of building up a great and thriving hill cattle industry on our hill and marginal lands, particularly in the Highlands of Scotland.

Much of the argument in favour of Highland cattle farming is based on the known fact that the Highlands once upon a time supported a cattle industry which formed the main source of exportable wealth out of that district.

Because of that argument and appeal to history, it is well to examine the evidence that history affords. There is a great deal of such evidence.

The first point to make clear is that at least until the seventeenth century Highland farming was, in the main, subsistence farming. The Highlanders grew food for their own support, and the food they grew included most things from oats to cockerels. There were many goats and some sheep. There were no pigs but ample poultry. There were cattle in numbers, dual-purpose, used for dairy produce and for meat but not for draught, the pony being the beast of burden the Highlanders preferred.

Subsequent to the Union of the Crowns in 1603 and more notably subsequent to the Union of Parliaments in 1707, Highland farming ceased to be purely subsistence and became partly commercial. Surplus cattle became the main article of trade and the export of cattle, being the readiest and sometimes the only means of acquiring wealth, was a policy energetically pushed by the Highland chiefs. There developed a great trade in store cattle out of the Scottish Highlands to the Lowlands of Scotland and into England, similar to the Irish store cattle trade of to-day. The Highland cattle, gathered together and assembled from all the Hebridean islands as well as from the Highland mainland, were driven over the recognised drove roads, converging together as they moved south, until the season's harvest of hill cattle debouched on the market stances of Crieff and Falkirk trysts. The story of the Scottish drove roads, of the cattle, and the drovers who used them, has been told and well told by Mr. Haldane in his recently published book, *The Drove Roads of Scotland*. (1)

Mr. Haldane in the Introduction to his very scholarly work advances the suggestion that the legitimate trade and droving industry in Highland cattle arose out of a much older tradition of cattle raiding and thieving. He makes it clear, also, that the export of Highland cattle, beginning with the Union of the Crowns, gained momentum with the Union of the Parliaments and thereafter persisted for some one hundred and fifty years. To quote Mr. Haldane:

" The Union of the Crowns helped the trend towards the legitimate movement of livestock, but it was only after 1707 that droving in the sense of large-scale organised movement of livestock on foot to established markets became a marked feature of Scotland's economy." (2)

In the eighteenth century cattle became Scotland's main source of sterling, and the rearing and export of cattle for the English market was favoured, encouraged, and sometimes pressed in much the same way as the dollar earning industries of Britain are to-day.

The Scottish Drove Roads and Droving hold a great deal of the essential romance of the country, the people and of the times. Contemporary accounts are filled with local colour, as for example how in the days when cattle were shod for their long journey south:

" Robert Gall of Kennethmont in Aberdeenshire once shod as many as seventy cattle in a day . . . " (3) Most probably his descendants are thereabouts to this day, still glorying in their hardihood and strength.

Perhaps the most vivid and contemporary account of droves of cattle on the Highland roads is that recounted by Bishop Forbes in his Journal of the year 1762. First his encounter with Allan

MacDonald, younger, of Kingsburgh in Skye, and husband of Flora Macdonald, on the high moorlands of Dalwhinnie.

"Tuesday, Aug. 31st.—In the Chaise by 5 o'clock and came to Dalwhinny 10 minutes after eight, qre we breakfasted, and near to which, before coming to it, we counted eight droves of black cattle moving to Crief-Fair. There would have been 1200 of them . . ." (4)

In referring to the cattle as " black cattle " the Bishop did not necessarily imply that the cattle were all black-coated, as already explained in an earlier section of this book.

After breakfast Bishop Forbes had a conversation with Kingsburgh, " . . . a handsome, comely Youth coming along with the Cattle, and dress'd better than ordinary in a Scarlet Vest and Philibeg . . . ". (4)

After some gossiping about mutual acquaintances in the island of Skye, the Bishop turned his attention to the cattle:

> I questioned him about the way and manner of their journeying with the Cattle. He told me they had four or five Horses with Provisions for themselves by the Way, particularly Blankets to wrap themselves in when sleeping in the open Air, as they rest on the bleak Mountains, the heathy Moors, or the verdant Glens, just as it happens towards the Evening; that they tend their Flocks by night, and never move till about 8 in the Morning, and then march the cattle at Leisure, that they may feed a little as they go along. They rest a while at mid-day to take some Dinner, and so let the Cattle feed or rest as they please. The proprietor does not travel with the Cattle, but has One for his Deputy to command ye whole, and he comes to the place appointed against ye Day fixed for the Fair. When the Flock is very large, as the present, they divide it, though belonging to One, into several Droves, that they may not hurt one another in narrow Passes, particularly on Bridges, many of which they go along. Each drove has a particular number of men with some Boys, to look after the Cattle . . .
>
> On the dusky Muir of Drumochter we had a full view of all the Cattle from Rear to Front, which would take up about a Mile in Length, and were greatly entertained in driving along through the midst of them, some of them skipping it away before us, like so many Deer. They were sleek, and in good Order and fit for present Use. This put me in Mind of the Patriarchal way of sojourning. We had now a fine view of Lochgarry, at the mouth of qch we saw another Drove of Cattle, about 300, resting, on their way to Crief Fair, some of them, through the Heat of the Day, wading into the Loch. (4)

It is a great pity that Bishop Forbes had no more to say of the cattle themselves, of their size, their coloration, their age, whether horned or polled, rough-coated or smooth. Coming out of Skye they would have been good cattle as Highland cattle went in those days.   Culley in his *Observations on Live Stock*, 1807, wrote that:

> It is in the northern and western Highlands and all the Islands and particularly the Isle of Skye and that tract of country near Kintail that you meet with the native breeds of kyloes; a hardy, industrious and excellent breed of cattle, calculated in every respect to thrive in a cold, exposed, mountainous country. (5)

The somewhat fragmentary evidence concerning these eighteenth-century Highland cattle is further examined in the chapter of this book dealing with the modern descendants of the ancient breed.

Suffice it to say here that they were in the first place small.

> While the figures available clearly do not make it possible to determine with any certainty the rate of increase over a period in the average weight of Scots cattle, it seems probable that until the early years of the nineteenth century only a small proportion reached a size which, by modern standards, would entitle them to be described as more than " stirks ". (6)

The Highland cattle being driven South to Crieff Fair in the eighteenth century would also have been considered old by modern standards.

> A farmer of to-day may pertinently ask the ages at which these beasts were sold. To this question no certain answer can be given, for circumstances and practice appear to have varied at different times and in different parts of the country; but many of the beasts were old cows and working animals past their useful life, while of the younger cattle it is probable that at least till near the end of the eighteenth century in view of the slow growth of beasts to whom each winter meant starvation, few were sold before three years and most at four years or older. (7)

It seems questionable, however, whether very many of the store cattle coming down out of the Highlands properly so-called were ever much older than three or four years of age. The accepted cattle unit was a cow and her followers—calf, yearling, two and three year old. In the Highlands, since ponies rather than cattle were used for agricultural labour, there could have been little point in retaining cattle not required for breeding or milking for any longer period.

In the adjacent agricultural North-eastern lowlands, from whence many cattle also travelled the drove roads to Crieff and Falkirk trysts, the age at which oxen came to be sold was—it would seem—entirely different. There, in the eighteenth century, the ox team pulled the plough, and it was only when too old for draught labour that oxen were disposed of in a store market that catered for beef.

An Agricultural Survey of Aberdeenshire in 1811 gives a table showing a calculation of the age of various classes of cattle sold from the county about the year 1770. This shows that few beasts were sold under twelve years old and many older. Most of the animals had been used in the plough for from one to four years before being put to grass. (8)

It may have been one of the reasons for the demand and ready sale of Highland cattle in the eighteenth century that, not being used for labour, they were, despite late maturity and poor feeding, available for fattening at a relatively early age when compared with the discarded cows and work oxen of lowland districts.

Such was the eighteenth-century cattle harvest of the Highland hills. What husbandry underlay and supported that annual harvest?

The sole reason for examining the question here is to draw attention to some of the salient points in the ancient Highlanders' use both of cattle and of land. It is necessary to examine the question because within recent years and in the praiseworthy efforts to revive a thriving cattle-rearing industry in the Highlands of Scotland, there have been so many references to history. In some cases there have been appeals to the authority of history in the sense that it has been argued that what has been done once, can quite easily be done again. That, in fact, is not necessarily so, since the modern hill-cattle industry of Britain— it must be confessed, still in a somewhat delicate infancy—bears a very faint resemblance to the cattle husbandry of the old Highland farming. That old cattle husbandry is a question far more of systems than of dates. It was universal, or almost universal, in the Scottish Highlands until the latter half of the eighteenth century. Big changes succeeded the repressive legislation of 1747. It survived in many parts of the Highlands far into the nineteenth century. In certain remote districts it retains some of the old features to this day.

In the first place the old Highland cattle industry was never an entirely beef cattle industry. The cattle were dual-purpose if there is any meaning in the phrase at all. The milking of the cows and the making of dairy produce was of equal or greater importance than the rearing of stores. Then, the unit of cattle husbandry was the cow and her followers, the oldest of the followers being at least three years of age. There was also a sharp and clear-cut distinction between winter and summer husbandry. All production was summer production, concentrated into the short growing season between May and September. It was then that the Highland communal farmers took all their stock—not merely the cattle but everything down to the very hens—to the summer pastures or shielings. These summer shielings were sometimes adjacent, sometimes at a considerable distance from the winter villages or clachans. They were, at times, at considerable altitude, right up among the high mountains. Their utilisation involved a seasonal migration on a wholesale scale. Thus, the writer of the Old Statistical Account of Boleskine and Abertarff, Inverness-shire, writing towards the end of the eighteenth century, says:

> As there were extensive shealings or grazings attached to this country, in the neighbourhood of the lordship of Badenoch, the inhabitants in the beginning of summer removed to these shealings with their whole cattle, man, woman and child; and it was no uncommon thing to observe an infant in one creel, and a stone on the other side of the horse, to keep up an equilibrium; and when the grass became scarce in the shealings, they returned again to their principal farms . . . . (9)

Pennant, in his Scottish tour of 1769, has left a vivid and charming description of one of these shielings where the Highlanders spent the summer months:

> Land on a bank covered with sheelings, the habitation of some peasants who attend the herds of milch cows. These formed a grotesque groupe; some were oblong, many conic, and so low that entrance is forbidden, without creeping through the little opening, which has no other door than a faggot of birch twigs, placed there occasionally; they were constructed of branches of trees, covered with sods; the furniture a bed of heath, placed on a bank of sod; two blankets and a rug; some dairy vessels; and above, certain pendant shelves, made of basket work, to hold the cheese, the produce of the summer. In one of the conic huts, I spied a little infant asleep, under protection of a faithful dog. (10)

Osgood Mackenzie has given a wonderfully vivid description of old Highland cattle husbandry which explains the whole system and its dual-purpose nature so well that I give the quotation in full and leave it at that. The district was Gairloch in Wester Ross, the period the early years of the nineteenth century, the account that of an eye-witness, Osgood Mackenzie's uncle.

> Having arrived at long last at the end of our three days' journey, we boys wanted but little rocking ere we were asleep in our hammocks. Next morning (Sunday) before six, all who were new to the place called out " Goodness gracious, what's the matter, and what's all this awful

noise about?" for sixty cows and sixty calves were all bellowing their
hardest after having been separated for the twelve hours of the night.
They were within eighty yards of the chateau, and, assisted by some
twenty herds and milkers screaming and howling, they made uproar
enough to alarm any stranger just waking from sleep, who expected a
quiet, solemn west-coast Sabbath morning. This was a twice a day
arrangement. Eventually the grass in the Baile Mor Glen was eaten
pretty bare, and then the whole lot of them went off to the shieling of
Airidh na Cloiche (Shieling of the Stone) for the summer.

There was a dyke about one hundred yards long between the entrance-
gates at the bottom of the lawn and the Allt Glas burn which kept the
cows and calves separate, to the great indignation of both parties, who
bellowed out their minds pretty plainly. Domhnall Donn (Brown
Donald) the head cowman, brought his wailing friends the cows to the
west side of the wall, and his subordinates, brought the calves from their
woody bedrooms where they had passed the night on the east side. And
then began an uproar of "Are you there, my darling?"   "Oh yes, mother
dear, wild for my breakfast." Then the troupe of milkmaids entered
among the mob of bawling cows by one of the small calf-gates in the wall.
They carried their pails and three-legged little stools and buarachs
(hobbles) of strong hair rope, with a loop at one end and a large button
on the other. The button was always made of rowan-tree wood, so that
milk-loving fairies might never dare to keep from the pail the milk of a
cow whose hind-legs were buarach bound.

All was soon ready to begin. A young helper stood at each gate with
a rowan switch to flick back the over-anxious calves till old Domhnall
sang out, looking at a cow a dairymaid was ready to milk, named, perhaps,
Busdubh (Black Muzzle), " Let in Busdubh's calf " who was quite ready at
the wicket. Though to our eyes the sixty black calves were all alike, the
helpers switched away all but young Busdubh, who sprang through the
wicket; after a moment's dashing at the wrong cow by mistake, and being
quickly horned away, there was Busdubh Junior opposite to its mother's
milker sucking away like mad for its supply, while the milkmaid milked
like mad also, to get her share of it. The calf, I suspect, often got the
lesser half, for the dairy people liked to boast of their heaps of butter and
cheese, leaving the credit or discredit of the yearly drove of young market
cattle to Domhnall and his subordinates. I have seen young Busdubh
getting slaps in the face from its enemy the milker, who thought she was
getting less than her share of the spoil; and then calfy was dragged to the
wicket and thrust out, and perhaps Smeorach's (Thrush's) calf halloaed
for next. This uproar lasted from six till nine, when, justice having been
dispensed to all concerned, Donald and company drove the cows away to
their pastures, and the junior helpers removed the very discontented
calves to their quarters till near 6 p.m. when the same operation was
repeated. (11)

This is of course a description of a laird's cattle fold. Those of
the peasantry were certainly less elaborate.

This cattle husbandry of the ancient Highlands was by no
means unique. The practice in Wales and North England was
fundamentally the same. Norway and Switzerland have re-

tained many of the essential features to this day. The ancient
Highland cattle husbandry was, in short, merely one example
of the pastoral methods almost universal among primitive com-
munities in hill country.

The essential revolution in Highland farming at the close of
the eighteenth century was something far more fundamental
and drastic than a change of stocking from cattle to sheep. It
involved the destruction of a peasantry. Nor can a mere reversion from sheep back to cattle re-establish a peasantry. There
may be many arguments for displacing sheep by cattle in the
Highlands of to-day, but those based on historical premises are
in this case unsound. The old cattle husbandry of the Highlands can never be re-established. New systems will require to
be adapted to fit new times.

Before proceeding to a consideration of these new systems, it
may be useful to summarise the essential features of the old. As
regards the cattle themselves it seems clear that these were the
ancestors and not so very unlike the Highland cattle of to-day.
The unit of production was the cow and her followers up to at
least three years of age. The cattle were used for two distinct
purposes, the provision of dairy produce for subsistence, the
rearing of beef stores for sale. The cattle husbandry and the
cattle were, therefore, dual-purpose in nature. The cattle were,
moreover, in summer and still more in winter, in most intimate
contact with human beings. They must, in consequence, have
been very highly domesticated, indeed, quite tame.

The utilisation of hill pasture differed quite fundamentally
from the practice common to-day. No attempt was made to
use mountain pasture for winter grazing. It was used in summer
only and during its period of active growth. In winter and
spring it was rested. All grassland experts would agree that in
this respect the ancient system was right and the modern system
wrong. The valleys and lower ground—what would to-day be
the marginal land adjacent to the hills—were cleared entirely of
stock during the summer months and their produce preserved
for the use both of man and livestock during winter.

Without presuming to idealise this ancient, seasonally migrant
and essentially communistic form of pastoral life, it is right to
admit certain of its advantages—advantages that cannot be
regained in the entirely different social circumstances of to-day.

Fig. 39. FRIESIAN STEER.

Fig. 40. HEREFORD CROSS CATTLE. These beef stores suitable for summer grazing were salvaged as calves by the Brecon W.A.E.C.

Fig. 41. THE ROAD TO BEEF BEGINS. Hill cattle being gathered off Lord Lovat's Range of Glen Strathfarrar.

Fig. 42. LORD LOVAT'S HILL CATTLE BEING DRIVEN FROM THE HILLS. The cattle seen are by Aberdeen-Angus or Hereford Bulls.

If then there can be no retreat into the past, what of the attempts to advance into the future?

Rather curiously the first suggestions for re-establishing a hill cattle industry in Britain were advanced with the avowed object of benefiting hill sheep. Highland sheep farming of the modern type is not much more than a hundred and fifty years old. Yet within that time it has become more difficult to farm sheep successfully in the Highland hills. The sheep carrying capacity of the pastures has declined. That process of pasture deterioration has been going on for a long time. Thus, the following passage, although strictly relevant to this subject, was written over seventy years ago:

> Farms will not carry so many sheep, or keep them in so high condition, as fifteen or twenty years ago. Considerable portions of the grazings are becoming foggy and rough, and of little value as hill pasture. We could point to one or two hirsels which carried stocks of from 1,000 to 1,100 over winter some twenty years ago, and which will now winter scarcely 800. The cause of this, we believe, is the covering of the land for so long a period exclusively by sheep, without any Highland cattle being allowed upon it, as was the case before sheep-farming reached its height. (12)

There are, of course, numerous reasons that might be advanced for the deterioration of hill pasture without bringing cattle or their absence into the picture at all. One of the excuses advanced for the Evictions was the necessity of providing wintering ground for sheep. The ruins of the dwelling places of the peasantry dispossessed to make way for the capitalist grazier's sheep can be traced, without difficulty, in practically every Highland glen to this very day. The houses are gone; the position of gardens still indicated perhaps by the rowan trees planted to keep the fairies at bay. Almost invariably there is a great wilderness of the bracken fern grown in upon and over what was once the arable ground of the crofting community. Following the Evictions, this arable land, fresh, green, cleared and so recently cultivated, must have been well-nigh perfect wintering ground for sheep off the neighbouring hills. Each year must, however, have seen more and more of it returning to its natural state of mixed hill vegetation or worse, because of the relative depth and fertility of soil, to an unchallenged monopoly of impenetrable fern.

Then, again, the stocking of the hills throughout the year on

11

the hefting system, by which every area of hill grazing has its own resident population of hill sheep, must, in itself, and inevitably if we are to accept the grassland teaching of to-day, have resulted over a long period of time in a change in vegetation that, from a stock-carrying point of view, was also a deterioration.

For, if a regular stock be maintained throughout the whole year on the same area of hill ground it must happen inevitably and no matter what type of stock be maintained, that the pasture is either over-grazed in winter and early spring of under-grazed in summer.   In most cases it is both, with the result that the carrying capacity of the pasture must decline.   No other outcome can be looked for, since it is known and has been well proved experimentally, that a combination of spring punishment and summer overgrowth will destroy the grazing value of the very best pasture in a surprisingly short interval of time.

While it may be queried, therefore, whether the mere introduction of cattle on to a hill sheep grazing really gets at the root causes of hill pasture deterioration, such introduction has sometimes been made with no other object in view.   And, certainly, on a rough, overgrown grazing, particularly with matted *Molinia* in the wetter places, the introduction of hill cattle is followed—at least for a time—by evident improvement in both the pastures and the sheep.   That statement, let it be added, is based on first-hand observation and the testimony of many reliable witnesses.   Yet, frankly, I know of no experimental work or quantitative evidence that confirms the point.

As a result of observation I am also convinced that too many cattle on a hill grazing over a period of years may actually reduce rather than improve its value for grazing sheep.   There is a balance in this business and the balance is a fine one.   Perhaps, at one time, too much was hoped for or expected from the re-introduction of cattle.   It would possibly be difficult to be quite so optimistic about this aspect of the hill cattle business in 1953 as, for example, was Mr. Duncan M. Stewart of Millhills in 1941, when he wrote:

> . . . I have come to the conclusion that the constant grazing of hill pastures by sheep alone is not a very good thing for the pasture, and that the establishment of a permanent cattle stock on a hill grazing, in addition to the sheep, can be both highly beneficial to the quality of the grazing from a sheep farmer's point of view as well as profitable by itself on the cattle account.

. . . not only can a limited number of cattle be put on to a hill grazing
without the numbers of sheep being reduced . . . the quality of the pasture
is improved for the sheep. In short, from the sheep farmer's point of
view, the quality of the grazing can be improved without its sheep-carrying
capacity being impaired. (13)

It was with the same object in view, improving hill pasture
for the sake of hill sheep, that Captain Bennett Evans first introduced Welsh Black cattle on to his Plynlimmon grazings over
twenty years ago. (14)

This general conception of using hill cattle somewhat as living
agricultural implements to improve hill pasture for the benefit
of sheep, although the basis upon which the Hill Cattle
Subsidy was first granted and, apparently, the accepted principle in New Zealand hill farming, already begins to wear a
somewhat old-fashioned look in this country of Britain. The
shortage of really good beef, whether home grown or imported,
has within recent years become acute; the national preference
for beef as opposed to mutton is so very well marked, that both the
general public and an increasing number of hill farmers have begun
to advocate the keeping of hill cattle, as it were, in their own right,
with the intention of increasing the meat output from hill areas
rather directly through beef than indirectly through mutton.

Two of the most notable pioneer efforts in this, the more
modern outlook on hill cattle, are those of Lord Lovat at Beauly
and Mr. J. W. Hobbs at Fort William. These two, now almost
classical enterprises, have several important points in common.
At their commencement both Glen Strathfarrar in the hills
above Beauly and the Great Glen Cattle Ranch near Fort William
carried sheep stocks. In both cases the sheep were cleared off
the ground in preparation for the coming of cattle. In neither
case were the native hill cattle breeds of Scotland—Highland
and Galloway—used for stocking. On the contrary, on both
cattle ranches Irish heifers were imported from Ireland and put
on the hills. To quote Mr. Hobbs:

" In selecting the foundation herd we chose the well-known
and recognised Irish cross of Hereford–Aberdeen-Angus, which
have proved the best beef producers in the West of Ireland." (15)

There is a superficial difference in the method by which the
cattle on the two farms are wintered. Lord Lovat's practice is
to clear Glen Strathfarrar in autumn, and to winter the cattle
summered there on coarse pit silage made and fed in lower and

more sheltered country, mainly around Beauly. Mr. Hobbs
also depends very largely on silage for the wintering of his cattle
but in his case the silage is both made and fed on the lower
reaches of the Great Glen Cattle Ranch itself. In both cases—
and herein lies a fundamental difference between hill cattle and
hill sheep—the cattle stock is dependent on forage additional to
grazing for its support during winter. The exact type of forage
to be used seems of relatively minor importance. Some hill
farmers have faith in silage, others prefer hay. In certain instances—Captain Bennett Evans' hill farm is one—sheaf oats
have been used with success. The main consideration, the
really important point to emphasise, is that without a forage
supplement of some kind to the pasture the hills provide, hill
cattle, no matter of what breed, cannot be successfully wintered
to-day, were never so wintered in the past, nor will they ever be
so wintered in the future.

Supplementary feeding of forage is a sine qua non *of the successful
wintering of hill cattle.* Whether the cattle are taken down to
the lowland during winter to consume forage grown there, or
the forage transported on to the hill to be consumed by cattle
wintered there, is, to some extent, a question of economics and
convenience. In one way or another the forage and hill cattle
must meet.

Not that a vast amount of such forage is required. On the
Ben Challum Estate, for example, a breeding hill cow, Highland
or Shorthorn–Highland cross, receives about 2 cwt. of oat straw
plus about 6 cwt. of good hay as supplementary forage, fed on
the actual hill, between January and mid-May. The ration
works out at some 7 lb. a day, which is not a great deal.

Captain Bennett Evans feeds his Welsh Black cattle on the
hill with 5 lb. of hay or with one unthreshed sheaf of oats daily
over roughly the same period.

Others have found it either necessary or advisable to feed
rather more. Jocelyn Gibb, for example, states that on his
farm in Wester Ross:

" . . . it takes nearly a ton of hay or three tons of silage to bring
a hill cow through the winter." (16)

No doubt the actual weight of winter forage a hill cow requires
will depend upon a wide variety of factors—the altitude and
fertility or infertility of the grazing; the severity or mildness of

the season; the breed of cow and, perhaps most important of all, the skill and conscientiousness of herding. It is far easier for a cow to consume forage laid down for her than to rake the hillsides for growing vegetation on her own account, and lazy habits in cattle, sheep, or men are more easily acquired than broken.

In any case there is general agreement that the scarcity and cost of winter fodder in hill districts is one of the main limiting factors in the expansion of hill cattle stocks. As Mr. Cameron of Glenfinlas has said:

" If we have the cattle, the limiting factor on expansion of hill breeding is feed over winter and spring." (17)

That is the reason behind the financial assistance towards the purchase of hay used for hill cattle now adopted as a further official incentive to the expansion of hill cattle farming.

In discussing methods of cattle husbandry in the old Scottish Highlands it was mentioned that the recognised stock unit of that period was the cow and her followers, her calf, her yearling, her two year old, and her three year old offspring. Doubtless, since hill cows have their occasional barren season and since young cattle are mortal, there must have been frequent gaps in the cow's following. Nevertheless that was the accepted unit, the ideal.

To-day the productive programme of hill cattle husbandry is, at least in one sense, a deal more modest. The cow and her suckled calf is the universally accepted production unit in modern hill cattle husbandry. Almost invariably the calf is sold off its mother in the first autumn of its life or, if retained in the herd, is certainly never retained on its native hill.

There is, admittedly, a popular delusion that hill land is capable of producing finished beef in the same way that hill sheep, given sufficient time to mature, are capable of producing finished mutton. As regards the Welsh hills, Captain Bennett Evans has, indeed, asserted that:

> Given time, we can even produce beef straight off the hills in the shape of four-year-old mature bullocks, in the same way that the mature four-year-old wethers become naturally fat in autumn. (18)

While stating that such a procedure is a possibility, Captain Bennett Evans evidently does not accept it as a policy, since he went on to say:

What I really favour is the rearing of good weanlings which the lowland farmer, with his protein, can turn into beef far sooner, keeping the foundation cows on the hills. (18)

Certainly it has never been claimed that the Scottish hills can produce finished beef. Even in the days of the old Highland farming, when beef standards were by no means high, it was store cattle—and store cattle only—that were the Highlands' export. To-day, in Scotland, the saleable product of hill cattle farming is the suckled calf. Foundation cows on the hills, weaned calves in the autumn markets, is the policy adopted. Quite evidently there remains a wide gap between the suckled calf and finished beef. The rearing farm—which quite frequently is a marginal farm— is required to carry on the weaned calf to the age and weight suitable for lowland fattening in winter courts or on summer fields.

Granted that the weaned calf is the product of modern hill cattle farming, how many of these calves could the hill country of Britain be expected to provide? Evidently that will depend upon the number of breeding cows the hills can carry. Everybody admits that the hills of Britain, and in particular those of the Highlands of Scotland, could carry a great many more breeding cattle than they have done in the more recent past or than they do to-day. The question at issue is *how* many more and the answer, quite naturally, can be nothing more than an estimate.

A common method of approaching the problem is to assert that the hills of Britain, and in particular those of the Highlands of Scotland, did actually and within historical times carry far more cattle than they have done at any time within the last century. That is quite true, the only matter at issue being how many more. There have been many guesses, fewer estimates, no proofs.

Mr. Duncan M. Stewart, in a paper read before the British Society of Animal Production in March 1949, was courageous enough to venture on statements of actual figures. He wrote:

We have reason to believe that about 150 years ago there were many more cattle in the Highlands than there are to-day. Books of that time refer to 150,000 cattle to be found on the 200-mile-long stretch of the Western Isles (mainly the Inner Hebrides). 25,000-30,000 stores were sent annually to the mainland—3,500 from the Island of Islay alone.

There were 44,000 cattle in the Orkney and Shetland Islands, from which droves were sent via Caithness to Carlisle. In addition there was an annual export of 25,000 Galloways from their native county to Norwich. (19)

These figures quoted from eighteenth-century writings must be accepted with a certain reserve. There was nothing comparable to annual agricultural statistics at that time. When we have said that there were many more cattle in the Highlands in the eighteenth than in the nineteenth or twentieth centuries we have said probably all that can, with any certainty, be said.

Modern figures regarding hill cattle populations are much more reliable. For one thing, there is a price on the head of every hill cow. There is a substantial subsidy to be earned by her. To quote Mr. Duncan Stewart again: (19)

" In 1947 the £7 was claimed—throughout the whole of Scotland—for only 90,000 cows."

Since there are some 12 million acres of rough hill grazing in Scotland alone, that figure of 90,000 works out at only one hill cow to every 130 acres of hill grazing.

These modern figures quoted by Mr. Duncan Stewart are, of course, entirely reliable. They may be used safely for making a simple deduction as to how many cattle the hills of Scotland *could* support. Since, *on the average*, it requires some three acres of hill grazing to support one sheep, and since one cow is usually assumed to require as much pasture as six sheep, it can be estimated that about twenty acres of hill grazing could support one hill cow. Accepting these very rough calculations and assuming that the hills of Scotland were devoted entirely to hill cattle husbandry, then the hill cattle population of Scotland could be increased from one cow to 130 acres to one cow to twenty acres— roughly a six-fold increase. Since the present population of hill cows in Scotland is 90,000, it may be calculated that this number could be increased to 540,000 head, over half a million breeding cows.

Such an increase in the number of hill cattle would lead necessarily to a reduction in the number of hill sheep. That reduction, however, would by no means be inversely proportional to the increase in cattle. Sheep and cattle on hill ground are complementary as well as competitive grazers. There is, however, a definite limit to the total stocking on any hill pasture, and if, say in Scotland, the number of hill cattle were increased six-fold, the number of hill sheep could not be expected to remain the same as it is to-day.

In addition to hill pasture, the suggested maximum number of 540,000 hill cattle in Scotland would require the equivalent of at least 6 cwt. of hay apiece to carry them through the winter. For 540,000 head of cattle, the hay requirements would thus be 162,000 tons. At two tons to the acre this would require 81,000 acres of land reserved for the winter feeding of the 540,000 hill cattle. Since about 500,000 acres of land in Scotland are used annually for hay, not more than one-sixth of the hay made annually in Scotland would suffice to support 540,000 breeding cows on her hills. Evidently there is no theoretical difficulty in finding sufficient winter forage to supplement the feeding of half a million hill cattle on the Scottish hills. The difficulties, if there are difficulties, are those of economics rather than of husbandry.

Provided, then, that by one method of feeding or another hill cattle can be wintered, either on or off the hill, there seems no reason why—ignoring an inevitable reduction in sheep stocks for the moment—half a million hill cows could not be maintained in Scotland alone. Now, Scotland contains by far the greater part of the acreage of hill grazing in Britain, some 12 million out of 16 million acres. Nevertheless, the remaining 4 million acres in England and Wales are quite definitely of higher stock-carrying capacity. On the Welsh hills particularly, there is far more ploughable land, and the possibilities of cultivation, reseeding and so on, as well as the capacity for growing winter forage for cattle, are far greater. Therefore, certainly no fewer, and probably considerably more, hill cattle could be carried on the 4 million acres of hill grazing in England and Wales than on a similar acreage of hill land in Scotland. It would be safe to say that the total hill land of Britain is capable of carrying 540,000 $+ \frac{1}{3}$ (540,000) or a total of 720,000 hill cows.

How many calves could these 720,000 hill cows produce annually? Calving percentage—*i.e.*, calves reared to cows kept—is seldom over 75 per cent in hill herds, so that about 540,000 calves could be expected each year. It would be necessary to retain at least 54,000 heifer calves on the hill for stock replenishments, leaving 486,000 calves available for sale.

In addition to the hills, marginal land deserves careful consideration as a source of store cattle.

Precise definition of the marginal farm, as of so many other matters agricultural, is difficult and may be impossible, although everyone with experience of farming has a mental picture, at least so far as his own district is concerned, of the type of holding implied.

In Scotland, then, marginal farms are usually upland farms, which, if in any way neglected, are quickly encroached upon by the natural vegetation of the adjacent hills. They require skilful cultivation if their somewhat low natural fertility is to be retained. They are usually small farms, with little if any hired labour regularly employed. In Scotland, they were, and indeed still are, predominantly cattle-rearing farms where calves, either bred on the farm itself or brought in from elsewhere, are reared to the stage at which the cattle feeders want them. In the past, these farms and the young cattle they reared played an essential part in the store cattle trade of Scotland. To-day this type of farm has fallen into difficulties, the fundamental reason being that the farms are too small to rear a sufficient number of cattle to yield an income adequate to support the standard of living country folk now demand.

This marginal land problem, particularly in the hill countries of Scotland and Wales, is no small one. In the year 1949, a Committee of the Scottish National Farmers' Union that had been studying this problem issued a report. This report stated that marginal and sub-marginal farms in Scotland amounted to 34 per cent of the total acreage of agricultural land, providing an agricultural output equal to 10 per cent of the gross output of Scottish farms and worth over 7 million pounds.

The Committee's long-term proposals included the amalgamation of uneconomic marginal land farms into larger units and the encouragement of cattle rearing.

There are many cogent reasons for farming marginal land on a much larger scale than at present. One is connected with buildings. On the typical marginal farm the steading is dilapidated and the farmhouse out of date. Building reconstruction on an adequate scale on these holdings at their present size would be quite uneconomic. The buildings would cost more to erect than the whole farm was worth.

Yet, young cattle need shelter. A marginal farm without a convenient and commodious steading may be little better than a hill farm, so far as the wintering of young cattle is concerned. Again, to make the most of marginal land, to reinforce cultivation in its long-drawn-out battle against reversion, requires machinery, and at present many marginal farms are too small and under-capitalised to afford anything more elaborate and expensive than a reaper. Moreover, the possibilities of increasing the stock-carrying capacity of the type of marginal land here envisaged are far beyond those of the actual hill. The land is under cultivation and in rotation. There is the possibility, not only of retaining fertility, but of building it up to a higher level. It is the ideal land on which to grow the winter forage crops that hill cattle require. In fact, it can be argued that by far the most useful function of the upland marginal farm is to provide winter quarters and winter forage for livestock summered on the adjacent hills.

Mr. George Jamieson, until recently farm manager at the North of Scotland College of Agriculture's hill station at Glensaugh, Kincardineshire, writes: (20)

> I believe great possibilities lie in the hill farm attached to a marginal farm where there is a good acreage of ploughable land capable of producing fodder. On many I believe it would be sound policy to cater entirely for stock feeding and give up the idea of producing cash-crops like potatoes and oats.

That, indeed, would seem to be the ideal method of cattle farming in hill country. Details, naturally, would depend on district, circumstance, and the judgement of management, but the general system would be a combination of upland marginal cultivated land, and the uncultivated high hill or mountain. All stock would be on the hill throughout the summer, while the attached marginal land was being intensively cultivated to produce forage for the cattle's use in winter. Under such a system the old Highland cattle farming unit of the cow and her followers could be revived. It would no longer be necessary to sell all stock surplus to breeding requirements as weaned calves in autumn. Further, the cattle-carrying capacity of the hill itself would be greatly increased.

REFERENCES

(1) Haldane, A. R. B. (1952). " The Drove Roads of Scotland." Nelson, Edinburgh.
(2) *Ibid*, p. 2.
(3) *Ibid*., p. 35.

(4) Forbes (Bishop) (1762), *Journal.* Edited, Ven. J. B. Craven, London, 1923, pp. 235–237.

(5) Quoted by Haldane, A. R. B. (1952), *ibid.*, p. 69.

(6) Haldane, A. R. B. (1952), *ibid.*, p. 61.

(7) *Ibid.*, p. 59.

(8) *Ibid.*, p. 60.

(9) The Statistical Account of Scotland (1798), Edinburgh, 20, p. 24.

(10) Pennant's Tour (1772), V. II, A Tour in Scotland, etc. London, 1790, p. 246.

(11) Osgood Mackenzie (1949). "A Hundred Years in the Highlands," pp. 24–26. Geoffrey Bles, London.

(12) Macdonald, J. (1877). *Trans. High. and Agric. Soc. Scotland*, Series 4, Vol. 9, p. 00.

(13) Stewart, D. M. (1941). "Cattle on Hill Grazings," *Scot. J. Agric.*, **23**, 253.

(14) Bennett Evans, Capt. G. L. (1949). "Raising Beef Cattle on the Welsh Hills," *Proc. Brit. Soc. Anim. Prod.*, p. 34.

(15) Hobbs, J. W. (1951). "The Great Glen Cattle Ranch," *Scot. Agric.*, **30**, 181.

(16) Gibb, Jocelyn (1952). "Mutton and Beef from Scotland's Northern Hills," *Times Agric. Review, Winter*, p. 8.

(17) Cameron, J. A. (1948). "Hill Cattle," *Trans. High. and Agric. Soc. Scotland*, Vol. 60, p. 56.

(18) Bennett Evans, Capt. G. L. (1949). *Ibid.*, p. 38.

(19) Stewart, D. M. (1949). "Store Cattle from the Scottish Hills," *Proc. Brit. Soc. Anim. Prod.*, p. 42.

(20) Jamieson, G. (1949). Private communication.

B.—DAIRY HERDS

T H E possibilities of increasing beef production by the more intensive use of hill and marginal land deserve careful consideration. They are, however, at the present moment, mainly possibilities. The national dairy herd, on the contrary, is something more than a future possibility. It is a present fact. Thus, while it can be argued that hill land developed to its maximum for the production of store cattle could produce annually some half-million calves, the national dairy herd, now and without any further development, produces over *one million* calves that are never reared. The figure (1)—in 1951 it was 1,302,000— of calves slaughtered annually represents an enormous wastage of beef. At the same time it constitutes a tremendous reservoir of store cattle were it but improved, developed, and used. It is, at the moment, somewhat of a paradox that while the country is short of beef, some million calves are slaughtered that might, if properly reared and fed, yield annually over 300 thousand tons of beef. Yet, because of their premature destruction, they add little or nothing to the meat resources of the nation. The figure of 300 thousand represents a very considerable quantity of beef, being roughtly half the amount produced in the United Kingdom in 1938. In general it may be fairly claimed that the present scarcity of British beef is due quite as much to a misuse of cattle as to a want of cattle.

Actually, the number of cattle in Britain has increased very considerably within recent years; from 8,800,000 in 1938 to 10,500,000 in 1951.

" The cattle population of the United Kingdom, after reaching a record level in 1950, declined slightly in 1951 but was still 19 per cent above the pre-war level." (2)

Estimated production of beef and veal in the U.K. during the same period, *i.e.*, 1938–1951, also increased, from 604·7 thousand tons in 1938 to 652·0 thousand tons in 1951. (3) This represents approximately a percentage increase of 8. The increase in beef,

8 per cent, is less than might have been expected from the increase in cattle, 19 per cent. It is, however, closely proportional to the increase in slaughterings. Thus the number of cattle (exclusive of calves) slaughtered in the United Kingdom increased from 2,209,000 in 1938 to 2,451,000 in 1951, a percentage increase of 10. (1)

The fact that a 19 per cent increase in the country's cattle population has been accompanied only by an 8 per cent increase in home-killed beef supplies is a clear indication that the recent increase in the cattle population is to be attributed to a continued expansion of dairying. That expansion is, of course, no new phenomenon and its effect on fat cattle production has been commented upon frequently before. For example, in the *Report on the Marketing of Cattle and Beef in England and Wales* published by the Ministry of Agriculture and Fisheries in 1929, it was stated that:

" The average annual number of home-bred fat animals produced for slaughter in the pre-war period averaged 1,116,000, but production has since declined, the annual average for the five year period 1924–28 being only 1,038,000, of which 600,000 were cows. The great increase in the dairying industry to which reference has been made is undoubtedly the main reason for this decrease in fat cattle production; farmers can only accommodate a limited number of animals, and, even although the total cattle population has not decreased, the fact that dairy cows are retained on the farm longer than feeding animals means that the output of mature animals from the farm must be slower and, hence, fewer in number than previously." (4)

The war referred to in this passage is, of course, the 1914–1918 war. The diagnosis of two of the main effects of dairying upon beef production—a relative decrease in the number of cattle slaughtered, and a relative increase of cow beef to other beef— are clearly brought out in this quotation. There is, however, at least one other effect of major importance.

It has been seen that the annual number of cattle slaughtered in the U.K. increased from 2,209,000 in 1938 to 2,451,000 in 1951, a percentage increase of 10.

It is of interest to compare these figures with those of the slaughter of calves during the same period. They increased, also, but to a much greater extent, from 836,000 in 1938 to

1,302,000 in 1951 (3), a percentage of increase of no less than
55 per cent. Whereas therefore, over the last thirteen years, the
increase in mature cattle slaughtered has been some 10 per cent,
that of calves has been five to six times greater. In that annual
sacrifice of over 1,000,000 calves from the national dairy herd
lies what is undoubtedly the biggest loss of the country's beef
resources at the present time. Moreover, it constitutes the
greatest and most practicable source of increased beef supplies
in the immediate future.

The increase in the number of calves slaughtered shortly after
their birth is one result of the concentration of British cattle
husbandry upon liquid milk production. On a specialised
dairy farm calves, other than those used for herd replacements or
those reared for sale as breeding stock, either heifers or bulls,
are unwanted. In particular, the bull calf not required for
breeding is a liability rather than an asset. To rear him would
demand an expenditure in milk, money, time, and labour which
the average dairyman refuses to incur. The male calf is unwanted and in the way and will be sent to the nearest collecting
centre for slaughter at the earliest opportunity. He becomes
" bobby " veal, bought for a few shillings by the Ministry of
Food and possibly diverted after slaughter to manufacturing
purposes.

Some have on occasion criticised the Ministry of Food for
accepting calves at such an early age and slaughtering them
before they are fit for the retail meat trade. Such criticism is
unjustified. If the M.O.F. refused to buy these young calves
they would, without doubt, disappear on the farms. They
would not be reared. Quite obviously the dairy farmer sends
these bobby veal calves to the Collecting Centres merely as a
convenient way of getting rid of them. The price they fetch—
30s. a head downwards to 3s. 6d.—can mean little or nothing to
a dairy farmer selling a reasonable quantity of milk.

The fact that a considerable proportion of these calves are not
worth the rearing—or generally considered to be so—is a further
difficulty. A dairy farmer chooses his breed of cow to satisfy his
personal preferences, his husbandry conditions, his potential
market for milk and stock. In general he is not particularly
concerned whether or not his surplus male calves are worth
rearing for beef. It is very widely held that the calves of quite

a number of our best known dairy breeds are useless, or very nearly useless for that purpose. For example, I have seldom heard anyone suggest that there is any alternative to bobby veal for surplus calves of the Channel Island breeds nor, with few exceptions, has any such claim been advanced for the Ayrshire. As regards the Friesian, by now the dominant dairy breed in Britain, opinions differ. Many would be prepared to class the modern Friesian as a dual-purpose breed—fitted for the production of both milk and beef in large quantity if not of highest quality—a breed of cattle, as it were, well fitted to the times. Rather curiously, the British Friesian Cattle Society have rather tended to avoid the dual-purpose label although the breed has been officially described as "supreme for milk and very valuable for beef". (5) It would seem, however, that the national circumstances of the times are driving, and that inevitably, the Friesian to become the standard dual-purpose cattle breed of England. It is of obvious significance that increased incentives for beef offered within the last two years in an effort to correct a previous over-emphasis on milk production have increased, rather than hindered, the expansion of the Friesian at the expense of other cattle breeds in this country.

It must be admitted, however, that in the case of all the dairy breeds, including the Friesian, the beef productive value of the calf is likely to be improved by crossing with one or other of the specialised beef breeds. Dr. John Hammond has pressed this point. His argument may be illustrated by the report of a quite recent speech he made in Aberystwyth. He suggested there " . . . that in most well-bred herds two-thirds of the cows should be sufficient for the breeding of herd replacements, and the other third, the less productive cows, should be mated to beef bulls to give colour-marked calves, for in this was a vast undeveloped source of beef type calves which should be transported to the poorer upland areas for rearing". (6)

The mating of lower-yielding cows in a dairy herd to a colour-marking beef bull seems at first sight to be sound breeding policy. The progeny of poor yielders are eliminated from the herd in such a certain and irreversible fashion that there can be no possibility of smuggling attractive-looking heifer calves of unsatisfactory milking parentage back into the herd.

I feel, however, that it is time the whole policy of the colour-

marking of these calves was reviewed in a rather more critical
manner than is usual. Colour-marking is certainly an intriguing
application of Mendelian genetics to cattle breeding. Superficial characters of certain of the specialised beef breeds are
strongly dominant. Thus, as is well known, an Aberdeen-Angus
bull will leave his calves polled and black-coated when mated
with horned cows of diverse colour. When a dairy cow has a
calf after an Aberdeen-Angus bull there can be no doubt, therefore, of the calf's paternity. The calf is said to be colour-marked
and since it is patently after a beef sire, there is very little chance
of its ever finding its way into a dairy herd, even one where
mongrel cows are maintained. Be it noted that the idea of
colour-marking of calves was designed quite as much with a
view to protecting the nation's dairy herds from beef infiltration
as to increase the number of calves suitable for the feeder of beef
cattle.

Now, the Hereford, just like the Aberdeen-Angus, will colour-
mark its calves. In practically every cross the white face markings
of the Hereford are dominant although the rich red coat colour is
not necessarily so and, partly because of this dominance, the
Hereford has become very popular of recent years as a crossing
bull.

The main criticism that may be levelled against the whole
idea of colour-marking is that it favours certain breeds to the
detriment of others on characters that are purely superficial and
that, apart from this one advantage of an automatic acknowledge-
ment of paternity, are of little or no economic significance.

In Scotland we have benefited—and let it be admitted also
suffered—from the superficially dominating characters of the
Aberdeen-Angus breed. Crossed with any of the common
Scottish breeds the Aberdeen-Angus leaves calves that are polled
and black or grey coated. The calves are all " colour-marked "
and all in the same way. Yet how very different are the feeding
constitutions the hornless head and black coat conceal ! Crossed
with the Beef Shorthorn the Aberdeen-Angus gives what is
probably the finest possible calf for specialised beef production.
" Gregor ", the 1952 Smithfield Supreme Champion and said to
be the finest beast ever exhibited there, was bred in Speyside to
that prescription. There are other breeds and crosses with
which the Aberdeen-Angus blends well—for example, the

Fig. 43. HIGHLAND COWS ON ROUGH HILL PASTURE.   Hill cattle are a most valuable
and economical means of improving hill pasture.

Fig. 44. WELSH BLACK CATTLE ON THEIR NATIVE HILLS.   The Welsh Black is the
native hill breed of Wales.

Fig. 45. BLACK HOST DOES AND THEIR WHITE YOUNG
from the transplanted ova from one superovulated
white doe. In this experiment 27 ova at the 32 to 64
cell stage (63 hour) were transplanted into 4 black
does and 22 young were born. (Dowling, 1949.)

Fig. 46. How beef bulls of breeds with dominant colours will
colour-mark their calves and so distinguish them from
dairy or dual-purpose bred animals. A Guernsey cow
which was mated with an Aberdeen-Angus and a
Hereford bull and produced twins, one by each bull.
(Vieth.)

Galloway or first cross of either Beef Shorthorn or Aberdeen-Angus itself on that breed. There are other breeds and crosses in which the Aberdeen-Angus cross, although it again leaves a black polled calf, is far less satisfactory. The Aberdeen-Angus cross with Ayrshire or with West Highland leaves much to be desired. In either cross the Shorthorn is preferable.

It is, in short, the fact that the Shorthorn does *not* colour-mark its calves that is the strongest argument against the whole principle of colour-marking. For, if the Beef Shorthorn has or ever has had any influence upon the world's cattle, it is in putting a beef frame on the progeny of thin-fleshed cows. That was its function and the basis of its reputation in the American continent. That should be its approved function in Britain to-day. Certainly, in Scotland, the Shorthorn is much to be preferred to the Aberdeen-Angus for a first and even a second cross on the Ayrshire or Highland cow. To scrap the Beef Shorthorn or to prevent the full utilisation of its most important economic qualities merely because it fails to " colour-mark " its calves would be to make too great a sacrifice to applied genetics. Colour-marking is useful but it is not sufficiently important to permit a system of crossing to be hinged on that alone. It is of infinitely greater importance to discover the most commercially useful crosses between different breeds, and then exploit them to the full.

Whether colour-marked or not—and it should not be beyond the wit of dairy farmers to distinguish beef breeding without the aid of colour—the calves sired by Beef bulls out of the less productive cows in dairy herds would not be raised in the dairy. They would have to be sold, and the main inducement to dairymen to breed them would be that they would sell for a price substantially higher than that offered by the M.O.F. in the Collecting Centres.

According to Dr. Hammond as reported (6) these " . . . beef type calves . . . should be transported to the poorer upland areas for rearing". The question arises as to whether the " poorer rearing areas " would be prepared to pay for and receive these calves. Present indications suggest that they would. The extent of the calf traffic between dairying and rearing areas was revealed by its influence in the extension of the 1952 Foot and Mouth disease outbreaks. Calves travelling up from South-

12

West England collected the virus *en route*—at Crewe station—and carried it north to Aberdeenshire. Some of the calves—although most fortunately not those infected—are said to have gone as far north as Orkney. There is, in fact, quite a trade in calves of cross Hereford or Devon type. These calves, born and bred in South-West England and surplus to stock replacement requirements there, are already and without further direction or propaganda, in keen demand in certain rearing districts at considerable distances away. Districts which still rear calves instead of selling liquid milk require more calves than are presently available.

A difficulty might arise from the fact that so many of the traditional rearing districts of Britain, rather less perhaps in Scotland than in England and Wales, were persuaded to change to milk selling during the war years. It would take a great deal more persuasion to get these districts out of the milk trade again than it took to bring them in. Apart from any economic considerations—and some of these are sufficiently important—selling milk is an easier job than rearing calves. It might, indeed, be found, were the investigation made, that there is actually a narrower bottle-neck in the rearing of suitable calves for beef production than there is in their birth and that, in consequence, the breeding of more calves of suitable beef type would result in no greater abundance of beef stores. To make Dr. Hammond's scheme really effective—and there is much to be said for his scheme—it might be necessary to discourage or, in the more modern phrase, apply disincentives, to milk production in districts and on farms better suited for rearing. This could, of course, be done by the Milk Marketing Board's ceasing their daily collection of milk from such districts and such farms. This the Board could quite easily do on the grounds that such milk collection was uneconomic as, indeed, it must be. Such action would be effective. Whether it would be either politic or just is, of course, quite another matter.

In addition to the essentially practical method of moving from milk towards beef by crossing a certain proportion of dairy cows with bulls of the specialised beef breeds, another more theoretical but also more radical procedure has been suggested. This procedure is concerned with the transplantation of fertilised ova, something that has been performed successfully and repeatedly in laboratory animals such as rabbits. So far as cattle are concerned, the idea would be to secure the fertilised ovum or egg of a specialised beef breed, say an Aberdeen-Angus, and then transplant it into the uterus, or womb, of a dairy cow undesirable as a dam of dairy herd replacements. In due course the dairy cow, let us say for purposes of argument an Ayrshire cow, would give birth to a pure Aberdeen-Angus calf. Similarly, to suggest another example, a pure Hereford calf could be incubated, as it were, within a Jersey cow. By this method, by this one big step, we could pass out from the world of specialised milk production into that of specialised beef.

Quite an amount of highly skilled research work has already been done on this subject. A full list of the work published on it up to 1949 is given by Dowling in a paper where he describes his own investigations designed ". . . to advance knowledge of the methods necessary for the practical application of the transplantation of fertilised ova in cattle". (7)

The essentials of the technique—well tested out in laboratory animals—is first of all to induce a beef cow, say an Aberdeen-Angus, to come into heat. This can be done by squeezing out the yellow body or corpus luteum from the ovary of the cow by manipulation through the wall of the back passage or rectum. Normally a cow in heat will only discharge one or at most two eggs or ova from her ovary. By ovarian stimulation she can be induced to shed far more, up to fifty. Stimulation is effected by injecting the hormone from the anterior pituitary gland (a small ductless gland but one of vast importance well protected in the bony floor of the skull at the base of the brain), in one form or another into the cow's blood. By the use of A.I. these multiple shed ova can be fertilised.

Now, if the cow that has been injected is a pure Aberdeen-Angus cow and the semen used in A.I. is from a pure Aberdeen-Angus bull, then each and every fertilised ovum has the innate capacity of developing in time into a pure Aberdeen-Angus calf and into no other thing. The fact that it might be destined to pass nine months within the womb of an Ayrshire cow or a Jersey cow would not make the slightest difference to the calf. It would be born a pure Aberdeen-Angus calf no matter what breed of cow sheltered it during its nine months' incubation. That is the essential fact to appreciate in this business of ova transplantation.

The rest is technique, of which the main object is to wash the fertilised ova out of the uterus of the beef cow and transplant them, one by one, into the uteri of a number of dairy cows. As already mentioned, the technique has been developed mainly in rabbits.

Until quite recently it had not yet been carried to a successful conclusion in cattle. Rowson (8) writing as recently as 1950 suggested, however, that, " . . . it is probably only a matter of time before success is achieved in the cow". That success, it would seem, has now been achieved since, according to a recent American report, a living calf has actually been born from a transplanted egg. (9)

Further details of the physiological principles involved and of the practical techniques employed in the procedure variously described as artificial pregnancy or the transplantation of ova are given by Hammond. (10) What of the possibilities of its practical application?

The fact that artificial pregnancy, at the moment, is still a laboratory procedure, some might call it a scientific trick, is no argument against the eventual and widest application of the new technique to practical cattle breeding. The industry has become accustomed to this type of scientific innovation through the enormous success of A.I. Were artificial pregnancy shown to have similar advantages its success, once the remaining technical difficulties were mastered, would be assured.

As a matter of logic there is a very strong case for A.P., as artificial pregnancy, were it ever to become commonplace, would undoubtedly be called. Using a bull of a beef breed on a dual-purpose or dairy cow with the object of procuring a beef store is an old and well-established husbandry procedure. Nobody could well deny that A.P. would result in a better type of beef store, since any feeder would prefer pure-bred Beef Shorthorn, Aberdeen-Angus, or Hereford stores to dairy cross breds from these same breeds. A.P. would do what cross breeding does already, but would do it more completely and do it better. Obviously, any beneficial influence that might be attributed to the hybrid vigour resulting from a cross would be sacrificed in A.P. Equally obviously, the main advantage of A.P. would depend upon the fact, if it be a fact, that a calf of a specialised beef breed would, environmental influences being equal, provide a better beef carcase than calves got by beef bulls out of cows of the specialised dairy breeds. To a certain extent this assumption seems somewhat questionable in view of the interim finding of the Cambridge cattle-rearing experiments described in some detail in another chapter.

Strangely enough, A.P. would probably make a stronger appeal to the majority of modern cattle breeders as a method of making the best of the two worlds of milk and beef than any attempt to popularise or repopularise designedly dual-purpose cattle. A.P. might be welcomed simply as a practical measure by which extremes might profitably meet. The breeder of certain specialised dairy breeds, say those of Channel Island or Ayrshire cattle, would be able to claim thereby that were additional beef stores required from dairy herds, then A.P. could provide calves from such herds as well suited for beef purpose as are those of the specialised beef breeds themselves. Certainly A.P. does offer possibilities of securing calves ideally *bred* for beef production purposes. That, however, would be only the beginning of a long journey. Without appropriate rearing, ideal breeding is merely wasted and given the birth of these pure-bred beef calves through A.P., who is to be responsible for their proper rearing?

Now, there have within recent years been a number of Government measures designed to encourage and stimulate beef production in Britain. The fact that the direct subsidy alone payable on a Scottish hill cow and her calf amounts to £15 shows that this aid is already substantial. Most of these official measures to increase the numbers of store cattle have been based on the assumption that the most probable source of increased beef production lies in hill country or on marginal land. The alternative source of the surplus calves born into dairy herds has received less direct official encouragement due, presumably, to the assumption that these calves, unless of recognised dual-purpose type, are not worth rearing. There have, however, been some noteworthy exceptions to this generalisation. The Brecon W.A.E.C. instituted a calf salvage campaign which gave good results and might serve as a pilot experiment to a much wider national effort. The object was to salvage those calves judged capable of turning into useful beef stores for summer grazing on the contention that, " In the present urgent need for meat no

calf suitable for rearing should be prematurely destroyed."
(11)

The enterprise was commenced in 1944 when the Breconshire
W.A.E.C. decided to salvage some of the beef type calves from
the Ministry of Food Collecting Centres. The selected calves were
reared on nurse cows on farms in the Committee's occupation.
The scheme worked very well and during 1946–1947 no fewer
than 800 calves were salvaged. Some calves were carried right
on by the Committee to eventual grading, but the majority were
distributed to various English counties.

" Only calves that would obviously turn out to be good stores
were selected. These were put on nurse cows for a period of
10–12 weeks, although the calves intended for dispatch to some of
the English counties would be retained for only a few weeks. At
no time were more than ten nurse cows used for rearing, and
during the year 1945–1946, 205 calves were salvaged. During
1946–1947 over 800 calves were salvaged. Approximately 700
of these were dispatched to Gloucestershire, Buckinghamshire,
Norfolk, and a few to Caernarvon." (12)

The calves deemed worthy of salvage were mainly Hereford
crosses but, no doubt, calves of other breeds, well reared on
nurse cows, might have turned out equally well. The scheme is
essentially sound and one well suited to official intervention.
Indeed it might be both wise and economic to make a greater
effort to rear or have reared the calves born into dairy herds as
a valuable but frequently unvalued by-product, as well as
subsidising cattle breeding on hill and marginal land. The
salvage and rearing of calves from dairies might prove a great
deal more productive and cheaper, and the beef stores finally
obtained little if at all inferior.

Additional to the store beef cattle—mainly steers—that the
dairy industry already supplies and the vastly greater number
that it could supply, there is the tremendously important contribution made to national beef resources through the carcases of
discarded cows.

" The very term cow beef has perhaps an uninviting sound "
(13) but it has, nevertheless, constituted between 40 and 50 per
cent of home-killed beef supplies for a considerable number of
years. Thus the annual average of fat cattle slaughtered in
England and Wales for the five-year period 1924–1928 was

1,038,000 of which 600,000 were cows. (4) In 1949, according to Shaw (14), cow beef constituted approximately 40 per cent of the total beef production in England and Wales. Shaw (14) predicted a substantial diminution in the relative proportion of cow beef in future years, his argument being that he found it " . . . very difficult to believe that improvements in veterinary science, in better housing, management and feeding will not add materially to the life of the dairy cow within the next decade, and so substantially reduce the number of fat cows marketed annually".

There is no immediate indication of Mr. Shaw's prophecy being fulfilled. The life of a cow in a dairy is certainly not becoming longer. It might, for a variety of reasons—better remuneration for beef compared with milk, increase of milk recording and elimination of more proved low yielders to mention only two—become, *on the average*, even shorter. If that were to result in a higher standard of both health and yield in those remaining, it could only be to the good. In any event Mr. Shaw's prediction, if fulfilled, while reducing the percentage of cow beef in the meat markets, would do so by reduction of the best quality of cow beef, that is to say from young cows, and retention of the worst quality from old cows. Beef from young cows may be excellent beef. It is beef from the old and worn out cow that is the real problem.

It seems that so long as we maintain a large dairy industry in Britain, as we seem likely to do for the foreseeable future, we shall, whether we like it or not, have a very large quantity of cow beef of which to dispose. It behoves us to make the very best use of it and that implies systematic and reliable grading. The best cow beef is quite good enough to go into the butchers' shops beside the beef from heifers and steers. The worst should not, and in most cases does not find entry to the butcher's shop except as sausage or pie meat and it would undoubtedly raise the reputation of home-killed meat if a higher proportion of cow beef was utilised in this way.

Dealing with the situation as regards cow beef at the end of the War years (circa 1945) Warman said:

" We do, however, see that cows only fit for manufacture go into manufacture. At present our manufacturing meat is about 8 per cent of our total supplies, as against perhaps 3 or 4 per cent in peacetime. That means that about a third of the cows go for manufacture. In peacetime rather more vigorous separation of manufacturing qualities might well be attempted." (13)

More careful grading of cow beef seems to be a solution to many of its marketing difficulties, that, and the diversion of all but the highest quality to manufacture. Careful grading, of course, implies a reliable grading system. The most serious criticism that can be brought against the present system of grading according to estimated killing-out percentage is that it is least accurate in the case of cows. (15) In other words it is a system of grading least effective in the class of beef requiring grading most. Undoubtedly, payment on carcase grades as advocated in the N.F.U. Livestock Marketing Scheme would be very greatly preferable in the case of cows.

REFERENCES

(1) " Meat," p. 3, Commonwealth Economic Committee (1952). H.M.S.O.
(2) *Ibid.*, p. 1.
(3) *Ibid.*, p. 4.
(4) Report on the Marketing of Cattle and Beef in England and Wales, *Economic Series*, No. 20, p. 8 (1929). H.M.S.O.
(5) " British Pedigree Cattle," p. 19, National Cattle Breeders' Assoc.
(6) Hammond, J. (1952). *Farmer and Stock Breeder*, **66**, 63.
(7) Dowling, D. F. (1949). " Problems of the transplantation of fertilised ova," *J. Agric. Sci.*, **39**, 374.
(8) Rowson, L. E. (1950). " Using cows as incubators," *Farming*, **4**, 201.
(9) Willett, E. L., Black, W. G., Casida, L. E., Stone, W. H., and Buckner, P. J. (1951). " Successful transplantation of a fertilised bovine ovum," *Science*, **113**, 247.
(10) Hammond, J. (1952). " Farm Animals," 2nd Edit. (London).
(11) Davies, J. (1947). " Calf salvaging in Breconshire," *Agric.*, **54**, 371.
(12) *Ibid.*, p. 372.
(13) Warman, W. H. (1945). " Meat supplies," *Rept. Brit. Soc. Anim. Prod.*, p. 11.
(14) Shaw, T. (1949). " Some national aspects of beef production," *Proc. Brit. Soc. Anim. Prod.*, p. 18.
(15) Callow, E. H. (1945). " The food value, quality and grading of meat, with special reference to beef," *Rept. Brit. Soc. Anim. Prod.*, p. 48.

BEEF begins with the unborn calf. The calf, once conceived, spends nine months within the body of the cow. From what has been proved in sheep, it is altogether probable that the nutrition of the cow, while pregnant, will influence the development of the unborn calf, but that effect will be confined, in the main, to the last three months or so of the cow's pregnancy. Moreover, since twin calves are exceptional and the most obvious effects of maternal under-nutrition in sheep are seen in twin lambs, the importance of the cow's nutrition upon the unborn calf may well be less than is the effect of a ewe's nutrition upon her unborn lambs.

In any event, optimum nutrition of the unborn calf is of the greatest importance in calves destined for true veal, and true veal is meantime of minor importance in Britain. If, however, the fate of a calf is to be highly fed on milk and slaughtered at an early age but fair weight, for veal, then the calf should be heavy and fat when born, for the profit of veal largely depends upon what the calf has on its back at birth. The calf is unlikely to be heavy or fat unless its dam has been well fed in the latter part of her pregnancy.

Calves, no matter what their condition when born, must be well fed after birth if they are to make the best beef. As M'Combie said:

" If the calf flesh is once lost, it can never be regained." (1)

The best method of calf-rearing is the natural method, and one of the strongest arguments in favour of hill cattle as a new source of the country's beef is that the calves from hill cows will be suckled calves. The advantages of suckling, as opposed to bucket feeding in calf-rearing, have been recognised in the cattle rearing business for a long time. Other things being equal, a premium has always been paid by the cattle rearer for a suckled calf. Some of these suckled calves—usually crosses by beef bulls out of hill cows—may not have received a very great quantity of milk in all, since the potentiality of the hill breeds for yielding milk is presumably limited, and the conditions under which they are kept may put a nutritional brake even on a low potentiality.

The secret of the superiority of suckling probably lies in the fact that the calf gets its milk, possibly in small quantities, but at frequent intervals, and over a long period. The milk it gets, moreover, is clean and of the correct temperature, and cows know nothing about week-ends or overtime!

Once a calf is weaned, either from dam, multiple foster-mother or from bucket it has, in general, to endure the relative austerity of a store period. Provided a calf has been well reared it can survive these austerities and still make good beef in the end. That is where the suckled calf shows up to advantage.

There are, of course, arguments both for and against the advisability of a store period in the feeding of cattle. To obtain the best quality of beef and the most desirable beef conformation cattle should, undoubtedly, be pushed ahead at the maximum rate of growth of which they are genetically capable. That was the principle behind the production of baby beef and beefling, becoming common practice before the 1939–1945 War. It is a method however, that requires an abundance of concentrated food, and nowadays concentrates are both expensive and scarce. The tendency during the last ten years has been towards feeding cattle off at a later age and that makes a store period essential.

Store cattle, in a sense, are the raw material from which finished beef is made. It is clearly impossible for the cattle feeder to produce good beef unless there are store cattle of the right quality and in sufficient numbers available for the job. That has been one of the main difficulties of beef production in Britain over the last thirty years. With the swing-over of the country's cattle industry towards specialised production of liquid milk, store cattle suitable for beef have become progressively scarcer. To what extent that lack of suitability is to be attributed to breeding or to rearing is the subject of detailed discussion later in this section. It must be admitted, however, that in the past, calves bred for the dairy and reared in the dairy have tended to be unprofitable propositions for beef production.

Shortage of the most desirable class of store cattle has meant their also becoming dearer, with the result that store cattle prices have been too high in relation to the price of finished beef. In fact, a kind of vicious circle has developed in the feeding of beef cattle. The scarcity of suitable stores has made beef production uneconomic, with a resulting tendency for beef producers to turn over to dairying, which, in turn, must lead to an even greater scarcity of stores well suited for feeding.

An increased supply of store cattle from hill and marginal land would do a great deal to break this vicious circle. With more good stores available at a more reasonable price, the prospects of profit in cattle feeding would be greater, and more farmers might be prepared to feed cattle. For, without store cattle, there can be no beef. That the shortage and cost of suitable stores may prove the bottle-neck in beef production is shown by the increasing number of farmers on what are by type and by tradition cattle *feeding* farms, who have, within recent years, begun to breed and rear stores for their own feeding purposes.

The scarcity of stores lies at the root of much of the present famine of good beef. Yet there are plenty of calves born in Britain annually were they but bred and reared in such a way as to answer the purposes of beef production. These calves are born but are not necessarily reared.

Possibly the most significant fact about cattle rearing in Britain at the present time is that such a vast number of calves—well over one million annually—are never reared at all. Yet, were they reared, and reared in the right way, it is possible that many, possibly the great majority, might make reasonably good beef in the end.

Taking the widest possible view, the sources of calves that might be so reared for beef are the male calves of any breed or the surplus heifer calves of any breed. It is a point highly controversial at the present time as to which, if any, of the dairy breeds supplies male calves worth rearing for beef. It is generally accepted that the Friesian is so worthy. Apart from this one breed, however, the general practice among dairy farmers of sacrificing the male calf of dairy breeds almost at birth is one frequently commended. It is generally agreed, however, that male calves of the dual-purpose breeds are worth rearing as beef stores. As regards those of the specialised beef breeds there can, of course, be no question.

We have always been told and have in consequence (perhaps rather uncritically) come to believe that there is a vast difference in the beef value of different breeds of cattle and that this difference is due to dissimilar genetic constitutions. Certainly were we to compare an average Aberdeen-Angus bullock with a Friesian steer, either on hoof or on hook, we should find this vast and easily recognisable difference. The point that is seldom raised and, until the Cambridge calf-rearing experiments were started, had never been effectively investigated, is how much of that difference is genetic and how much is the effect of early environment. The point is, of course, of quite fundamental importance, one that is apt to be obscured by legitimate breed propaganda, and one clearly in need of impartial scientific investigation.

An Aberdeen-Angus steer is admittedly a fine butcher's animal. That part of its excellence for beef purposes is due to breeding is, I presume, something that no sensible person would be prepared to deny. The question at issue is—*How much?*

It is known to all practical cattlemen that poor nutrition or bad husbandry, or both, may so ruin an Aberdeen-Angus beast of the most impeccable breeding that it develops neither the beef conformation nor the beef quality proper to its breed. The impression of practical feeders has been amply confirmed by the results of scientific investigation.

" Extensive experiments . . . in U.S.A. have shown that when well bred stores are fed on a low plane of nutrition the development of the more valuable parts of the body is inhibited and they come to look like badly bred animals." (2)

The experimental work here referred to is the classical investigations of the Missouri Agricultural Experimental Station on the effect of limited food on the growth of beef cattle. (3)

Now, in the rearing of cattle of the beef breeds the nutritional plane is exceptionally high if the cattle be pedigreed and in a herd maintained for the production and sale of breeding stock. Granted the capacity for growth exists in the first place, the plane of nutrition requisite to support that growth to the limits of its fullest genetic expression is totally uneconomic in relation to the production of beef as distinct from that of pedigreed beef cattle.

In herds of beef cattle kept for the commercial production of beef and hides rather than for the more specialised purpose of breeding pedigreed stock, the nutritional plane is, of course, at a very much lower level. It is seldom that herds of the specialised beef breeds are kept in Britain solely for the production of beef and hides.   In fact and in Britain, unless these breeds, to name them—Beef Shorthorn, Aberdeen-Angus, and Hereford—are kept for the production of breeding stock, they are very unlikely to be kept at all.

In other countries the situation is quite different.   In many of the newer pastoral countries vast herds of beef cattle are maintained and these beef cattle are in most cases, nowadays, pure-bred or so highly up-graded as to be for all practical purposes indistinguishable from pure-breds.

" We all know the high quality of Argentine beef, produced as it is entirely from herds of pure-bred Shorthorn, Aberdeen-Angus, and Hereford.   In the Argentine there is no indiscriminate crossing with dairy breeds, in fact there is no crossing of any kind in these breeds . . .   Most of the big herds have been graded up from the native cattle, but they are now absolutely pure Shorthorn, Aberdeen-Angus and Hereford." (4)

These beef cattle in Argentine, as in the United States, Australia, and other pastoral countries are—contrary to what is customary in Britain—run under range conditions with the prime object of producing beef stores of the highest quality.   The nutritional plane is not necessarily high; it is never uneconomically high, it may on occasion, as during drought, be exceptionally low, and yet the quality of the final product—the carcase of beef—in respect of conformation and of quality in many cases leave nothing to be desired.   What, apart from breeding, can be the secret of this success?

In contrasting beef with dual-purpose or dairy cattle there is— apart from breeding altogether—one important environmental difference that requires to be observed.   Beef calves, whether in stud or range herd, are suckled calves.   Dairy calves, apart from some bull calves reared for breeding purposes, are never suckled calves.   To what extent, if any, does this general environmental distinction explain the presumed superiority of the specialised beef breeds of cattle for beef production?

Undoubtedly, the mere fact of being suckled is favourable to a calf.   It is generally admitted that no other method of calf rearing is quite so successful.   As M'Combie wrote, " . . . it will generally be found that the sure way to make first-class calves is to allow them to suckle." (5)

There always has been a premium paid for the suckled calf as compared to the pail-fed calf, at least in the cattle markets of Scotland.

Moreover, the profound effect of nutrition during early life in affecting the later capacity of store cattle to fatten satisfactorily has been known to practical feeders for a very long time. To quote M'Combie again:

" The calf should be allowed to suckle or to be fed from the pail for six or eight months. It has then strength to stand weaning, and, if properly cared for, will not be checked in its growth, and it will retain the good calf-flesh it has put on. The loss of the calf flesh cannot be remedied, and great care should be taken to avoid this. If the calf-flesh is lost the animal will be reduced in value, and can never be made to yield first-class meat. Great care, therefore, must be taken by the breeder when his calves are weaned." (6)

It follows from this discussion that two points regarding the presumed superiority of the specialised beef breeds of cattle in relation to beef production require emphasis. They are:

1. That it is the easiest thing in the world by wrong feeding and poor husbandry to reduce the finest strain of pedigreed beef cattle to scrub level.

2. This being admitted, the question must then be put as to what extent the general excellence of beef cattle for beef production is to be attributed to correct feeding and good husbandry directed to that purpose.

The question and its correct answer have this profound importance. If, on the one hand, the superiority of the specialised beef breeds of cattle for beef production purposes is due to the genetic constitution of these breeds, to their breeding and to that alone, then it becomes impossible to attempt a satisfactory adaptation of dual-purpose or dairy cattle to beef production purposes by environmental means only.

If, on the other hand, much of the superiority for beef production purposes of the specialised beef breeds is due to the methods of husbandry, particularly the suckling of calves, almost universal among these breeds, then it should prove possible, by imitation of these beef husbandry methods, to raise up cattle of good beef quality out of the dual-purpose or even out of some of the dairy breeds. That, in fact, is one object of research, although by no means the only one, in the cattle rearing experiments at the Cambridge University Farm which now fall to be described.

These experiments, which have been in progress over a number of years now, are, undoubtedly, the most important and illuminating experiments on the rearing of beef cattle being conducted at the present time. They have been designed in the attempt to answer at least three questions of the first importance. To quote Mr. A. J. Brookes who is in direct charge of these experiments, these questions are:

" 1. How should calves bred in milking herds be reared to make reasonable beef?

2. How do such calves compare with beef bred calves as regards efficiency in turning food into meat?

3. Can these ' dairy bred ' calves be reared profitably for beef purposes? " (7)

The experiments, then, are concerned primarily with testing the feasibility of developing beef as a profitable by-product of milk, on the argument as stated by Mr. W. S. Mansfield.

" . . . that it is now generally admitted that the raw material for any great expansion in beef production in this country must come from our milk producing herds." (8)

Developing this general thesis on a more detailed and personal note, Mr. Mansfield continued:

" It has always seemed to me that for feeders to demand nothing but stores of pure beef breeding is crying for the moon and I do not for one moment believe the oft repeated statement that it is only such cattle that are both acceptable to the butcher and profitable to the feeder, for I know very well that cattle which have no beef blood in them at all can be both. This does not mean that I think that all calves, no matter how they are bred, are suitable for beef production. Obviously I rule out calves from Jersey and Guernsey cows. I would also rule out calves from Ayrshires and Ayrshire crosses as well. But I would include calves from all the dual-purpose breeds, and also calves from what I may describe as the improved modern type of Friesian . . . " (9)

Possibly Mr. Mansfield is a little drastic in his sweeping aside of the Ayrshire and its crosses. The Ayrshire, admittedly, is a dairy breed and neither a beef nor a dual-purpose breed. Yet, the same can quite justifiably be said of the Friesian. The

Ayrshire is not quite such an entirely hopeless beef proposition as Mr. Mansfield would have us believe. Scottish experience is not universally so unfavourable and discussing the Ayrshire in the United States, Professor Petersen writes:

" The Ayrshire ranks high among the dairy breeds for beef. Dry cows, as well as steers and heifers, fatten readily. The fat of the Ayrshire does not possess the high yellow colour of the fat that detracts from the beef value of the Jersey and the Guernsey." (10)

In any case, too sharp a differentiation between the beefing possibilities of the various dairy breeds would seem somewhat illogical on Mr. Mansfield's general argument since, after dismissing the Ayrshire because of its breeding, he proceeded to develop the thesis that early environment is if anything of rather greater importance than breed in the rearing of desirable beef store cattle.

In developing his argument, Mr. Mansfield began very logically and sensibly by discussing the problem of baby beef. This type of beef, it may be recalled, was produced in pre-war (1939) days by the lavish feeding of milk and concentrates to young cattle so that they grew at a great rate and were ready for slaughter at an early age. Baby beeves have been well defined as:

" . . . young cattle that have been fattened while still in rapid growth—*i.e.* they have not passed through a definite 'store period' but have been fed somewhat intensively from birth. They reach the meat market at from twelve to twenty months old, and usually scale from 6 to 10 cwt. live weight." (11)

Now, rather curiously and perhaps unexpectedly, certain dual-purpose breeds established an excellent reputation as a source of the best raw material for baby beef production. Of these dual-purpose breeds, the Red Poll was outstanding.

The question then arises—and it is, biologically speaking, a most intriguing question—why is it that, if certain dual-purpose breeds can provide baby beeves as good, or even better, than those produced from the specialised beef breeds, they cannot also provide mature beef of equal quality. Mr. Mansfield, in his address to the British Society of Animal Production in 1949 essayed both question and answer.

" If calves of dual-purpose breeding can make good *baby beef*, why can't they make good *mature beef*, and the answer I believe

EXPERIMENTAL CALVES AT SIX MONTHS.

In each picture the calf on the left has been reared on a high plane, the one on the right on a moderate plane and each is six months old.

Fig. 47. DAIRY
SHORTHORN CALVES.

Fig. 48.
HEREFORD CALVES.

Fig. 49.
FRIESIAN CALVES.

EXPERIMENTAL STEERS ALL AT 16 MONTHS.

Fig. 50. HEREFORD STEERS.
(*Left to right*) High-high, high-moderate, moderate-high, moderate-moderate.

Fig. 51. FRIESIAN STEERS.
(*Left to right*) High-high, high-moderate, moderate-high, moderate-moderate.

Fig. 52. DAIRY SHORTHORN.
(*Left*) High-moderate.
(*Right*) Moderate-high.

Fig. 53. DAIRY SHORTHORN.
(*Left*) High-moderate.
(*Right*) Moderate-moderate.

Fig. 54. FRIESIAN STEERS.
(*Left*) Moderate-moderate, $3\frac{1}{2}$ years old.
(*Right*) High-moderate, $2\frac{1}{2}$ years old.

Fig. 55. DAIRY SHORTHORN STEERS.
(*Left*) Moderate-moderate, $3\frac{1}{2}$ years old.
(*Right*) High-moderate, $2\frac{1}{2}$ years old.

HIGH-MODERATE AND MODERATE-HIGH STEERS READY FOR SLAUGHTER
(fat off grass).

Fig. 56. HEREFORD STEERS.
(*Left*) Moderate-moderate, $3\frac{1}{2}$ years old.
(*Right*) High-moderate, $2\frac{1}{2}$ years old.

is that *provided they are reared* on the same high plane as calves destined for baby beef, then they *will* make good mature beef." (12)

Mr. Mansfield then went on to explain that: "Since the time when the making of farm-house butter was abandoned in this country, dairy bred calves, except when intended for baby beef, have generally been reared on a low plane of nutrition, and calves reared on a low plane of nutrition will never make really good meat however well they may be done subsequently. Even beef bred calves if they are reared on a low plane of nutrition suffer (though of course in the ordinary way they never are so reared, since they always suckle their own dams)." (12)

It is clear that Mr. Mansfield's argument is rapidly approaching the point where it might be suggested justifiably that a calf's early environment had an equal or even greater importance than its breeding upon its subsequent development as a beef animal. In fact, Mr. Mansfield actually arrived at this conclusion when discussing the effect upon the calf of generous feeding throughout its first eight months of life. He said:

" It is the fact that these calves were reared on a high plane that enables them to thrive in this way on such poor fare, rather than the fact that they were beef bred, though it is their breeding which usually receives all the credit." (13)

Perhaps it is a trifle unfair to follow the arguments of a speaker towards an inevitable conclusion with which he might not be altogether prepared to agree. For that conclusion is revolutionary, to say the least. In a period when hopes of livestock improvement are based so very largely on the science of genetics, we are faced with the somewhat startling proposition that one of the most important and valuable branches of the livestock industry, namely beef production, is quite as much a question of early environment as of breeding. That seems to me to be far the most important outcome of these Cambridge cattle-rearing experiments. It is something much more fundamental, if true, than considerations dealing with the most economical methods of producing beef under the special economic circumstances of post-war Britain although, very naturally, it is these economic questions which have aroused most interest among the farming community. Certainly the conclusion is no hasty one or one arrived at without due consideration, for the suggestion made by

Mr. Mansfield to the British Society of Animal Production in 1949 was repeated in even plainer terms by his colleague Mr. Brookes addressing the Farmers' Club in 1951, when he said:

" I have formed the opinion that much of the merit of beef breeds is due to nutrition, and the high plane of rearing in early life, and not so much to breeding as some would have us suppose." (14)

What are the theoretical extensions of this hypothesis? Are we to assume that were Friesians to suckle their calves, be excused the dairy, and be exported to the Argentine, that they might give rise to a new beef breed? Or, conversely, that if Beef Shorthorns were reared parsimoniously on the pail, were milked to capacity in the dairy, and were exported to Holland, that we might have the makings of a new dairy breed? That would be to bring Cambridge unexpectedly close to Moscow and yet these opinions of Mansfield and Brookes are based, not on theoretical speculations, but on the results of the careful and well-planned experiments on which they have been long engaged. What are, then, these experiments which appear to be leading to conclusions of such unexpected novelty?

They began in the spring of 1946, so that, at the time of writing (1953), they have been in progress some seven years and are planned to continue until 1955.

Three breeds of cattle are being used, Hereford, Dairy Shorthorn and Friesian, representing beef, dual-purpose and dairy breeds respectively. The comparison between these three breeds over a number of years and on a variety of levels of feeding or nutritional planes is designed to establish the value of dairy bred steers as beef animals in comparison with a specialised beef breed. That is the first object of this series of experiments.

In 1946, and in each subsequent year, a batch of twenty-four calves (eight of each breed) is added to the experiment and these are carried on to slaughter and in some cases to dissection at somewhere between 2 and 3 years of age according to the method by which they have been reared. The cattle are reared on four different levels of nutrition and the calves are allocated initially in such a way that there are two calves of each breed under each system of treatment.

In the four systems of rearing adopted, the only essential difference lies in the amount of food the cattle receive.

In the nutritional work on farm animals conducted at Cambridge University within recent years it has become customary to refer to " planes of nutrition ". Let it be said at once that the phrase has no recondite scientific meaning. It merely implies that certain groups of animals have been better fed, in a general way, than others. It has also become customary at Cambridge to refer to " high ", " moderate ", " low " planes of nutrition. In many cases these terms have meant no more and no less than that certain groups of animals have received respectively a surfeit, a sufficiency, a modicum of the same kinds of food. There is, therefore, nothing either mystical or learned about the term " nutritional plane " or " plane of nutrition ". A loaf, half a loaf, crumbs would express the conception adequately and in plainer language.

With these introductory remarks it is now possible to return to the consideration of the Cambridge cattle-rearing experiments in slightly more detail. The four feeding treatments are as follows:

" 1. High plane during calfhood (*i.e.* up to eight months of age) followed by high plane. (High-High, HH.)

2. High plane during calfhood, followed by moderate plane. (High-Moderate, HM.)

3. Moderate plane during calfhood, followed by high plane. (Moderate-High, MH.)

4. Moderate plane during calfhood, followed by moderate plane. (Moderate-Moderate, MM)." (15)

The essential difference between the High and Moderate plane of feeding during calfhood is that those calves on the High plane are multiple suckled on nurse cows for six months, with liberal allowances of both good hay and concentrates; whereas those on the Moderate plane are restricted to forty gallons of milk in all (pail-fed) during the first nine weeks, followed by a restricted ration of hay and concentrates supplemented by straw.

Subsequent to calfhood—*i.e.*, after the first eight months, the difference between the High and Moderate nutritional planes is, perhaps, a little less clear cut. It is certainly less continuous, being merely a difference in winter dietary. During summer, cattle of both groups graze together. In winter, cattle on the High plane of nutrition receive three times more concentrates and rather more hay and sugar beet pulp than those on the Moderate plane. The hay is also of better quality. Details of the actual rations used are available in the original publications.

Those, very roughly, are the outlines of the experiments. What of the results? Strictly speaking there are none, since the research workers concerned with these experiments have always maintained—and with the most abundant and complete justification—that the experiments should be completed before conclusions are drawn from them. It may be recalled that the experiments are estimated to continue until at least 1955.

Because of the enormous interest these experiments have aroused, particularly in official and farming circles, there have already been several publications of first importance. It is only fair to the research workers concerned, however, to regard these publications as progress reports. What results do they meantime suggest?

1. *" How should calves bred in milking herds be reared to make reasonable beef? "* (7)

The provisional answer to this, the first question, is that the calf must be well fed during the first eight months of its life. Since " well " is always a comparative term, it might be better and safer to be blunt about the matter in admitting that the calf must receive a much larger quantity of milk than it is at all likely to get in a modern dairy if it is to make a good beef animal within a reasonable time.

One of the more surprising results of this aspect of the experiments has been the profound and prolonged impression a nutritional difference during calfhood has upon the subsequent development of the calves concerned.

" Long after the nutrition treatments are subdivided at eight months the difference in size between calves reared on a high or moderate plane initially remains visible." (14) After detailing the differences between the experimental groups, Mr. Brookes continued:

" All these figures emphasise the value of a really good start in life and also the fact that the calf reared on a high plane initially is better able to deal with bulky and less digestible foods in its first winter than its moderately reared brother." (14)

2. *" How do such calves compare with beef bred calves as regards efficiency in turning food into meat? "* (7)

The general answer to this second—and fundamentally important—question is that they appear to compare more favourably than could well have been predicted. The results of these experiments indicate that method of rearing has a greater influence on growth and development than the animal's breeding. Naturally those conducting the experiments have to be extremely cautious in making such a suggestion. It is, or would seem to be, against practical experience. It is certainly contrary to preconceived opinion. It is, quite obviously, one subject to the most searching and severe criticism in that it contradicts the previously unquestioned claims to beef supremacy of the leading beef breeds.

Nevertheless, Mr. Brookes who conducted the experiments had this to say:

" In each year the moderate plane calves have assumed what might be described as a ' dairy type ' appearance, showing narrow hind-quarters and lack of second thigh. This has been common to all three breeds, indicating the important effect of nutrition on conformation." He then went on to make the very important statement already quoted:

" I have formed the opinion that much of the merit of beef breeds is due to nutrition, and the high plane of rearing in early life, and not so much to breeding as some would have us suppose." (14)

Replying to the discussion on his paper, Mr. Brookes somewhat modified his earlier statement by saying:

" I do not want to give the impression that breeding does not matter; of course it does, but nutrition matters even more." (16)

When the results of these experiments are finally worked out, the differences between breeds, whether beef, dual-purpose, or dairy on the same level of nutrition may prove to be surprisingly small. The contribution to the discussion on Mr. Brookes' paper made by Dr. E. H. Callow of the Low Temperature Research Station, Cambridge, is of extraordinary interest in this connection. (17) Dr. Callow said:

" The Low Temperature Research Station at Cambridge have had the privilege of carrying out dissections of the carcases from seventeen of the beef animals which Mr. Brookes has been describing. Work on the chemical analysis of the dissected tissues has proved a laborious task but is almost completed.

The results obtained still await a detailed study and nothing can yet be said about the finer points of beef quality, such as the marbling fat of the lean.

"Two points, however, have already been established. In spite of its larger frame, the Friesian does not give carcases with undue proportion of bone. The butcher is interested in the percentage of bone in a carcase. This percentage falls as the carcase gets fatter and it is, therefore, necessary to discount the level of fatness of the carcase, before comparisons can be made. When this is done, to our surprise the Friesian may even give a carcase with slightly less than the average percentage of bone for its level of fatness.

"So far only one factor due to breed has been discovered. The Hereford steers undoubtedly had heavier hides than those from the Shorthorns or Friesians. Again a comparative basis must be used and the weight of hide has been considered as a percentage of the live-weight because this affects dressing-out percentage. Expressed as a percentage of the live-weight, the hides of the Herefords were on the average 7·8 % as opposed to the average figure of 6·1 % for the hides of both the Shorthorns and Friesians."

3. *'Can these 'dairy-bred' calves be reared profitably for beef purposes?'"* (7)

The first and clearest cut answer to at least a section of this question is that with the background of modern production costs and controlled beef prices, intensive feeding subsequent to calfhood does not pay. The average profit per head of the High-High group was estimated at a mere threepence, that of the Moderate-High group rather better at £5 8s. 1d. (18)

A Moderate plane of nutrition subsequent to calfhood paid much better. Thus the profit from the High-Moderate group was, per head, £15. 2s. 4d., that from the Moderate-Moderate group, £17. 1s. 4d. (18) Of these two groups the High-Moderate group was to be preferred, since the cattle were sold fat off grass a year sooner, thus leading to a much quicker turnover.

This part of the Cambridge experiments, presumably because of its direct economic implications, has received what might perhaps be considered a somewhat undue share of the relative publicity. It has been proved to the hilt that under present economic circumstances it does not pay to feed beef cattle intensively, either because the price of concentrates is too high, the price of beef too low, or from both these circumstances combined. There is, however, nothing of enduring biological significance in the elucidation of these facts. A change in the price ratio of beef to concentrates could change the whole picture, radically and immediately. A combination of dear beef and cheap concentrates would make baby beef production profitable again. The reverse picture—cheap beef and dear concentrates—might render even the feeding of concentrates during calfhood an uneconomic policy in spite of its advantages in production. It might lead to a situation where the feeding of concentrates to cattle was uneconomic under all circumstances and at all ages. In the special terminology of the Cambridge experiments it might result in the Moderate-Moderate (MM) groups being more profitable than the High-Moderate (HM) group, at present favoured by the Cambridge experimenters, and that in spite of the longer period required by the MM group to attain maturity.

These and other questions will, without doubt, become clearer once the experiments have been repeated sufficiently often to permit of statisticians passing judgement upon the significance or otherwise of the measurable differences revealed. Perhaps even more illuminating will be the final and detailed results of carcase examination, dissection, and analysis carried out at the Low Temperature Research Station, Cambridge. Until all this massive amount of work has been completed it would be wrong to criticise or attempt to criticise the interim findings. It would, however, be equally wrong to base any general or national cattle policy upon them, and that statement, especially in view of the close linkage between Cambridge and Whitehall, requires to be made.

In these Cambridge experiments the cattle have been reared and fattened on the same farm. That has never been a general custom and was, indeed, and until quite recently, a rather exceptional practice. For, in the course of centuries, a certain division of labour, as it were, has grown up in the beef producing industry. Thus, the fattening pastures of the English Midlands were accustomed to draw largely upon Wales for their stores. Scotland has for long imported Irish store cattle to such an extent that even in the war years 1940–1944 " . . . nearly half the store cattle fed off in Scotland were of Irish origin ", while " . . . the reliance on imported store cattle was even greater before 1939 than in war time". (19)

The ramifications of the store cattle trade are most complicated, so much so, in fact, as to give occupation to a considerable number of cattle dealers and other intermediaries and to raise, perhaps unnecessarily, the production costs of the finished article. The restriction on the movements of stock an outbreak of Foot-and-Mouth disease entails, displays, as it were at a glance, the scope and complexity of the constant traffic of store cattle throughout Britain. In the severe and prolonged outbreak of 1952, for example, the disease was first notified in Scotland from a rather remote corner of Aberdeenshire. It had been carried there by calves bought in South-West England, at that time free of the disease, and infected by contaminated milk fed to them in the course of their long journey north. At first sight it seems strange that Aberdeenshire, by tradition a cattle-rearing county, should import calves from Somerset and Devon. The reason is that, nowadays, the Aberdeenshire calf rearer has to depend, to a very large extent, apart from his own breeding, upon what the dairy farmer gives him. Since it is always possible to rear more calves than can be bred, these rearing farms buy in calves deemed suitable for rearing. The Scottish dairy herd of to-day is, in the great majority of cases, an Ayrshire herd, and the rearer—rightly or wrongly—does not consider Ayrshire calves repay rearing as beef stores. Therefore, the Aberdeenshire calf rearer, through dealers, prefers to buy Devon, cross Hereford, Dairy Shorthorn, or other types of dual-purpose calves, even from a great distance. One result of this division of labour, this coming and going of store cattle of various ages, breeds, sizes, and conditions throughout the country, is that the cattle feeder usually feeds cattle that others have bred. This is but a right and proper division of labour, since cattle can be bred, and probably better bred, under conditions of soil, climate, husbandry quite unsuitable for cattle feeding. Again, it is somewhat of a waste of good land to breed cattle—always and of necessity an extensive form of husbandry—on farms where cultivation is intensive and cattle can be fattened and carried on to slaughter.

Cattle feeders, in consequence, are dependent on others for their stores and a great deal of the success or failure, the moderate profit or the more frequent loss, resulting from the fattening of cattle is undoubtedly influenced by the skill or otherwise of the feeder in purchasing his stores.

The selection of stores is an art, a high art at that, but one that is being forgotten. The weighing of store cattle at sale induced many feeders to buy by weight rather than by character. The practice seems fundamentally unsound, although many arithmetically minded farmers indulged in it. It is not, however, a method likely to appeal greatly to the highly skilled stockman. After all, when store cattle are bought, the weight at the time of sale while admittedly of great importance, is little more so than the capacity to thrive and to put on beef after they *are* bought. The ability to judge the possibilities latent in store cattle is possibly one reason why, amid the somewhat depressing unanimity of agricultural economists that cattle feeding, particularly winter cattle feeding, does not pay, one comes across the exceptional farmer who apparently makes quite a satisfactory living out of the business. Admittedly, a sure judgement of store cattle is not, and never was, a common gift. As M'Combie very truly said: (20)

" To be a good judge of store cattle is exceedingly difficult. We have many judges of fat cattle among our farmers and butchers, and a few good judges of breeding stock; but our really good judges of store cattle are exceedingly few. A judge of store cattle ought to be able to say at a glance how much the animal will improve, how much additional value you can put on him on good, bad, or indifferent land, and on turnips, in three, six, or twelve months. Unless a grazier is able to do this, he is working in the dark, and can never obtain eminence in his profession. Since my first speculation, already referred to— the half of the £12 field—I have bought and grazed store cattle for nearly fifty years. No one has been able to put upon paper a clear definition, such as can be understood by the reader, of the characteristics of a good store beast. It is only practice and a natural gift that can enable anyone to master the subject."

There are very few men alive to-day who have the experience or the ability to judge and select store cattle as M'Combie did. Nor are the men with something of that experience and ability of the type likely to make written record of their knowledge. There is, however, and has been for many years, a great trade

and traffic in store cattle, and the traditional knowledge of some
of the men in that trade is vast, and, although incoherent, not to
be despised.   There are, undoubtedly, biological principles
buried in the wisdom of the cattle dealer which the professional
biologist would do well to explore.

REFERENCES

(1) M'Combie, W. (1886).   " Cattle and Cattle Breeders," p. 14, 4th Ed. (Edinburgh).
(2) Hammond, J., Edwards, J., and Walton, A. (1941).   " Animal breeding in relation to environmental conditions," *J.R.A.S.E.*, **102**, 156.
(3) Trowbridge, P. F., Moulton, C. R., and Haigh, L. D. (1918).   " Effect of limited food on growth of beef cattle," *Missouri Agr. Exper. Stat. Res. Bull.* 28.
(4) Stewart, D. M. (1945).   " Proc. Hill Cattle Confer., Oban," p. 24.
(5) M'Combie, W. (1886).   *Ibid.*, p. 129.
(6) *Ibid.*, p. 130.
(7) Brookes, A. J. (1951).   " Some aspects of rearing cattle for beef," *J. Farmers' Club*, Part 5, p. 65.
(8) Mansfield, W. S. (1949).   " Beef from dairy and dual-purpose calves," *Proc. Brit. Soc. Anim. Prod.*, p. 21.
(9) *Ibid.*, p. 23.
(10) Petersen, W. E. (1950).   " Dairy Science," p. 140 (Chicago).
(11) Watson, J. S., Cameron, J., and Garrod, G. H. (1926).   " The Cattle-Breeders' Handbook," p. 126 (London).
(12) Mansfield, W. S. (1949).   *Ibid.*, p. 24.
(13) *Ibid.*, p. 25.
(14) Brookes, A. J. (1951).   *Ibid.*, p. 67.
(15) Brookes, A. J., and Vincent, L. S. (1950).   " Beef production experiment at Cambridge," *J.R.A.S.E.*, **3**, 100.
(16) Brookes, A. J. (1951).   *Ibid.*, p. 80.
(17) *Ibid.*, p. 79.
(18) *Ibid.*, p. 69.
(19) Heath, W. E. (1946).   " Irish cattle on Scottish farms," *Scot. Agric.*, **26**, 109.
(20) M'Combie, W. (1886).   *Ibid.*, p. 10.

Chapter Thirteen
CATTLE FATTENING—WINTER

BEFORE considering the problems involved in the fattening of mature cattle, it is convenient here to discuss the production of meat from cattle of more tender ages. Veal calves, baby beeves, and beeflings have been in abeyance since the outbreak of war in 1939. Their production has never been revived, largely owing to the scarcity and high cost of the milk and concentrates on which these forms of cattle meat production so largely depended. At any future period, however, should it so happen that surplus summer milk became cheaper, or should there ever come a time when cereal and other concentrates were in plentiful supply, then the production of veal and baby beef might become profitable once again. It is therefore wise to keep these possibilities of alternative production under periodical review.

Veal. The production of true veal is a highly specialised procedure. It has been discontinued for so long now that it is necessary to refer to some of the older books about beef and beef cattle to find veal production adequately described. Such a description can be found in an excellent little handbook published in 1926 by Sir James Scott Watson and collaborators. (1) The description is as follows:

> The best class of veal is produced by feeding the calf on whole milk only. Commencing with ½ to ¾ gal. of colostrum on the first day, fed in four meals, the daily ration is gradually increased to 1½ gal. of whole milk at the end of the first week and later to 2, 2½ or perhaps, finally to 3 gallons per day. Veal calves should always be fed at least thrice daily. They are confined in small individual boxes, or tied by the neck, and must be kept warm and comfortably bedded. A lump of chalk may be put before each, so that the animal may be able to counteract any tendency to acidity in the stomach. A good marketable calf may be produced in from four to six weeks, and it rarely pays to feed beyond the eighth or ninth week. Until about the twelfth week the product is still of excellent quality, but the cost of production per pound steadily rises. After twelve weeks the flesh is liable to become dark in colour and to lose the characteristic flavour and appearance of true veal. As regards the live-weight increase, the calf at first makes 1 lb. of gain for each 7 or 8 lb. of milk fed; at about a month old the ratio is approximately 1 lb. to 10 lb. of milk, and at two months 1 to 12. At six weeks a good calf, weighing 80 lb. at birth, may reach 160 to 180 lb. live weight, giving a carcase of 100 to 110 lb. weighed with the skin on. (2)

The peculiar and agreeable flavour and texture of real veal

depended upon the all milk diet of the fattening calf. The pallor of true veal was due, at least in part, to the anæmia a dietary of milk alone and too long continued causes in the young of most mammals.

Some specialists in veal production deliberately intensified this anæmia by repeated bleeding of the calf. This custom did not meet with universal approval:

" The old practice of bleeding veal calves, with the idea of whitening the flesh, was of extremely doubtful efficiency and, apart from humane considerations, is not to be recommended." (3)

At the present time it would be uneconomic to use such large quantities of milk to produce true veal even were there an open and luxury market to absorb the product. True veal, then, is not being produced to-day and the flesh from the so-called " veal calves " hung in the butchers' shops is of a quite different type and of far inferior quality.

Veal is, in fact, mainly of historical interest at the present time and so also are two other classes of fat cattle, frequently referred to in pre-war publications dealing with beef production. These two classes were (1) Baby beef and (2) Beefling.

(1) *Baby beef* is obtained from " . . . young cattle that have been fattened while still in rapid growth—*i.e.* they have not passed through a definite ' store period ' but have been fed somewhat intensively from birth. They reach the meat market at from twelve to twenty months old, and usually scale from 6 to 10 cwt. live weight." (4)

(2) *Beeflings* are cattle rather older than baby beeves, but still under two years of age, and weighing 10–12 cwt. when slaughtered.

According to Garner, (5) " For baby beef production much the same conditions are required as for veal, namely, constant growth and fattening without any check; this is only achieved when the calves are fattened on the farm on which they are bred, since any movement from one farm to another often hinders growth. Thus the baby beef production may be an important side-line to the dairy industry, but this is only possible in the case of dual-purpose stock, the pure dairy stock being unsuitable for fattening. Of the dual-purpose breeds, the Red Poll stands out as being ideal for baby beef production. First, the stock fatten very readily at young ages, and, secondly, the conditions prevailing on the farms in which Red Polls are kept lend themselves to baby beef production . . . Baby beef stock are kept entirely indoors, never on grass, they are fattened on arable land crops (summer and winter) . . . The calves are usually bucket fed."

These two classes of beef cattle, baby beef and beefling, noteworthy for early maturity, light weight, and high quality, are not being produced at the present time. Their production, like that of veal, ceased with the war.

" The shortage of concentrated foods prohibited the production of baby beef, though no regulations appeared on the subject . . . for baby beef production, cattle were fed liberally with concentrated foods from birth until sold fat. This produced quality meat but quantity was the demand during war-time. In a similar way, the production of beeflings disappeared except for the cases where the animals intended for mature beef naturally got fat." (6)

For purposes of discussion the fattening of *mature* cattle may be separated into two fairly clear cut divisions. There is the winter feeding of cattle in courts, stalls, or byres; and the summer fattening of cattle on pasture.

In the past, winter feeding resulted in the production of much first-class beef. It would be untrue to suggest to-day, what with the scarcity and high cost of feeding stuffs, that the quality is quite so good. Moreover, neither in the past nor in the present is there any clear evidence that winter beef production is in itself at all a profitable proposition.

There are, it is true, certain districts where the winter fattening of cattle has continued, although over wide areas of the country dairy cows are now kept in buildings originally designed for the winter fattening of beef cattle. Particularly with the " milking parlour " system of dairying, it is not too difficult to make this husbandry conversion. In most cases where the change could conveniently be made it *has* been made, and it is mainly on farms where the buildings cannot be easily adapted to comply with the enactments of the Milk and Dairies Order that the winter fattening of cattle continues. There are certain important exceptions to the above statement. This will become evident when discussing the production of winter fed beef as a by-product of dung on many of the larger arable farms.

Certain districts, in the past, have rather prided themselves on producing high quality, winter-fed beef. The North-East corner of Scotland—particularly Aberdeenshire—was one such area. There was a certain element of competitive rivalry in producing the finest type of finished cattle, especially about Christmas time. To a modified extent the tradition persists in that district to this day. It is usually claimed by the feeders that they are operating at a profit and there are, undoubtedly, some farmers who, presumably by a special degree of skill or knowledge, appear to achieve a satisfactory measure of financial success where others fail. That the majority *do* fail is shown beyond doubt by the results of recent economic surveys conducted throughout the whole of Britain. Nor is the unprofitability of winter beef production a novel phenomenon of post-war times. It has been going on for far longer than that as the following selection of quotations plainly shows:

Year 1919.—" It may be said without hesitation that no practice is more typical of empirical British industry than that of winter beef production. Its produce ' Roast Beef ' is supremely typical of our home life, and yet, wheat growing possibly excepted, few items in our agricultural practice have brought more men to financial ruin." (7)

1928.—" It is clear that a very considerable part of our winter beef production is not, in itself, remunerative." (8)

1945.—" Collected experiences of war-time feeding of cattle in Wales over three consecutive summers and two winter periods have led to the conclusion that while pasture feeding has been moderately profitable, yard feeding has shown direct profits only in a small number of cases." (9)

1949.—" . . . it is generally agreed in the arable districts of Scotland that if you can turn over your cattle so that they cover your costs, and do no more than give you the dung for the cost of handling, you are doing as well as you have any right to expect." (10)

Recently, Wheldon and Hall (11) have given summaries of eight independent agricultural economic studies conducted in very widely distributed districts of the country. In every case these studies, conducted by professional economists, reveal a direct loss on winter beef production. The summaries, in more detail, are as follows, references to the original sources being available in Wheldon and Hall's paper. (11)

" Messrs. D. H. Dinsdale and J. B. Butler report an average

loss per head of £4. 18s. 5d. for 1,100 winter-fed cattle in Northumberland in 1944–45.

2. J. B. Butler—an average loss per head of £3. 4s. 5d. on 800 winter-fed cattle in Northumberland in 1945–46.

3. J. B. Butler—an average loss per head of £1. 6s. 8d. on 530 winter-fed cattle in Northumberland in 1946–47.

4. S. T. Morris—an average loss of just over £4 per head for 215 winter-fed cattle in Devon and Cornwall.

5. R. E. Jeffrey—an average loss of £4. 1s. 9d. per head for 336 winter-fed cattle in Worcester and Hereford in 1948–49.

6. J. A. MacLennan—an average loss of £7. 9s. 6d. per head on 1,522 cattle in S.E. Scotland.

7. J. D. Nutt and J. A. MacLennan—an average loss of £1. 8s. 3d. per head on 3,093 winter-fed cattle in S.E. Scotland.

8. D. J. G. Heggie—an average loss per head of £2. 6s. 5d. for 879 animals in the North of Scotland."

It seems justifiable, in view of this evidence, to conclude that in general, winter beef production is to-day, as it has been in the recent past, a quite unprofitable proposition. Doubtless there are exceptions to this general statement because there do appear to be certain farmers producing winter beef and doing so, or at least claiming to do so, at a profit.

Rather a greater number of farmers, while admitting to a direct loss on cattle fattened indoors during winter, continue the practice for the sake of the dung the cattle make. The economic question at issue then becomes rather what value should be put upon dung than what monetary loss is incurred by the cattle.

The actual value of dung may be considered from two distinct angles—biological and financial. As regards the first—the biological—there is the Biodynamic School of thought in agriculture that would—if I understand its theories rightly—maintain that in a sound system of balanced husbandry there can be no satisfactory substitute for dung. Apart altogether from the somewhat mystical conceptions of Biodynamic theory, there is a certain virtue of completeness in dung that is reassuring. Agricultural chemical analysis, at times somewhat crude chemically, and inevitably and always incomplete, may do but scant justice to dung. There may be more in it than can be accounted for in routine analysis and indeed some novel lines of research—into Vitamin B_{12} for example—suggest that this may well be so.

On the contrary, it can hardly be maintained that dung is the absolute essential to good farming it was once thought to be. There have, within more recent years, been too many examples to the contrary. Both knowledge and use of alternatives to dung in maintaining the fertility of arable land have increased greatly. Artificial manures are used more systematically and with a greater discretion. Again, the extension of ley farming has offered the ploughed-in ley as a substitute for dung in the maintenance of soil fertility and humus content. Some have even advocated the growing of leys especially for this very purpose.

On the whole the verdict on dung, from the biological point of view, would seem to be that while eminently useful there is no sound proof, as yet, that it is in any way essential. If this view be accepted then it merely remains to attempt to put a value upon dung in comparison with other material sources of soil fertility. Mr. W. H. Long, among others, has tried to do so. His conclusion is that, broadly speaking, what is lost on the winter beef roundabouts is made up, and perhaps a little more than made up, on the manurial swings.

" Experiments at Saxmundham on the value of the increased crops grown by using farmyard manure suggest that at 1943–44 prices the value of dung was 45s. per ton. The quantity of dung made should be not less than one ton per beast per month, and on a five-month feeding period the value of the dung should usually, therefore, be enough at least to offset the cash loss on feeding." (12)

Dung is reputed to be of especial value to the potato crop although I must confess that I know of at least one successful potato merchant who grows a vast acreage without any dung at all. That, however, is a rather exceptional case and the majority of potato growers use large quantities of dung. Thus, Mr. J. A. Stodart writes of East Lothian in Scotland:

" . . . the potato crop is the backbone of this great arable farming county ", and that " the dung-midden is the nerve centre of it all". (10)

To produce that dung, large numbers of cattle—usually well-grown and mature Irish store cattle—are fed under cover or in yards. As to the actual profit or loss on these cattle:

" Naturally it depends on the value placed on the dung that the cattle leave behind them; if you care to inflate the value of

that, you coax yourself into thinking your cattle have done very
well by you." (10)

It is, then, abundantly clear that the whole question of winter
beef production is bound up with the presumed value of dung in
increasing the yield and profit of important cash crops.
Naturally, dung, in this connection, must be, to a certain degree,
in competition with other forms of fertiliser. It might even be
suggested that an effective subsidy on artificial manures might,
by discouraging dung making and in consequence cattle feeding,
lead to an even greater scarcity of winter-fed beef!

The apparently wasteful systems of feeding that used to be
associated with winter beef production were also bound up with
this question of dung. Cattle fed on the produce of a farm and
on that alone can conserve the farm's fertility, but it is difficult
to conceive how they can increase it. Granted that feeding
cattle, as contrasted with dairy cattle, will leave more fertility
behind simply because they take less away; nevertheless, even
feeding cattle fed on home-produced crops and on these alone,
will tend to carry away a farm's fertility no matter at how slow a
rate.

But feed these same cattle lavishly on feeding stuffs imported
on to the farm, in many cases imported into the country, and the
fertility situation is entirely altered. The dung left by cattle fed
and fattened on this more generous principle will not merely
conserve fertility, it will actually add to it. In times, therefore,
when the only possible supplements or alternatives to farmyard
manure were " bones, ashes, shoddy and soot " (13) " wasteful "
feeding of cattle, while genuinely wasteful so far as the actual
fattening of the cattle themselves was concerned, was very far
from wasteful in relation to the general fertility level of the farm
upon which they were fed. The case was quite the reverse.
" Wasteful " feeding of cattle in the times when guano was a
novelty and other effective forms of artificial fertiliser undreamt
of or unused, was a sign of high farming. So long as the value
of the increased yields of cereals or other cash crops outbalanced
any loss upon the feeding cattle, that loss was justifiable. When,
subsequent to 1875, corn production in Britain ceased to pay,
this justification of the lavish and at least superficially quite
uneconomic system of feeding cattle was swept away. There is
an old saying " Up Horn—Down Corn! " It would be more

14

true to say in general, as it was certainly true to say of British farming in the last quarter of the nineteenth century, that once Corn went down, Horn followed. These considerations should be kept in mind when reading modern criticism of the generous and apparently wasteful feeding of oil cake to cattle in earlier times.

Somewhat similar considerations apply to the old practice of feeding turnips in huge quantity to fattening cattle. When the root break formed an essential element in the Norfolk four-course rotation, the turnips were there to be eaten. That is not to imply that in all cases they were *grown* to be eaten. The root break replaced the bare fallow, so that it is evident that the primary object in root cultivation was to clean land and not to feed cattle. The cleanliness of land, like the fertility of dung, was repayed financially by the larger yield from the cereal cash crop. Once cereals ceased to pay, then the main reason for root cultivation, and the utilisation by feeding cattle of the roots grown, ceased also. Nevertheless, in days when cereals *did* pay and when artificial manures were in guanic infancy, then the feeding of cattle on great quantities of oil cake and roots was a sensible procedure in the general management of an integrated farm. Although not, admittedly, as a special device to make a direct cash profit off the winter feeding of cattle. But was it, in fact, ever so devised?

It is the accepted custom of the agricultural economist to separate out one farm activity and to contrast its relative profitability with that of others. In practice, however, what the farmer is concerned with is a profitable farm. So long as the farm as a whole is profitable and, by conservation of fertility, is likely to remain profitable, it is of much less moment to the farmer than it is to the economist whether one section or another of the complete farming enterprise pays or fails to pay. These considerations are elaborated here because the general conclusion that might be gathered from the economic studies of the winter feeding of cattle is that farmers who fattened cattle during winter both are and were rather foolish to do so. Yet one has met farmers who did so or who continue to do so who are very far from being fools!

These preliminary remarks may serve to introduce the methods of winter feeding of cattle in former times and the changes that have been brought about by the pressure of economic circumstances up to the present day.

" Farmers who belong to the ' old school ' still feed large quantities of roots up to 168 lb. or even 224 lb. (sliced) daily, a little hay and 4 or 5 lb. of both linseed and undecorticated cotton cakes daily. This has been shown to be a very wasteful system of feeding, . . . " (14)

This criticism of what might be termed the classical English, often referred to as the Norfolk system, must be judged in relation to the considerations already referred to in which it is suggested that the Norfolk system of feeding cattle was quite a natural outcome of the four-course rotational system of farming that originated in the same county. The outstanding advantage of the Norfolk four-course rotation was that it enabled England to increase its cereal output without soil exhaustion, an important thing in its time.

But to-day there are so many other means of achieving the same objects. For instance, sugar beet cultivation and selective herbicides have, to a great extent, destroyed the land cleansing monopoly of turnips and associated root crops such as mangolds and swedes. Artificial fertilisers have destroyed the monopoly of the fertility enhancing value of dung enriched by the manurial residue of oil seed cakes. The Norfolk system of cattle feeding produced fine cattle, clean land, and fertile fields in its time, but that time is not our time. Consequently, much of the research work dealing with feeding cattle presently in progress is concerned with a search for home-grown substitutes for roots, especially one less expensive and laborious to grow and to feed.

Certainly at its highest development the indoor feeding of cattle on a basic ration of turnips was indeed laborious. Thus, dealing with the duties of the cattleman of his time, M'Combie wrote: (15)

" They must not be oppressed with having too many in charge, or the owner will suffer by his ill-judged parsimony. From August to November a man may take care of, and pull turnips for, thirty cattle very well, or a few more, if the cattle are loose; but when the day gets short, twenty to twenty-five are as many as one man can feed, to do them justice, if tied up."

Fine results were got in this old, laborious way. Prime beef was produced on very simple and homely rations. Yet the proposition of one able-bodied man acting nursemaid to a score of feeding cattle is, with the modern cost of labour, hopeless as an economic proposition.   It is still possible with pedigreed breeding stock; it cannot hope to survive in the modern production of commercial beef.

Apart from the laborious method of the individual care and feeding of beef cattle customary in M'Combie's time and so closely interwoven with turnip feeding, the wider subject of turnip cultivation has been attacked by a succession of economists ever since 1918.   Certainly, the steep rise in agricultural wage levels which occurred during the First World War, to be far exceeded by that of the Second World War, has provided ample ammunition for those launching the offensive.   Root cultivation involves much manual labour and manual labour has become expensive but, to conclude this paragraph on a note of inquiry, are the labour costs of turnip cultivation which the agricultural economists condemn, any greater than those of sugar beet cultivation which the same economists frequently applaud? Might it not be argued that the economic trouble with the turnip crop is not that its cultivation is too costly but rather that the final product—meat—into which it is converted, is possibly too cheap?

Admittedly, however, if winter fed beef of as good quality can be produced more cheaply by feeding stuffs other than turnips it would be mere stubborn conservatism to cling to roots.

The possibilities of silage in this respect certainly deserve to be explored and within recent years there has been no lack of energetic exploration.   Professor J. Morrison of the University of Belfast, Northern Ireland, has published some encouraging results on this subject. (16)

In one experiment, Shorthorn crosses of about 10 cwt. live-weight in forward store condition were fed grass silage at the rate of 112 lb. daily.   They gained 2·8 lb. daily between January 3rd and March 14th, killing out at SS, S or A1 at an average of 60 per cent.   The number of cattle (two groups of five) was small and they scoured rather badly but, on the whole, silage proved a satisfactory fattening ration equal to a ration in which silage was replaced partially by oats.   The age of the cattle used in this experiment is not stated.   Apparently they were fairly mature, since the experiment was repeated subsequently with cattle of

younger age. (17) This second experiment also gave good
results.

Work along similar lines has been in progress for some years at
the North of Scotland College of Agriculture, Aberdeen, where
comparative feeding trials between silage of varying quality and
the classical Aberdeenshire cattle feeding ration of turnips and oat
straw have been conducted in an exhilarating atmosphere of
forthright controversy and debate. Silage has come out quite
well from what has proved a veritable contest and in general
the work at Aberdeen confirms that carried out at Belfast.
There is, in fact, no apparent reason, theoretically, why silage, of
proved utility in milk production, should not be equally valuable
in the production of beef. Its economic advantages, if any, will
depend largely on the yields per acre of grass silage compared
with that of alternative crops, for example, swedes. This point
has been brought out clearly by Dodsworth and Campbell in a
recent publication. (18)

It has been asserted frequently that silage-fed cattle " kill out "
poorly; in other words, that the estimate formed by the grader's
eye tends to be more flattering than the ultimate verdict of the
scales. At least a partial explanation of this tendency may
be found in the observation made by the Aberdeen workers that:

" . . . cattle fed solely on silage build up a bigger ' gut fill ', to
the extent of 40 lb. ($\pm$11), than similar cattle fed on swedes and
straw." (19)

In these Aberdeen experiments it was further found that silage
made from grass cut at grazing stage and before " shooting "
gave better production results as regards fattening than silage
made from grass after the grass had " shot ". Possibly, the
feeding of dried grass—were it economic to use—would have
given production results that were even better.

There can be no doubt that grass, in one form or another, and
at one season or another, offers what is perhaps the most promising
means at the present time of increasing beef production in this
country. That idea is, of course, very far from new, and most of
the theoretical basis on which practical application can be based
was worked out at Cambridge and at Aberystwyth a good many
years ago now. Thus, Wood and Newman wrote in 1928 that:

" It has been shown quite recently, at Cambridge, that grass
not more than a fortnight, or, possibly, three weeks old, possesses,

when dried, the composition, digestibility and nutritive value of bean meal or linseed cake. It is, in fact, a concentrated food. If, however, grass is allowed to grow long, it becomes more fibrous and indigestible. Long grass, like hay, is a coarse fodder." (20)

In spite of a vast amount of work done on the subject of grass and grassland since that time, the above quotation still contains the really important facts regarding grass and its preservation.

Presumably the underlying economic difficulty of applying that knowledge to the profitable fattening of cattle during winter is that the more nearly grass approaches the composition of a concentrate when harvested, the more expensive it is to harvest. With the associated motives of increasing yield per acre and decreasing cost per ton, there is therefore a constant economic temptation to delay harvesting. In consequence, dried grass frequently and in practice has a composition little superior to that of good silage, and silage is found, when analysed, to be not so very much better than a sample of good hay. The whole question is really one of economics rather than of production, no matter whether that production be of grassland or of beef.

A further possibility in the winter fattening of cattle is to use them rather in the nature of farm scavengers on arable farms. At first sight such a suggestion seems almost sacrilege to the fine breeds of beef cattle this country has produced.

On the other hand, it may well be that in the feeding-stuff plethora of pre-war days we were tending to forget the true agricultural purpose for which ruminants are so ideally designed. Cattle, particularly dairy cattle, were coming to be fed on food that was certainly better suited to poultry or to pigs.

Actually, the true and historical purpose of the ruminant in animal husbandry is to convert grass and roughage, upon which non-ruminants cannot live, let alone profitably produce, into animal food-stuffs, be they of meat or from dairy, of direct importance to the optimum nutrition of mankind. It may not be either economic or necessary to grow roughage specially designed for the feeding of ruminants. On the other hand, the roughage resulting from the cultivation of crops grown primarily for direct human consumption, or for the feeding of pigs and poultry, should not be wasted. The ploughing in of crop residues or the burning of straw may be fashionable. These practices may, superficially, appear economic. Perhaps, on a short term basis they may be so. Yet surely it would be more sensible and more productive of real wealth to pass the maximum quantity of crop residues through some species of ruminant, thus adding to the variety and health value of human food.

The crux of the argument would seem to be this. There is a present shortage of concentrated food on which to feed livestock. That shortage is quite likely to continue and in any competition for the available supplies beef cattle are quite unlikely to achieve a priority position. Therefore, if we are to have winter-fed beef in future, we may have to drop all idea of returning to the pre-war objective of early maturing cattle, fed to fit consumers' preference on concentrated food. Although to many it may seem a retrograde step, we may have to return to the old practice of fattening maturer cattle on roughage or on roots. More modern crop by-products, such as those of the sugar beet, may well come to replace much of the root crop grown specifically for cattle feeding.

In this respect, winter beef production, if we are to have winter beef production, may have to be based very largely on mature beasts acting as farm scavengers. For example, Mr. Frank Garner, at the 1949 summer meeting of the British Society of Animal Production held in Cambridge, told how he had fed cattle successfully on market garden surpluses. He had fed cattle on parsnips and carrots. He had fed them on cabbages. He had even fed them upon onions! Along such lines—the feeding of crop residues and unsaleable surpluses to fairly mature cattle—there would seem to be a hopeful possibility of the economical production of winter beef.

If that be true, and there is every indication that it may have to be true—since, unless the costs of winter-fed beef are substantially reduced, its production may still further decline—then a great part of the art associated with the winter feeding of cattle may have to go by the board.

In addition to the old art, a good deal of the more recent scientific method of feeding beef cattle may have to go too. Actually the method is not, in its fundamental principles, so very recent. Nor is it, despite a great array of tables, equations, calculations, and technical phrases, so very scientific. The system of rationing for beef production is applicable mainly to winter beef production, since it is very difficult to make the necessary calculations when cattle are on grass. Such calculations have been made, but in many cases they are little better than shrewd guesses. In winter beef production, however, the actual food consumption of the animal can be directly ascertained, and the complications due to estimations of energy expenditure during grazing do not arise.

Even so, the accuracy of the rationing is more apparent than real. It is based on three main concepts: dry matter content, starch equivalent, and digestible protein. This is not the place to go into a detailed criticism of these conceptions except to say that, some fifty or more years ago, they were doubtless legitimate applications of the nutritional physiology of that period to farming practice. Contemporary physiological teaching, in the days when the old German agricultural scientists, Wolff, Kellner and their associates formulated their theories, was that—given a sufficiency of carbohydrate, fat, protein, minerals, and water in the diet—then an animal's food requirements were fully met. It was, however, shown by Hopkins and others in the early years of this century that no animal would live, let alone produce, on such a ration when actually fed it. A passage from Hopkins' classical paper (21) published in 1906 is well worth quoting in this connection. He wrote there:

"No animal can live on a mixture of pure protein, fat and carbohydrate, and, even when the necessary inorganic material is carefully supplied, the animal still cannot flourish. The animal body is adjusted to live either upon plant tissues or other animals, and these contain countless substances other than protein, carbohydrates and fats."

It would seem, therefore, that the so-called "scientific" method of feeding farm animals in general and of beef cattle in particular, being based on somewhat out-of-date physiology, must of itself be a trifle out-dated. Nevertheless it continues to receive official recognition, approval, and wide publicity, since the official bulletin on the subject (17) has run through no fewer than twelve editions between 1920 and 1952. Dr. H. E. Woodman, of the School of Agriculture, Cambridge, has been responsible for the sixth and subsequent editions and has succeeded in introducing some order and clarity into what is fundamentally a confused subject. Those desiring further information should consult the Bulletin already referred to. (22)

In any case, an exact system of rationing—even were it based on modern physiology—must assume a certain range of available feeding stuffs from which to choose, and must also assume the practicability of adjusting the ration to suit the productive capacity of the animal. To-day, with the choice of feeding stuffs so much more restricted than in the pre-war period, it may on the contrary become necessary to permit the production rate of the animal—live-weight increase in the case of beef cattle—to adjust itself, as it were automatically, to the nutritional plane provided by the available food. Improvisation, in many cases, may have to take the place of attempted calculation. One probable outcome of the more restricted range of feeding stuffs is that when cattle are fattened they may fatten more slowly. Yet they may, in the end, fatten quite as cheaply. Given rather more time, they will still make beef.

REFERENCES

(1) Watson, J. A. S., Cameron, J., and Garrod, G. H. (1926). " The Cattle Breeders' Handbook " (London).

(2) *Ibid.*, p. 141.

(3) *Ibid.*, p. 142.

(4) *Ibid.*, p. 126.

(5) Garner, F. (1946). " The Cattle of Britain," p. 118 (London).

(6) *Ibid.*, p. 148.

(7) Mackenzie, K. J. J. (1919). " Cattle and the Future of Beef Production in Britain," p. 34 (Cambridge).

(8) Wood, T. B., and Newman, L. F. (1928). " Beef Production in Great Britain," p. 15 (Liverpool).

(9) Thomas, W. J. (1945). *Agriculture*, **52**, 349.

(10) Stodart, J. A. (1949). *Agriculture*, **56**, 77.

(11) Wheldon, R. W., and Hall, J. S. (1950). " Beef Production," *Farming*, **4**, 210.

(12) Long W. H. (1949). " Some economic aspects of bullock feeding," *Agriculture*, **56**, 244.

(13) Watson, J. A. S., and More, J. A. (1949). " Agriculture," p. 74, 9th Ed. (London).

(14) Garner, F. (1946). *Ibid.*, p. 84.

(15) M'Combie, W. (1886). " Cattle and Cattle Breeders," p. 26, 4th Ed. (Edinburgh).

(16) Morrison, J., and Heaney, I. H. (1949). " Grass silage for winter fattening of bullocks," *Agriculture*, **56**, 71.

(17) Morrison, J., and Stephenson, W. A. (1950). " Winter fattening of bullocks with grass silage," *Agriculture*, **57**, 251.

(18) Dodsworth, T. L., and Campbell, W. H. McK. (1952). " Studies on the productivity of first year ley grass when cut at different stages of growth, ensiled and fed to beef cattle," *J. Brit. Grassland Soc.*, **7**, 151.

(19) Dodsworth, T. L., and Campbell, W. H. McK. (1952). " Report on an experiment to compare the fattening values, for beef cattle, of silages made from grass cut at different stages of growth," *J. Agric. Sci.*, **42**, 402.

(20) Wood, T. B., and Newman, L. F. (1928). *Ibid.*, p. 20.

(21) Hopkins, F. G. (1906). Quoted by Maymard, L. A. (1951). " Animal Nutrition," p. 169.

(22) Woodman, W. F. (1952). " Rations for Livestock," *Bul.* No. 48, Min. of Agric. H.M.S.O.

Chapter Fourteen
CATTLE FATTENING — SUMMER

In comparing winter and summer beef production, it may in general be conceded that while winter fed beef is of somewhat better quality, summer fed beef is a good deal cheaper to produce. This, the economic aspect, seems to be the crux of the whole affair. It is generally agreed that at present price levels beef can still be produced off grassland at a profit. Recent studies of a number of economists give support to that conclusion.

In the preceding chapter dealing with winter beef production, figures were quoted showing clearly that, were it not for the manurial value attributed to dung, winter beef production would, in the majority of cases, be conducted at a loss. If, therefore, there has been a profit in winter beef production, it has seldom been a direct profit on the main product, beef, but rather an indirect profit on the by-product, dung.

The economic outlook as regards grassland beef production is more favourable. Recent figures have been collected, summarised, and published by Wheldon and Hall. (1) Their main conclusion, supported by the results of economic studies is that:

" The following summary of grass fattening costs so far published indicates that winter fattening losses can be turned into profits by grass finishing.

1. J. B. Butler reports an average profit of £3. 10s. 2d. per head on 904 animals wintered on Northumberland farms in 1946–47 and grass fattened in the summer of 1947.

2. D. H. Dinsdale and E. M. Carpenter report an average profit of £8. 6s. 0d. per head on 924 farms," (apparently a misprint for " animals ") " for cattle store wintered 1947–48 and grass finished 1948.

3. A. J. Wynne found that for grass feeding in East Midlands there was an average profit of £4. 5s. 0d. per head in 1946 for 1,348 cattle and an average profit of £3. 1s. 0d. per head in 1947 for 758 cattle.

4. D. J. G. Heggie publishes a preliminary report comparing winter and summer fattening costs and reveals that for groups of farms in the North of Scotland an average profit of £6. 2s. 3d.

per head has been obtained on a limited group of farms that have changed over to winter fed stores and grass finishing."

Agricultural economics is such a very complex subject, however, that it would be wrong to assume from these studies alone, excellent and useful as they are, that winter beef production being unprofitable is therefore something to be discouraged and summer beef production being profitable, is something to be praised. The question is not quite so simple as all that. For one thing the profit on summer beef production appears attractive mainly in comparison with the loss on winter beef production. In itself that profit is not so very impressive. Consider, for example, the figures worked out by Wynne for the East Midland region, an average profit per head of £4. 5s. od. in 1946 and of £3. 1s. od. in 1947. Now, even on the best of land and pasture, it requires one acre to fatten one cattle beast, and, subsequent to 1939, a profit of £3–£4 an acre off good land and during the most naturally productive season of the year is nothing to boast of.

" The capital involved in bullock feeding is enormous; there is no other money turned over for so little interest as that employed in cattle grazing." (2)

Probably any other form of crop or animal husbandry would do rather better. Of course, let one man own or rent sufficient acres, and let him have access to sufficient working capital to purchase the cattle to correspond with those acres, then he may do very well for himself and do it, moreover, in a relatively pleasant and leisurely manner. But for the small man with limited acreage a profit of £3 or so per acre won't do at all. On a small farm it requires a much higher profit per acre to support a modern family.

There is really but little excuse in a book of this kind to labour such a point. I do so only for the one reason and I think it is a good and sufficient reason. Because the profit and loss account of summer beef production compares rather favourably with that of winter beef production, it might be imagined or suggested that summer beef production is on that account a desirable farming operation. Compared to barley, dairying, or even to sheep I don't think it can really be held to be so. Beef is slow and expensive to produce. No beef, not even summer fed beef, can ever be cheap and pay.

Nevertheless, under modern conditions the fattening of cattle on summer pastures *does* hold more promise than their winter fattening in courts or byres. Indeed, even previous to 1939, it had come to be regarded as the most economic—indeed, the only economic—method of fattening cattle at all. The greater economy of summer fattening might, indeed, be deduced from the first principles of animal husbandry. Where herbivorous animals are concerned, summer production, at least in this country, must always be more economic. The cheapest method of feeding a herbivorous animal must always be to put it where its food grows and let it do its own harvesting.

In the past, two economic circumstances militated against an extension of grassland beef production in Britain. One was a relative scarcity of suitable beef stores; the other an autumnal glut of grass-fed beef. Store cattle, of the right type, were apt to be over-dear in spring. Then, with the coming of autumn, too many cattle were slaughtered in too short a period, so that beef prices fell. It might happen, and on occasion *did* happen, that cattle cost more in spring as stores than they fetched in autumn after a summer's grazing. Yet neither of these two economic obstructions to an extension of grassland beef production is insuperable.

An increased cattle population on both hill and marginal land, by bringing store cattle supply into more reasonable relation with summer grazier's demands, would remove what has always proved to be one of the greatest obstacles to the maximum utilisation of grassland for the production of beef.

Moreover, in these days of controlled and guaranteed prices there is no reason for the price of beef to fall merely because of seasonal abundance. We are still very inclined to carry the hangover of depression and free markets into the more modern circumstances of agricultural prosperity and controlled trading. When increased supply led almost inevitably to a fall in prices already too low for sustained and profitable production—then, indeed, a flooded seasonal market was something the producer might justifiably dread.

To-day, circumstances are different. There is a genuine scarcity of livestock produce, especially of meat, in this country, that is likely to be prolonged. A return to the days of abundant and cheap meat imports seems exceedingly remote. Consequently, the marketing of beef, guided by official price control, could be quite easily regulated to encourage rather than to restrict the maximum production of beef off summer grazing— the system offering the best prospects of an economic supply under the conditions prevailing since the war.

It has on occasion been argued that concentration of beef production on grassland is a retrograde step. In a sense that argument is true since, until relatively recent times, all beef was grass-fed beef. It was the introduction of the turnip crop and of oil seed residues as feeds for cattle that enabled winter fattening and the sale of fresh beef in quantity during the winter and spring months. Before the latter half of the eighteenth century it was in general only in autumn that finished, fresh beef was in supply. Beef surplus to the requirements of fresh beef consumption at that season was preserved salted, and the salting of beef had the importance of a major industry.

In modern meat preservation ice has replaced salt, and while chilled or frozen beef is—other things being equal—inferior to fresh beef, it is quite as certainly preferable to salted beef.

The economic tendencies of the times appear to have been driving our beef production into the summer period. At the same time the prices offered by the Ministry of Food have aimed to encourage a spreading of beef supplies throughout the year, by offering appreciably higher prices at seasons other than those of the autumn glut. This question of the seasonal glut of grass-fed beef; of the advisability or inadvisability of encouraging it; and of the capital expenditure in the way of increased abattoir and refrigerator space required if it were to be encouraged; all these questions being matters of policy rather than of production are discussed more fully in the final chapter of this book.

Meanwhile on the production side there can be no doubt that good beef can be, has been, and still is produced off summer pasture. Such beef may not have quite the prime quality of the best winter fed beef. It is likely, for example, to have a more pronounced yellow coloration of the fat, a character in beef to which the British consumer was wont to object. It is unlikely, however, that the modern British consumer, after more than a decade of reduced beef supply and an even greater deterioration in general level of beef quality, is at all likely to be over-particular on such minor points.

A general system of grassland beef production, well suited to the conditions of to-day, was outlined by Mr. W. S. Mansfield when addressing the British Society of Animal Production in 1949. (3) He was referring specifically to the treatment of beef stores made available from the dairy industry, particularly from dual-purpose dairy cattle. What he said, however, is applicable also to the beef stores from hill cattle.

"From the national point of view", Mr. Mansfield said, "(and I believe also from the farmers' point of view) the ideal way of turning calves of these types into beef is to rear them on a high plane of nutrition until they are eight months old, to follow with a store period of some eighteen months when the object should be just to keep them growing, feeding them practically nothing but hay, straw and possibly a few roots in the winter and grass in the summer, and finally to fatten them on grass, and by grass of course I include leys. In this way cattle weighing 11–12 cwt. at two and a half years old can be obtained with a minimum expenditure of concentrates . . . "

These conclusions of Mr. Mansfield are based on the progress reports of the Cambridge University Farm cattle rearing experiments already discussed in Chapter XII. The importance of these experiments has already been stressed.

The value of a good start as a calf has also been sufficiently enlarged upon. Something more, however, requires to be said on the treatment of beef stores that are to be finished on grass, for their management during winter makes all the difference to their progress on pasture in the following summer.

Cattle that are to be grazed in summer should not be too well done during the previous winter. That is, perhaps, the most essential point in wintering them. The idea of getting cattle into a forward condition in spring so as to give them a good start on grass was tried out fairly extensively by graziers aiming to get the cattle away fat during summer. By so doing they hoped to avoid the glut of grass-fed beef coming on the market in the autumn months. The system has never worked well in practice. Store cattle intended for grazing should have fresh air and hard rations during the previous winter. The reverse—confinement and high feeding—has repeatedly proved fatal to their subsequent progress on grass. On this subject M'Combie wrote many years ago: (4)

" If you put upon grass cattle which have been fed through the winter upon cake, corn, brewers' wash, grain or potatoes, and kept in hot byres or close strawyards, and look to them to pay a rent, you will find that they will soon make a poor man of you. This mode of feeding is unnatural. Before the animals begin to improve, three months will have passed. If half fat cattle are bought, which have been kept close in byres or strawyards, and put to grass in April or the first two weeks of May, and cold stormy weather sets in, with no covering to defend them, they will fall off so much that the purchaser will scarcely believe they are the beasts he bought. Thus he not only loses all his grass, but the beasts will be lighter at the end of three months than when they were put into the field."

There have been many practical confirmations of these facts since M'Combie's time. There have also been several experimental investigations dealing with the same subject. One such investigation conducted by the North of Scotland College of Agriculture between 1928 and 1935 dealt with the effects of different methods of wintering store cattle upon their progress on grass during the subsequent summer. Although the main subject of investigation was concerned with the relative advantages of wintering cattle inside or outside, other, nutritional, factors were also taken into consideration.

The results, in general confirmatory of M'Combie's experience, showed that the advantage lay with store cattle out-wintered and unforced. Any temporary advantages due to shelter and high feeding in winter were lost during the following summer. Cattle out-wintered on turnips and straw throve best on summer pasture.

Thus, cattle that had been tied up in byres during winter lost weight when first put out to grass in the following summer.

" When put out to grass after they ceased getting turnips, cattle tied up in a byre lost considerably in weight in the first week, whereas those wintered outside in a field lost very little, if any." (5)

Moreover, " . . . the outside field lot gave the largest total live-weight increase for the winter and summer periods and were generally ready to sell first and gave a larger dead-weight percentage." (5)

The advantage, therefore, lay with outside as compared with

inside wintering of store cattle intended for subsequent fattening off on grass. It should be added, however, that the out-wintered cattle had access to a comfortable, straw-littered open shed.

The ill effects of feeding " artificials "—*i.e.*, corn and cake, during winter to cattle intended for grazing during the following summer was clearly demonstrated in another of this series of experiments. Thus:

" The groups that got artificials in addition to turnips and straw during the winter gave much larger live-weight increases than the groups getting no artificials. On the grass, however, the groups that got no artificials in winter gave much greater live-weight increases than the groups that got artificials, even when the artificials were continued in summer." (5)

This effect of the mode of treatment of store cattle during winter upon their rate of fattening during the subsequent summer is of considerable interest not only because of its economic importance but because of its significance to biological theory. Clearly, in view of this effect, any attempt to predict the probable progress of cattle on grass requires something more than a knowledge of the animal's live-weight on which to base an estimate of maintenance requirements, and of the quality of the pasture with which to calculate probable live-weight gains. Cattle of the same live-weight and on the same pasture may react very differently because of a difference in their previous history. One reason for this may be connected with their grazing behaviour. Cattle that have been out-wintered as stores may spend a longer time grazing and a shorter time waiting at gates in the hopes of getting back to shelter. Quite evidently the behaviour of cattle on grass must make a considerable difference to their food consumption and food utilisation. In this connection we are, unfortunately, still too ignorant of what could quite easily be observed. Professor Johnstone-Wallace has very truly said:

" A knowledge of the behaviour of grazing animals when continuously on pasture is essential for a proper understanding of the principles involved in grazing management." (6)

Yet, presumably because of the over-emphasis on chemical conceptions in conventional agricultural science, we remain rather less well informed about what one might term the natural history of both grazing cattle and grazing sheep than we are of that of birds such as the greenshank or the fulmar petrel. It is, however, known, that in addition to the influence of previous treatment as stores, the class of cattle grazed—for example whether bullocks, heifers, or barren cows—will make a considerable difference to their rate of progress on the same pasture. Since the grazier's aim is to finish the cattle and to finish them on grass before the end of the grazing season, he will endeavour to stock each field with the most appropriate class of cattle. The general rule of the grazier is the best land for bullocks, the next best for heifers, and the poorest for cows.

" . . . some of the land will not finish a bullock, in which case heifers are grazed, and, if it is not good enough for them, cows are grazed." (2)

Within more recent years, some land previously thought too good for cows has been grazed by cows simply because they were the class of cattle most readily available.

" Due to the growth of the national dairy herd and to the decline in the supply of stores from hill country an enormous number of barren cows are grazed, and not so many old bullocks." (7)

There is thus a well-recognised distinction between bullocks, heifers, and barren cows considered as classes of cattle suited for summer grazing. There is also the distinction between mature and immature cattle, the grazier definitely showing preference for the former. As regards breeds and crosses between breeds, there is far more propaganda than evidence. It is frequently affirmed that Herefords and Hereford crosses are supreme, but this is denied by some graziers, particularly in Scotland, where it is frequently stated that the Hereford cross as contrasted with the Aberdeen-Angus cross flatters in the field to disappoint upon the scales. Consistent differences between breeds are almost certainly far less than is currently supposed. On the contrary the variations in the capacity of grassland to fatten cattle are undoubtedly extreme. Moreover, under modern conditions, the possibilities of ironing out these differences by supplementary feeding of the cattle have been greatly reduced.

Previous to 1939 it was customary, except on what was regarded as the best fattening pastures, to feed cotton cake or other concentrate, sometimes in amount up to 6 lb. per head daily, particularly in the latter part of the grazing season. The custom, at least in the Scottish Border counties, was to put out small individual cattle feeding boxes on the grass fields and to feed cake to the cattle grazing there. The date at which supplementary feeding commenced and the quantity of supplement fed depended upon the progress of the cattle. The aim being to get the majority if not all the cattle fat off the grass, supplementary feeding of concentrates was pushed either when the cattle were backward in progress or the pasture in growth. Where cattle were thriving in a good grass season, feeding with concentrates was both little and late. The residue of cattle that were unfinished by late autumn were either put into yards for final fattening or were sold as forward stores.

The reason for using cotton cake as a supplement to pasture, as alleged by the actual graziers, was that cotton cake, being costive, tended to firm the animals' dung. In view of what is now known of the chemical composition of pasture, with its tendency, at least early in the grazing season, to be over-rich in nitrogenous constituents in relation to its energy value, it would probably have proved more advantageous to feed a carbohydrate concentrate such as maize. That, however, at the moment is mainly of historical interest since to-day it is improbable or even impossible that either the one supplement or the other—cotton cake or maize—would be fed as a supplement to grazing beef cattle. The aim to-day is to fatten cattle on grass without concentrates.

Now, there was always a certain, rather limited proportion of the pasture lands of Britain reckoned capable of fattening cattle without the support of any supplementary food. This bullock to the acre land, this fatting pasture, was situated mainly, at least according to tradition, in the English Midlands, although not confined strictly to that region. Thus, according to Garner (8):

"The real old fattening pastures are found in many more districts than people realise: sometimes one is led to believe that the fattening pastures are only in Northamptonshire and Leicestershire, but the fattening area extends in the Midlands to Buckinghamshire, Worcestershire, Staffordshire, Herefordshire, and Lincolnshire. Various river valleys and other low-lying areas are also famous for the fattening grassland they produce, *e.g.*, the river valleys of the Severn, Trent, and the marshland extending mainly around the coastline from Somerset (Bridgwater), Pevensey Level (Sussex), Norfolk, Lincolnshire, Northumberland, and along parts of the north-east of Scotland. Thus it cannot be stated that the fattening is in any way localised."

Nevertheless, although there is considerable justification for Garner's statement, it can still be safely affirmed that the English Midlands are the classical, if not the exclusive, centre of the fattening pastures. According to Maurice Passmore:

" The Midlands have been recognised for years as the fattening pastures. I suppose because the land is so strong, or perhaps because it is where grassland management became a highly specialised part of farming." (2)

To what extent the excellence of these old fatting pastures is to be attributed to the nature of the land and to what extent to system of management is a somewhat debatable point. Management is of undeniable importance. Referring to these first-class Midland pastures of which he has had a life-long experience, Mr. Passmore has said:

" The grassland has been maintained by careful stock management; the manure was regularly ' beaten ' (*i.e.*, spread) and still is in some cases. On every farm there is the best field, and the farm usually goes into four grades. The first will finish a bullock, the next a heifer and the third a cow, and the last is store land." (7)

An interesting deduction may be made from this system of management Mr. Passmore has described. If all the farm were first-class pasturage it would, presumably, prove impossible to maintain any of it permanently in first-class condition. In other words, the excellence of the very best is protected if necessary by the sacrifice of the second and the third best. These considerations, however, appertain rather to grassland management than to the feeding of cattle. On the other hand the relative value of permanent pasture versus temporary ley is more strictly relevant to the professed subject of this book. Fortunately there is here a considerable measure of agreement.

It appears to be admitted by all practical graziers that while the highest class of permanent pasture is their ideal for the summer fattening of cattle, nevertheless permanent pasture of second quality is inferior to the best temporary ley for this purpose. There may be some conflict of opinion as to whether or not the feeding value of the best fatting permanent pasture is equalled or surpassed by the most productive types of temporary ley. As regards anything but the best, there is none. Now, that unanimity of opinion is of great importance. The area covered by permanent pasture of fattening quality is strictly limited even if we allow the extension into a number of rather widely scattered districts as Garner (8) suggests. The potential expansion of first-class temporary ley is infinitely greater. Consequently the area of the country that can be used for summer beef production is also far greater than it could otherwise be. Moreover, the use of the temporary ley allows of the pasturing of less mature cattle. Graziers always have and still do prefer matured cattle for the grazing of permanent grass. One reason for this is that anything but mature cattle are inclined to scour on such grass. Temporary ley does not have this effect. As Garner says: (8)

" It is an interesting fact, however, that while young cattle will not fatten on the first-class permanent grassland, because they scour too profusely, these younger cattle will fatten quite satisfactorily on temporary leys."

Now, while in England long tradition has given an air almost of sanctity to the best permanent pastures, that has never been the case over the greater part of Scotland, the reason being, presumably, that in the poorer country there is far less land capable of supporting really first-class permanent grass. There is a little of that land, particularly on the East coast, but not very much. Consequently, the majority of Scottish farmers were practising the temporary ley long before Stapledon began to preach it, and it was well recognised in Scotland, probably a full century ago, that the temporary ley and the fattening of cattle go well together. This, for example, is what the great M'Combie first wrote on the subject in 1875, towards the end of a long life among cattle and when in his seventieth year.

" A week's new grass in Aberdeenshire at the first of the season is worth at least two and a half upon old grass, . . ." Again:

" Where there is new grass, first year, it is a most difficult matter to get full advantage of it. There is no other grass to be compared with it for putting on beef in Aberdeenshire.

" At the middle and end of the grazing season, old grass upon fine land may improve cattle nearly as much; but if new grass is properly shifted—take the season all through, equal quality of land, and in the same condition—no second, third year, or older grass is equal to it, or will put on the same weight of meat." (9)

Whether on permanent or on temporary ley one of the major difficulties of fattening cattle on grassland is the shortness of the really productive grazing season. By the end of July the best of the season is over and so far nobody quite knows why. Discussing the utilisation of pasture, Professor S. J. Watson writes:

" Analysis and digestibility alone are not the only criteria, and pastures from late August onwards are, in practice, found to be of low productive value even if they are of good analysis. This has been attributed to the lower biological value of the protein in autumn grass as compared with spring and summer grass. This, however, cannot be the whole story since the biological value of autumn protein, though admittedly lower than spring protein, is still higher than that of many foods which are nevertheless used with every success in the winter feeding of farm animals.

" The real reason is to be sought elsewhere, it may be in the higher water content of the grass, in lower morning temperature, in higher amounts of sand in and on the herbage, acting as an irritant. Whatever it is, the fact remains that in autumn the best of pasture will not give the results which might be expected from its computed feeding value." (10)

Possibly a clue to this extraordinarily interesting and unsolved problem might be found by correlating the vagaries of season with the known variability of the finish of grazing cattle when they come to slaughter in the autumn of each year. Certainly the difference in average finish from year to year is quite pronounced. Thus, Major W. H. Warman, dealing with meat supplies during the war years of 1939–1945, stated that:

" The weight of all cattle has averaged about 570 lbs. in October in every year of the war. Cattle that we get in September are generally rather heavier, but their weights seem to depend much more on the season than on any great changes in production. For instance, in 1940, when there was a drought, the September figure was only about 575 lbs., normally it has been about 600 lbs., while in an exceptionally good year it has risen to 625 lbs. Since cattle nowadays get very few concentrates on grass, these varied weights must be attributed to seasonal influences. It is of interest to note that the variation between a good and bad

season amounts to almost half a hundredweight dead weight." (11)
It follows that in a bad grazing season, a considerable proportion
of cattle offered for grading in autumn will be in an unfinished
condition. According to Major Warman, during the war years
the situation was far from satisfactory.

" The B grades run up to 40 and 50 per cent. We have even
had 60 per cent in a year of drought. That really means that in
a normal year for two or three months in the back end from
20 to 25 per cent of the home-breds are below the standard for a
good butcher's beast. It may be that most of these cattle are
fed on land which will not fatten them properly without concentrates, which have been unobtainable." (12)

There seems no reason to suppose that the general picture
outlined by Major Warman in 1945 is any different to-day.
Nevertheless, the situation he revealed is not necessarily confined
exclusively to grass-fed cattle. In former times when winter
beef production depended on the turnip, and turnips, later in the
season, were in short supply because of a poorish crop, large
numbers of half-finished cattle used to come on the market in the
spring of the year. Possibly, in the case of grass-fed cattle the
situation might be substantially improved by the better management of grass. On some farms the summer grazing of cattle
consists in putting cattle in a grass field and leaving them there.
This system may answer well enough on the Midland fattening
pastures where stocking is regulated to suit pasture growth by
adding to or reducing the number of cattle on the first-grade
pasture. Even then, while an exact balance between stocking
and pasture growth can be struck on the first-grade pasture, this
can only be brought about by a certain degree of sacrifice of the
balance on the lower grades of pasture on the same farm.

On land of poorer quality where none of the permanent pasture
is really of fattening quality, it is probable that this system might
be supplanted with advantage by the temporary ley and the
purposeful shifting of cattle. There is nothing theoretical,
new-fangled, nor particularly " scientific " in the idea. It was
tested and tried out successfully by William M'Combie the better
part of a century ago. His methods and ideas of the best method
of grazing cattle have, moreover, a strangely modern ring.

" In regard to my own farms, I cut scarcely any hay. I pasture
almost all my own grass, and the moment the cattle's feet begin

to injure the grass, they are removed. If cattle are changed to
an old grass field, so much the better; but they will be safe on
second or third year's grass, provided the land is naturally dry.
By the 1st July, the new grass land gets consolidated, and you
are safe. New grass fields are bad to manage in another respect.
The grass comes very rapidly about the 10th June, and if you are
not a very good judge of what you are about it will get away in
a few days, become too rank, and will lose its feeding qualities
during the remainder of the season. By the middle of July it
will be nothing but withered herbage. Young grass ought to
be well eaten down, and then relieved for two or three weeks;
then return the cattle, and the grass will be as sweet as before.
It requires practice to know the number of cattle, and the proper
time to put on these cattle, to secure the full benefits of new grass.
Three days miscalculation may cause a heavy loss." (13)

The possible advantages of strip-grazing, using the modern
technical device of the electric fence, obviously deserve careful
consideration. The method is known to be advantageous in
milk production and is already widely used by commercial dairy
farmers in the summer grazing of cows. It is a method that
should answer, also, for beef. It has, in fact, been tested out
successfully at the Grassland Research Station, Stratford-on-
Avon. (14)

From what has been said in this chapter, it is clear that the
successful summer fattening of cattle depends upon a great
number of highly variable factors. First, the response of the
cattle to the same grazing will vary according to the broad class
to which the cattle belong, that is to say whether bullocks,
heifers, or cows. That response will vary also according to the
previous treatment to which the cattle have been subjected, to
their age and, presumably, to their breeding.

Secondly, the pasture will vary according to the land on which
it grows, and to the skill with which it is managed. It will vary
according to whether it is permanent pasture or temporary ley.
Broadly, it will vary according to season, and more narrowly
with the minor variations in rainfall, sunshine, and temperature
met with from day to day.

It follows that a grazier, if he hopes to be successful, must be
a master of his craft. It is a craft that looks easy, but isn't.

"The whole business is not one of just looking over the gate or sitting on a horse, but is one of very keen observation of cattle and grass." (2)

That is the art of the grazier. What of science as applied to the study of the fattening of cattle on grass? Probably, in a strictly logical sequence, the study of what might be termed the observational natural history of the grazing animal should have come first. Actually, it has tended to come much later and it is only now that we are beginning to have accurate information of how cattle behave on grass, what they do with their time there, how much grass they consume, and how long they take collecting it. Such studies cannot fail to be useful aiming as they do to give a quantitative and systematic assessment of the principles embodied in the grazier's art. The work of Johnstone-Wallace (6) is a model of its kind.

The chemical approach to the problem, as exemplified in Woodman's ingenious attempts to apply Kellner's conceptions and the official system of rationing to the very difficult circumstances of cattle on grass, is of more doubtful utility. Woodman himself summarises the main difficulties as follows: (15)

1. " It is not possible to assess with any degree of reliability the grass consumed daily by grazing animals."

2. " The energy expended by the animal in grazing is not taken into account in the standard allowance of starch equivalent for maintenance."

3. " The feeding value of grass is subject to very great variation under the influence of a variety of factors, such as the general nature of the season, the particular time of the season, and the system of pasture management."

In view of these difficulties, Dr. Woodman admits that:

" The scientific principles that largely govern the rationing of dairy cows during winter cannot be applied with the same precision when the animals are subsisting on pasture during the summer." (15)

And, of course, what applies to dairy cows in this connection applies also to fattening cattle. The grazing of cattle of any type is at the moment—and it is perhaps wiser to confess it—more of an art than a science but it is an art, nevertheless, with a sufficiently promising future.

Young leys and their skilful management, keeping a watchful eye on the progress of both grass *and* cattle, offer the greatest hope of increasing beef production in this country to-day, because, unless permanent grass is of exceptional quality, and as M'Combie put it, " on fine land ", it will not fatten cattle. The areas where such permanent " fatting " pastures are to be found are limited, and the number of cattle they are capable of fattening could never hope to satisfy the beef requirements of this nation. The temporary ley, on the contrary, with skilful management and a moderate rainfall, can be established successfully on much poorer land and over much wider districts of the country. The number of cattle that could be fattened off the temporary ley is, therefore, infinitely greater.

REFERENCES

(1) Wheldon, R. W., and Hall, J. S. (1950). " Beef Production," *Farming*, **4**, 210.

(2) Passmore, M. (1952). " Grazing—sheep and cattle," *J. of Farmers' Club*, Part 3, p. 41.

(3) Mansfield, W. S. (1949). *Brit. Soc. Anim. Prod. Rpt. Proc.* 11th Meeting, p. 26.

(4) M'Combie, W. (1886). " Cattle and Cattle-Breeders," p. 12, 4th Ed. (Edinburgh).

(5) Findlay, W. M. (1936). " Experiments at Craibstone on wintering cattle inside and outside, 1928–35," *Bull.* No. 41, p. 15, N. of Scot. Coll. Agric.

(6) Johnstone-Wallace, D. B., and Kennedy, K. (1944). " Grazing management practices and their relationship to the behaviour and grazing habits of cattle," *J. Agric. Sci.*, **34**, 190.

(7) Passmore, M. (1951). " Cattle feeding in the Midlands," *Proc. Brit. Soc. Anim. Prod.*, p. 63.

(8) Garner, F. (1946). " The Cattle of Britain," p. 85 (London).

(9) M'Combie, W. (1886). *Ibid.*, p. 21.

(10) Watson, S. J. (1949). " Feeding of Livestock," p. 123 (London).

(11) Warman, W. H. (1945). " Meat supplies," *Reports Brit. Soc. Anim. Prod.*, p. 8.

(12) *Ibid.*, p. 10.

(13) M'Combie, W. (1886). *Ibid.*, p. 22.

(14) Hughes, G. P., and Redford, R. A. (1952). " Controlled Grazing for Beef Production," *Agric.*, **58**, 505.

(15) Woodman, W. F. (1952). " Rations for Livestock," *Bull.* No. 48, p. 70, Min. of Agric. H.M.S.O.

" THERE is a wider demand for beef than for any other meat. Indeed, among a meat-eating race such as ours, there is perhaps a wider demand for beef than for any other foodstuff except bread and milk." (1)

That passage was written almost a quarter of a century ago yet, undoubtedly, the potential demand for beef in Britain is no less to-day. It may well be greater, because of the relatively increased purchasing power of what for convenience may be called the British working class. Mutton and lamb, as alternatives to beef, have never been particularly popular with British working people. In pre-war days it was the middle class that formed the main body of customers for mutton as opposed to beef and, within the last decade, the relative purchasing power and, in consequence, the economic importance of that class has been substantially reduced.

Granted, then, that the potential demand for beef exists and is likely to persist, how is that demand to be met or, to put the matter in its bluntest form, *can* it be met?

In 1938, the *per caput* consumption of beef and veal in the United Kingdom was 55 lb., a figure that compared quite favourably with that of other countries. In the same year the corresponding figure was 62 lb. for the U.S.A. and no more than 39 lb. for Western Germany and 34 lb. for the Netherlands.

By 1951 the beef consumption in Britain relative to that in other countries had altered substantially, the corresponding figures as compared with 1938 being U.K. 33 lb., U.S.A. 63 lb., Western Germany 28 lb., Netherlands 33 lb. (2)

Expressed in this way the fall in British beef consumption is not so drastic as is sometimes supposed. What has happened is that British beef consumption, as in the case of many other items of food consumption, has tended to fall very much below American standards and by doing so, approximate more closely to that of industrial countries on the continent of Europe.

British *per caput* consumption of beef has fallen from 55 lb. in 1938 to 33 lb. in 1951. The latter year was, however, one in which beef consumption in Britain was exceptionally low. It was 46 lb. in the previous year. It is fairly clear, however, that future consumption depends largely on the success or failure of negotiations designed to secure adequate supplies of beef imported to this country.

It has been the failure to secure these beef imports that has led to the reduction in British beef consumption. The reduction in beef imports has been both substantial and progressive. The relevant figures, expressed in thousands of tons, for the immediate pre-war and the post-war periods are as follows:

1938=585·4	1949=362·2
1947=507·1	1950=332·3
1948=326·6	1951=156·9

The reasons for that failure are bound up with international economic problems of the deepest significance which it is quite beyond the purpose of this book even to attempt to discuss. From the point of view of the present argument the really important point is that these problems appear likely, in a certain sense, to prove insoluble. In other words, world economics and the position of British economy in relation thereto have not only received a most thorough shaking up and mixing during the war years but have begun to settle down into a permanent pattern which is not the pre-war pattern. One evident result of this economic earthquake is that the housewife Britannia has lost her priority position in the world's beef queue. Instead of being served first she has, on occasion, been served last and there has at times been a degree of justifiable dubiety as to whether she were likely to be served at all.

The reduction and perhaps even more the uncertainty of the position regarding beef imports has compelled Britain to pay the closest attention to the maintenance and, if possible, the substantial increase of her own beef production. Faced with numerous and substantial difficulties that attention has not been without a measure of reward. Beef production in Britain *has*, in fact, risen although, so far, it has not risen sufficiently to compensate for the reduction in imports. The increase has been particularly encouraging during the last two years for which complete statistics are available. Thus, the estimated production of beef and veal in the U.K. expressed in thousands of tons,

for the immediate pre-war and for the post-war years was as
follows: (3)

1938=604·7	1949=528·2
1947=509·4	1950=633·7
1948=498·5	1951=652·0

The increase since the war years appears to be progressive as
well as substantial. That increase, however, will require to be
immensely greater if, as appears probable, a permanent decrease
in beef imports has to be compensated for by a corresponding
increase in home production. In 1938, home production of beef
was able to support certainly no more and probably less than
50 per cent of a *per caput* beef consumption of 55 lb. Even to
restore that consumption, the production of beef within Britain
would require to be roughly double that of 1938. The task is
colossal. It may prove impossible. According to some authorities it may not be worth attempting, yet, at least in modified
form, it *is* being attempted.

Other solutions might have been sought and favoured—the
acceptance without struggle of a predominantly vegetarian diet
in Britain; more dependence for meat upon sheep and less upon
cattle. Possibly even greater incentives to pig-rearing and
feeding, leading to an abundance of bacon and pork in substitution for beef, might have been adopted as official policy
were it not for the difficulty of finding food for pigs. But pigs
do not, to any great extend, consume grass, and grassland
farming in the shape of the temporary ley is an accepted canon
of modern good farming. Moreover, where dairying is devoted
to the liquid milk market and dairy by-products are unavailable
for feeding pigs, an expanding pig population is apt to be faced
by the limiting factor of progressive scarcity and cost of nitrogenous foods.

In any case, increased beef production is accepted official
policy. Apart from propaganda there are figures—in pounds,
shillings, and pence—to prove it. The guaranteed prices for
beef negotiated between the Government and Farmers' Unions
at the periodical price reviews have been considerably increased
over the last two years. The subsidy designed to encourage
calf-rearing, discontinued for a time, has been revived. Financial
encouragement to cattle breeding and rearing on hill and
marginal land has become very substantial. To-day, a hill cow

in Scotland, and to a very slightly less generous extent in England and Wales, is set off to a flying start. She receives £7 annually just for being a hill cow and another £2 if she belongs to an attested herd freed from tuberculosis. A sum of £3 annually is available to assist in providing her with winter forage. Her calf gets a bounty of £5 just for being a beef-worthy calf. There is thus a payment of £17 made by the State to anybody willing to run a healthy cow out on a hill. In addition there are numerous methods of financial assistance less direct in nature. Obviously that generosity means one thing and one thing only; that the State is desperately in need of beef and is determined to have it. In this case the State, in practice as well as in theory, and that, moreover, without a shadow of a doubt, represents the people. The average consumer in Britain to-day desires more beef, desires it keenly, and is willing to pay for his desires both directly in the shops and indirectly through taxation. The question at issue, then, is how best to satisfy his needs.

The answer, in its broadest terms, would seem to be:

1. To produce more calves,
2. To rear more calves,
3. To feed more cattle,

and to do these things in a manner sufficiently economic to maintain beef as a staple of the people's diet rather than as an occasional item on the menu of our luxury hotels.

Discussion of the first problem need not detain us very long since, as has been sufficiently indicated in earlier chapters, there are already far more calves born than are ever likely, under present conditions, to be reared. To find a method of putting a stop to this wastage of young calves—this slaughter of the innocents to the tune of over one million a year—is one of the first as it is also the most sensible and effective method of increasing the raw materials—namely the store cattle—from which beef can be made. The apologia for this bovine holocaust is that either:

    (a) The calves are not worth the rearing, or
    (b) The calves don't pay to rear.

The calf wastage is almost entirely confined to the male calves born on dairy farms. It used to be generally assumed and even to-day is frequently asserted that steer calves of the specialised dairy breeds, debarred from milk production because of their sex, are useless for beef production on account of their genes. As regards dual-purpose cattle, however, it is very generally admitted that the male calf is worth rearing for beef, as is indeed implicit in the definition of a dual-purpose cattle breed. Since one of the features of dairy history in this country within recent years has been the replacement of dual-purpose cattle by specialised dairy cattle, it might be considered that the ever-increasing calf slaughter was thereby justified. Actually, the distinction between dual-purpose and specialised dairy cattle has never been very clearly defined, is certainly exaggerated, and in any event may not be, in the end, of such fundamental importance. Thus, the most numerous breed of dual-purpose cattle in England is the Dairy Shorthorn. The most numerous breed of specialised dairy cattle is the British Friesian. Yet, as regards beef production, there seems to be little to choose between the two breeds. Indeed, in a number of recent tests, the Friesian has appeared to make beef of as good quality and at a rather faster pace.

Granted that the Friesian is, by universal consent, by far the best beef proposition among the specialised dairy breeds, are the other breeds entirely useless? The Ayrshire, in numbers the third most numerous breed of dairy cattle, dual-purpose or specialised, in Britain, is not, as has been mentioned already in this book, so entirely useless for beef production as is often supposed. From time to time, Ayrshire steers of a reasonable degree of merit have been marketed as beef. Even as regards Channel Island cattle—the Guernsey and Jersey—opinions may differ. In Britain it is customary to class these breeds as useless for beef, partly because of their yellow fat. Yet the inhabitants of Guernsey actually prefer what they call the " yellow beef " of their native cattle to the " white beef " of English breeds. (4)

Almost certainly the difference between the various dairy breeds with reference to beef production potentialities have been exaggerated, just as the more general distinction between dual-purpose and specialised dairy cattle has been exaggerated. In all breeds there are wide variations in type and conformation, far wider than any Breed Society would be prepared to admit, or the carefully selected entries at the leading Shows or Sales would lead one to believe. There is often wider variation between individuals within one breed than there is between the average of two breeds. So much so, that certain calf-rearers of experience have come to select calves suitable for rearing into beef stores on their individual conformation rather than upon their breeding.

Moreover, recent experiments on cattle rearing, particularly those in progress at Cambridge University Farm, certainly indicate that the method of rearing a calf is, with reference to its future beef-producing capacity, of quite as much importance as the breed to which it belongs. This outcome is somewhat surprising, and indeed, if confirmed, revolutionary, but does not necessarily prove that in selecting for beef as we have done in our specialised beef breeds we have been pursuing a will-o'-the-wisp. To argue the case out fully would involve more space than we can presently afford, but it would certainly appear that, *because of the limitation of concentrated foodstuffs at our disposal*, the relative advantages of cattle bred specially for beef as contrasted with those available as a by-product of the dairy have been very substantially reduced.

The facts as presently assumed may be liable to revision, but it does seem that the main advantage of cattle specially bred for beef production is that they are more rapidly maturing and of superior conformation. They reach a desirable state of finish at an earlier age and at a less weight and they carry a greater proportion of their beef in the more valuable cuts. Dairy-bred steers on the other hand are more slowly maturing and their conformation poorer. They will not attain the requisite finish until they have grown heavy and somewhat old, and, at least superficially, they would appear to carry too small a proportion of beef in the most valuable regions.

That is, in short, the main apparent difference between the beef-bred steer and the dairy-bred steer. There may be others. It used to be said and is still very widely believed that the proportion of bone to the other carcase constituents is less in beef-bred steers than in dairy-bred steers and certainly their superficial appearance gives ground for that belief. Nevertheless a comparison of skeletons and the results of dissections at the Low Temperature Research Station, Cambridge, prove this belief to be erroneous. The dairy-bred steer, whatever its weaknesses and faults may be, is not a "bag of bones" as it has frequently been miscalled. Actually, this result might have been predicted from the work of Dr. John Hammond on sheep. He found that far from the proportionate weight of inedible bone being reduced in the improved mutton breeds of sheep, that the bones of such breeds are actually both thicker and heavier than those of breeds unimproved or wild. (5)

There may, nevertheless, be other definite advantages in conformation, finish, and quality favouring the beef-bred as distinct from the dairy-bred steer. It would be extremely difficult, in view of the world-wide preference of beef cattle breeders for one or other of the three leading specialised beef cattle breeds, to believe otherwise. What is quite certain, however, is that unless the beef-bred steer is reared and fattened on a high nutritional plane its inherent advantages are unlikely to be expressed. In other words, on a medium or low nutritional plane the beef-bred steer may develop no better; it may, indeed, develop rather worse than the more slowly maturing store animal the dairy provides.

There is, in fact, no best or worst breed in any branch of animal husbandry. There are only breeds which are fitted or are not fitted to the particular set of environmental conditions in which they happen to be placed. It may well prove that in the circumstances prevailing in post-war Britain, rapid maturation in cattle is, economically speaking, out of the question and that, in consequence, the more slowly maturing steers of certain dairy breeds may answer as well, or in certain cases better, than the more rapidly maturing steers of the specialised beef breeds.

For, without concentrate feeding there cannot be the fullest expression of early maturity. An illuminating calculation in illustration of this fact was made by Wood and Newman. (6) The calculation was concerned with the consumption of concentrates per lb. of saleable meat in the case of (a) a baby beef animal, killed at 18 months old, and (b) a bullock fattened and killed at three years old. The comparative figures they brought out are as follows:

(a) " A baby beef animal, killed at 18 months old, has eaten 7,000 lb. of food, weighed dry, of which 1,500 lb. is concentrates. His carcase yields 600 lb. of saleable meat. He has, therefore, consumed per lb. of saleable meat, $11\frac{3}{4}$ lb. of food, weighed dry, of which $2\frac{1}{2}$ lb. is concentrated food." (6)

(*b*) " A bullock fattened and killed at three years old has eaten, since birth, 18,000 lb. of food, weighed dry, of which not more than 1,000 lb. is concentrates. His carcase yields 800 lb. of saleable meat. He has, therefore, consumed, per lb. of saleable meat, 22½ lb. of food, weighed dry, of which only 1¼ is concentrated food." (6)

The disappearance of baby beeves, beeflings, and other forms of young and early maturing beef cattle from our modern British markets is not due to any alteration, nor to any deterioration in the early maturing capacity of the cattle we breed. It is due simply to the altered diet on which these cattle are being fed. The fact that our cattle, when they come to be slaughtered, are some six months older on the average than were the cattle slaughtered previous to 1939, is due to exactly the same cause.

Now, it seems altogether improbable that feeding stuffs, particularly imported feeding stuffs from dollar area countries, will ever again be as cheap and plentiful as they were previous to 1939. And if they ever were to become cheap and plentiful it would probably lead to a more rapid and substantial increase in the British meat ration were such concentrates fed through pigs rather than through cattle.

It would seem therefore that the proposition that the male calves out of dairy herds are not worth rearing for beef is hardly one that can be successfully defended under modern conditions either of the national larder or of animal husbandry. These calves, while in all probability incapable of responding to an environment most favourable to early maturity and ideal beef conformation are, nevertheless, reasonably well suited to what is probably the most economic environment for beef production under modern conditions in the Britain of to-day.

Admitting for the moment that these calves from the dairy are worth the rearing, will they pay to rear? One very important answer to that question is that it depends upon who rears them! Yet there are other considerations more readily capable of assessment.

There is, for example, the substantial inducement of the calf-rearing subsidy. The Agriculture (Calf Subsidies) Act of 1952 is designed to encourage the rearing of calves for beef. It authorises the payment of a subsidy of £5 a head for any steer or heifer calf born in the United Kingdom on or after October 1,

1951, and not later than October 29, 1955, which has been reasonably well reared and is suitable for further rearing for beef production.

The description of calf specified for the purpose of the scheme is any steer or heifer calf, except a heifer calf of the Jersey, Guernsey, Friesian, or Ayrshire breeds, which has been reasonably well reared and is suitable for further rearing for beef production, or if a heifer calf for use for breeding for beef production, being in either case an animal which after rearing and fattening would be likely after slaughter to yield a carcase of good-quality beef.

The intention of this scheme is excellent but its administration in practice is bound to prove difficult. Knowledge permitting a livestock officer inspecting a calf to decide the ultimate quality of the beef it will yield two or three years later simply does not exist. Nevertheless, if the scheme results in even the first hundred thousand calves out of dairy herds being saved from premature slaughter, it will have done much good. The possibilities of supplementing this scheme by official calf salvage on the lines of the Brecon experiment have already been discussed (p. 169).

As regards private individuals and private enterprise there is every evidence on theoretical grounds that calf-rearing, if properly organised and technically efficient, should pay reasonably well. There is, on the one hand, a surplus of calves born; on the other a definite deficiency of store cattle marketed. There should be a profit in converting a surplus article into one in short supply. Moreover, provided the calves are approved for subsidy and attested they should, like hill cows, start off with an attractive dowry. A sum of seven pounds would go far towards the purchase of a suitable calf to rear.

In short, to save a substantial proportion of dairy-bred calves and to rear them reasonably well seems to be the first, the most promising, and the most essential step in bringing about that increase in British beef production which everyone so greatly desires.

There are, of course, other means which it would be folly to neglect. There is, for example, the possibility of increasing the production of beef-bred cattle from both hill and marginal land. The possibilities have already been sufficiently discussed (Chapter 11). The main conclusion arrived at was that while the possibilities were less than certain exaggerated statements might lead one to believe, nevertheless the possibilities were there, and that the main physical limiting factor, namely the quantity of available winter keep, was one that could be over-come.

I should do wrong, however, and indeed be guilty of the grossest hypocrisy, were I, merely because at the moment engaged in writing a book about cattle, to disguise my personal and strongly held conviction that the bulk of our hill country is more naturally suited to sheep. That view, I fully realise, is at the moment both unpopular and unfashionable. It is one, nevertheless, very widely held by professional hill farmers. Quite frankly, the reason that there are so many more sheep than cattle on the hill grazings of this country is that, over a long period of years, hill farmers have found sheep pay better. More-over—at least in my opinion—an extension, or rather the revival, of wether sheep farming promises a more rapid and successful increase in meat production off hill areas than does any enterprise connected with cattle.

The public preference, however, is for beef rather than for mutton and, no doubt, if hill cattle are made more profitable than hill sheep, hill farmers will very quickly come to keep cattle in preference or, at least, in addition to sheep. In any case, on many hill pastures, there should be a limited stock of cattle if only to benefit the grazing for its more profitable exploitation by hill sheep.

In addition to the publicity hill cattle have received, there have been, as already mentioned, substantial inducements offered in the form of subsidies of one kind and another, to persuade hill farmers to keep more cattle.

One of the most recent steps adopted in implementing the Government's declared policy of favouring the extension of cattle breeding in hill areas is the Hill Lands (North of Scotland) Commission set up in 1951 under the chairmanship of Lord Balfour of Burleigh. Its main remit is:

> To consult with the Hill Farming Advisory Committee for Scotland and with the Agricultural Executive Committees and other agencies, and arrange with the Department of Agriculture for Scotland for any necessary field surveys with a view to ascertaining in what areas and by what methods schemes of cattle rearing development could, with most advantage, be promoted.

To date, the most material result of the Commission's deliberations has been the recommendation, since officially adopted, of a grant of £3 per head towards the cost of providing winter keep for hill cattle. The recommendation was based on the Commission's conclusion,

> ... that the kernel of the problem of greater beef production from the Scottish hills is that of increased production of winter keep. It is to that objective that the maximum effort of all concerned must be directed. (7)

The Commission has laid stress upon the contribution the crofter can make to the increase of hill cattle stocks in the Scottish Highlands.

> One of the main objects to which the Commission must direct its efforts is to induce the crofter who has one cow to keep two, and himself to create the winter feed to make this possible. (7)

It is my own opinion that the Commission have erred in laying such weight on the potential contribution of the crofter. Discussion of the place of the croft and of crofting in the agriculture of a modern state would lead us too far afield from the present subject of discussion, which is hill cattle, yet this much, without fear of contradiction, may be safely said; that the future of crofting is even more problematical than that of hill cattle.

The nomination of several persons of distinction and with experience of forestry to the Hill Lands (North of Scotland) Commission gave promise that we might at last begin to see some effective co-operation between afforestation and stock farming, a co-operation which, at the moment, is apt to be replaced by a rear-guard action of the guerrilla forces of hill farming against the well-organised, disciplined, and regular troops of the Forestry Commission invading hill country. The result of this somewhat unequal struggle is a foregone conclusion. Many, all too many, imagine that this approaching victory is one of right over wrong, and of trees over sheep. It is nothing of the kind. It is one of a well-organised Department of State, with the full resources of the State behind it, over a somewhat intimidated and disorganised opposition.

The lesson to be drawn regarding hill cattle farming is surely perfectly plain. Without the Government's establishment, organisation, and financing of a national Forestry Commission there would have been precious few trees planted in the hill lands of

Britain during the last thirty years. Without some similar and closely associated Hill Cattle Commission there will be equally few cattle herds established in our hill country during the next thirty years. Indeed, should the Forestry Commission remain unopposed by an equally powerful organisation responsible for hill farming, there may be very little hill land left unplanted in thirty years' time sufficiently low-lying, fertile, and sheltered to support hill cattle. Possibly the best solution of all would be to make the Forestry Commission responsible for the grazing, sporting, and recreational uses of the land it dominates as appears to be the accepted practice in the United States wherever similar circumstances arise.

In short, the store cattle raising potentialities of our hill country are unlikely to be developed by the mere substitution of three acres and two cows for the proverbial three acres and one cow. The successful development of a really productive hill cattle industry would require resources in capital, equipment, organisation, and technical skill which the small-scale crofter or marginal farmer cannot hope to command.

Whatever contribution hill country may make to the national resources in store cattle, the fattening of these cattle will have to be undertaken somewhere else than in the hills. Calves born in the dairy rather than on hill ground will also have to be fattened somehow and somewhere before they will make edible beef. Where and when is that fattening to be done?

The economic circumstances of the day seem likely to provide the inevitable answer that the future fattening of cattle in Britain will be done on grassland and in the summer. Any attempt to equalise slaughterings over the twelve months of the year will almost certainly fail. It has been shown in previous chapters of this book that even with a price differential designed to favour winter fattening rather than summer fattening of cattle, winter fattening has failed to pay. Yet the price differential in recent years has been quite heavily and deliberately weighted in favour of cattle sold fat in spring in comparison with those sold fat in autumn. Thus, for example, in the year 1951 whereas the price per cwt. for SS. beef was 133s. 3d. on April 30, it was only 115s. 3d. on October 8.

On the contrary, despite a price differential deliberately weighted to discourage the practice, the summer fattening of cattle on grass has shown a small profit in post-war years. Possibly without this deliberate discouragement, the profit on summer fattening of cattle might have been reasonably attractive.

It is further of significance that in the pre-war era (previous that is to 1939), the summer fattening of cattle was increasing at the expense of winter fattening despite the two substantial economic impediments to profitable summer fattening of high price of store cattle in spring and a low price for beef in autumn.

Finally, the cattle rearing experiments in progress at Cambridge University Farm have shown conclusively that winter storing and summer fattening, with the grading of the fat cattle at 2 to 2½ years off grass, is the most profitable method of beef production at the present time. The cattle, grass-fattened, may be even more mature when slaughtered.

It must be emphasised, however, that the older the cattle are at slaughter, the slower the turn-over of cattle within a given time. At the moment, with the scarcity of suitable store cattle a limiting factor in production, this is of less importance than it would be should measures to increase the numbers and quality of store cattle succeed.

The question of weight in cattle is also of importance in relation to social changes and their influence upon effective demand. Prior to 1939 the general tendency in cattle breeding and feeding, as is very well known, was towards early maturing animals slaughtered at an early age and at a relatively light weight. Considerable emphasis was laid upon the small joint and the type of light weight carcase that could best provide such a joint. The small joint was associated with the small house, the small kitchen, and the small family of the average household of the inter-war years.

Beef, in those days, was consumed mainly in the home whereas, to-day, an ever increasing proportion is eaten communally in factory canteen, school, hostel, and restaurant. Under these new social conditions small size of joint is of far less importance. Indeed, where cooking is communal and for large numbers, large joints from heavy cattle have definite advantages. Large joints (at least according to some butchers) have even greater advantages when, as has been so necessary in the post-war years, a large number of small meat rations has had to be cut off one and the same joint.

In short, the somewhat heavy grass-fed beast of full maturity and reasonable finish is much better suited to the circumstances, economic, pastoral, and social of 1953 than it would have been to those of 1939. It is, moreover, the circumstances of 1953 with which we are mainly concerned. Fourteen years is quite a long time and it would be a mistake to further limit our inadequate beef supplies by carrying over the standards of excellence appropriate to one generation to those of the next. Early maturity when concentrates were available to support it; ideal beef conformation when the nutritional plane and rapidity of growth permitted its development; small joints when a whole joint of beef was available for one family; all these things were excellent in their time, but that time is not our time. Unless we learn to be contented with beef that is largely cow beef, or beef from heavy dairy-bred steers in their slowly developed maturity; beef moreover that, whether from cows or steers, is mainly grass-fed beef; we may find in the end that we have very little beef to eat at all. Probably in dealing with cow beef, it would be wiser to divert more to manufacture and less to the butcher's shop on the unassailable contention that a good sausage is preferable to a poor steak.

Finally, a proportion of grass-fed beef, coming to grading as a seasonal crop, may require to be chilled or even frozen. Provided refrigerator space is made adequate to the purpose, that is no disadvantage. The assistance in orderly marketing that cold storage provides compensates for any deterioration in quality meat may suffer from refrigeration. Certainly, if beef production is to substantially increase, then the requisite facilities must be forthcoming in order to deal efficiently with that increase. Mr. Maurice Passmore put the point excellently when he said:

" I have mentioned the grazing area of something about four million acres plus five million acres of rough grazing. It is not a bit of good improving this land unless you can cash in on what you spend. The cashing-in point is the finished product—a fat beast or sheep. Unless there are killing and storing facilities for the output of this vast area, it is more than likely we shall be wasting out money improving it." (9)

To allow slaughtering or refrigerating facilities to become the limiting factor in the most productive utilisation of the grasslands of this country would indeed be a confession of ineptitude and failure. We have, most fortunately, been moving towards rationalisation of slaughtering facilities for some time. As long ago as 1929 it was stated in the Ministry of Agriculture's Report on the Marketing of Cattle and Beef in England and Wales that:

" Central slaughtering in up-to-date abattoirs is, in fact, an inevitable development in the meat trade." (10)

During the 1939–1945 war, under the Ministry of Food, this centralisation was tremendously accelerated. " Slaughtering was concentrated at a limited number of abattoirs." (11)

This concentration was effective, even drastic for:

" Of some 16,000 slaughter houses in use in England and Wales before the war only some 600 are still in operation, whilst in Scotland the number has been reduced from some 600 to approximately 80, as a result of the concentration carried out by the Ministry of Food." (12)

The declared policy of the National Farmers' Union as, expressed in their draft plan for a Fat Stock Marketing Scheme is that the appropriate Board, if and when established, should have " power to build new abattoirs where they are found to be needed " (13) and that at these abattoirs proper provision should be made for the preservation and collection of valuable beef by-products such as hides, other offals, and glandular products.

The draft scheme does not deal with the associated question of refrigeration, although it might well be argued that such, to-day, is an essential adjunct to the orderly marketing of any highly perishable product. Doubtless the necessity for capital expenditure on abattoirs and cold storage will be questioned and the difficulties of finance and raw materials under present conditions of national stringency strongly expressed. In this connection let it be declared once and for all, that whatever difficulties this country may in future be compelled to face, none is of quite such dangerous urgency as that of fifty millions of people confined on an island which in its present state of agricultural development produces food sufficient for only half that number. Under such circumstances talk of steps to avoid a seasonal glut of beef or of any other food-stuff appears frankly dangerous as well as absurd. We should on the contrary be prepared to receive and welcome the bounty of the naturally productive season with both hands. Nor is there any insuperable reason why we should do otherwise.

" The meat-producing countries, particularly New Zealand, have killing facilities to fit production. Here we are trying to fit production to facilities, one you can control and the other you can't." (14)

In this connection we in Britain would be abundantly justified in following New Zealand's example, for while their organisation is designed to favour national prosperity, ours might well prove eventually to be an important factor in securing our survival as a nation.

REFERENCES

(1) Report on the Marketing of Cattle and Beef in England and Wales, *Economic Series*, No. 20, p. 25, 1929, Min. of Agric. and Fisheries.
(2) " Meat," p. 5, Commonwealth Economic Committee, 1952. H.M.S.O.
(3) *Ibid.*, p. 4.
(4) Report on the Marketing of Cattle and Beef, p. 21, 1929, *ibid.*
(5) Hammond, J. (1932). " Growth and Development of Mutton Qualities in the Sheep " (London).
(6) Wood, T. B., and Newman, L. F. (1928). " Beef Production in Great Britain," p. 19 (Liverpool).
(7) The Hill Lands (North of Scotland) Commission, 1952 (May). Press statement.
(8) Passmore, M. (1952). " Grazing—sheep and cattle," *J. of the Farmers' Club*, Part 3, p. 42.
(9) *Ibid.*, p. 43.
(10) Report on the Marketing of Cattle and Beef in England and Wales, *Economic Series*, No. 20, p. 25, 1929, Min. Agric. and Fish.
(11) " Marketing of Fat Stock," p. 7 (1952). N.F.U.
(12) *Ibid.*, p. 17.
(13) *Ibid.*, p. 18.
(14) Passmore, M. (1952). *Ibid.*, p. 43.

INDEX